DREAMLAND'S
GRADED
MATHEMATICS

(As per the latest NCERT Syllabus 2002-3)

PART - 8

TIRTH RAAJ BHANOT
Hons. (Maths), MA (English), B. Ed.
Formerly Sr. Teacher
Air Force Central School,
Subroto Park, New Delhi

SUSHMA NAYAR
M.Sc. I (D.U.), B. Ed.
H.O.D Mathematics
Delhi Public School,
Mathura Road, New Delhi-3

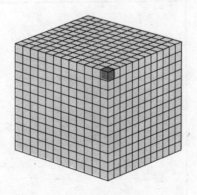

DREAMLAND PUBLICATIONS

J-128, Kirti Nagar, New Delhi - 110 015 (INDIA).
Phone : 011-2510 6050 Fax : 011-2543 8283
e-mail : dreamland@vsnl.com
www.dreamlandpublications.com

Published in 2013 by
DREAMLAND PUBLICATIONS
J-128, Kirti Nagar, New Delhi - 110 015 (India)
Tel : 011-2510 6050, Fax : 011-2543 8283
e-mail : dreamland@vsnl.com
www.dreamlandpublications.com

ISBN 978-93-5089-257-2
Printed at : **Shalini Offset Press**

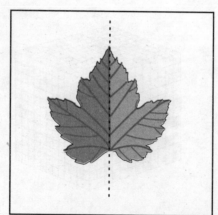
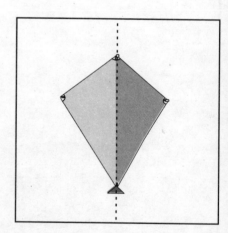

PREFACE

The present series—**GRADED MATHEMATICS**—has been brought out to meet the needs of the students of Middle Classes in the subject of mathematics. Till recently, this subject was considered to be a bug-bear by students only because of the stereo-typed methods of its teaching. But our treatment of the subject is altogether different and so the present series is certainly a series *with a difference*.

The series has been brought out in conformity with the latest syllabus issued in 2002. It encourages the student to develop a mathematical, *i.e.* logical thinking which is so useful in day-to-day life. Liberal use of *diagrams* as well as *illustrations* and the choice of *sums from day-to-day life* are some salient features of the book.

The present volume is meant for class VIII. Topics in this book have been given an easy-to-difficult order while exercises contain numerous sums with a view to giving ample practice and generating self-confidence in the pupils. Two chief features of the book are a **miscellaneous exercise** at the end of each unit followed by a list of **memorable facts** studied in the unit.

We feel highly delighted to place the series in the hands of the teachers and the pupils hoping positively that it will admirably meet their approval from every angle. Still improvement has its scope in every human effort. So, constructive suggestions for the betterment of the series are highly welcome.

—T. RAAJ BHANOT

LATEST SYLLABUS 2002

CLASS-VIII (Periods 180)

UNIT-I NUMBER SYSTEMS *(Periods 30)*

Powers and Roots

Square of a number and cube of a number. Finding square roots of perfect squares, and cube roots of perfect cubes by factorization (Square root and cube root should not exceed two digits).

Using division method, finding square roots of (i) positive integers which are perfect squares. (ii) decimals which are perfect squares (Square root should not exceed three digits including decimal digits). Finding square roots of numbers which are not perfect squares by the division method up-to two or three decimal places (The 'Why' aspect of the process may be excluded). Problems based on square roots (Simple problems only). Idea of rational exponents. Laws of exponents including rational numbers as exponents. Idea of *radical* and *radicand*.

UNIT-II COMMERCIAL MATHEMATICS
(Periods 30)

Applications of percentage

Problems on *profit and loss* including discount (rebate), marked price, selling price (Only single discount to be discussed). Meaning of *compound interest*. Calculation of amount and compound interest by unitary method. Calculation of amount and compound interest by formula upto three years, compounded annually.

UNIT-III ALGEBRA *(Periods 40)*

Indentities

$(x+a)\,(x+b) = x^2+(a+b)\,x+ab,$

$(a+b)^3 = a^3+3a^2b+3ab^2+b^3,$

$(a-b)^3 = a^3-3a^2b+3ab^2-b^3,$

$(a+b+c)^2 = a^2+b^2+c^2+2ab+2bc+2ca$

(These identities may also be verified through cardboard models). simple cases of factorization based on these identities. Idea of a polynomial in one variable and its degree. Division of a polynomial in one variable by a monomial or a binomial (Restricted to polynomials in one variable of degree 4). Verification of

Dividend = Divisor×Quotient+Rremainder

(Explain the cases of remainder non-zero and remainder equal to zero). Concept of a factor of a polynomial.

Equations

Solving equations of the type $\frac{ax+b}{cx+d} = k$, $(cx+d) \neq 0$. Word problems could be framed from daily life situations like age, coins, number of students of a class etc. with emphasis on ability to translate word problems into mathematical statements).

UNIT-IV GEOMETRY *(Periods 40)*

Parallel Lines

Varification of the following properties : *(a)* Two lines parallel to the same line are parallel to each other *(b)* Two lines perpendicular to the same line are parallel to each other *(c)* Equal intercepts and properties and their use in the following constructions : *(i)* To divide a line-segment into a given number of equal segments. *(ii)* To divide a line segment in a given ratio internally (Constructions should be by using a ruler and compasses).

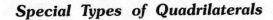

Special Types of Quadrilaterals

Square, rectangle, rhombus, parallelogram and trapezium (Example of kite may also be given as a special type of quadrilateral). Verification of the following properties : *(i)* Opposite sides of a parallelogram are equal. *(ii)* Opposite angles of a parallelogram are equal. *(iii)* Diagonals of a rectangle are equal and bisect each other at right angles. *(iv)* Diagonals of a square are equal, perpendicular to each other and bisect each other (Simple problems based on these properties involving one or two logical steps).

Construction of Quadrilaterals

Construction of a quadrilateral given : *(i)* Four sides and one diagonal. *(ii)* Three sides and both diagonals. *(iii)* Two adjacent sides and three angles. *(iv)* Three sides and two included angles (The sides should be in whole numbers of centimeters or at most multiples of ½ a cm. Angles should be in multiples of 5°).

Circles

Concyclic points. Opposite angles of a cyclic quadrilateral. Angle subtended by an arc at the centre of a circle. Verification of the following properties : *(i)* Opposite angles of a cyclic quadrilateral are supplementary. *(ii)* Perpendicular from the centre to a chord bisects the chord. Converse of the above. *(iii)* Equal chords of a circle subtend equal angles at the centre. Converse of the above. *(iv)* Equal chords of a circle are equidistant from the centre. Converse of the above. *(v)* Angle subtended by an arc at the centre is double the angle subtended by it at any point on the remaining part of the circle (Simple problems based on these properties involving one or two logical steps).

UNIT-V MENSURATION *(Periods 25)*

Area

Area of a parallelogram, triangle and trapezium The following formula for area of a triangle to be taught :

Area of a Triangle = ½ Base × Height.

Circumference of a circle and its relationship to its diameter. The number π. Area of a circle. simple problems involving areas.

Volume and Surface Area

Idea of a right circular cylinder, right circular cone and sphere. Volume and surface area of a *(i)* Right circular cylinder. *(ii)* Right circular cone. *(iii)* sphere *(iv)* Simple problems on volumes and surface areas (Direct problems may be given on surface area and volume, taking one solid figure at a time).

UNIT-VI STATISTICS *(Periods 15)*

Data and its Representation

Raw data Frequency. Making frequency table from the given raw data. Ungrouped and grouped data. Class size and class limits. Grouping given data into classes. Reading and interpretation of histograms (Drawing of histograms not required). Mean of raw data (Number of observations should not exceed 10).

CONTENTS

REVISION OF WHAT WE HAVE LEARNT

A. Answer :

1. Is 0 an integer or a rational number ? ....*rational*..........
2. What is a number expressed in the form $\frac{a}{b}$ called ? — ....*fraction*..........
3. Is $\frac{0}{1}$ a rational number or $\frac{0}{2}$? ....*both*..........
4. How is a written as a rational number ? ....$\frac{a}{1}$..........
5. What does the word—*rational*—mean ? ....*Not Irrational*..........
6. Which is a rational number $\frac{0}{2}$ or $\frac{2}{0}$? ....$\frac{0}{2}$..........
7. Is it correct to write $\left(-1\frac{3}{4}\right)$ as $\left(-1+\frac{3}{4}\right)$? ....*No*..........
8. What is the *additive inverse* of zero (0) ? ....*(0)*..........
9. What is the *multiplicative inverse* of zero ? ....*No number*..........
10. By what number must $\frac{5}{11}$ be divided to get $\frac{2}{3}$? — ....$\frac{10}{22}$..........
11. How will you write $\frac{2}{3}$, 0 $\frac{-2}{3}$ in ascending order ? — ....$-\frac{2}{3}, 0, \frac{2}{3}$..........
12. What is the decimal form of $\frac{1}{9}$? ....0.0101..........
13. What is $\frac{a}{b} \times \frac{a}{b} \times \frac{a}{b}$ .... m times equal to ? ....$\frac{a^m}{b}$..........
14. By what should 25 be multiplied to get 2·5, 0·25 ? — ....$-10, -100$..........
15. What is the standard form of 1500000 ? ....15×10^5..........
16. What is the standard form of 0·29 ? ....$29 \times (10^{-2})$..........

B. Explain the difference between :

17. a *rational number* and an *irrational number*.
18. an *additive inverse* and a *multiplicative inverse*.
19. *density* and *absolute value*.
20. a *terminating decimal* and a *non-terminating decimal*.
21. a *pure recurring decimal* and a *mixed recurring decimal*.
22. a *base* and an *index*
23. *direct variation* and *inverse variation*.
24. a *factor* and a *common factor*
25. a *variable* and a *constant*.
26. *centroid* and *orthocentre*
27. *circumcentre* and *incentre*.
28. *concurrent* and *concentric*
29. a *chord* and an *arc*
30. *area* and *volume*
31. *perimeter* and *diameter*

C. 32. Arrange $\dfrac{-5}{11}, \dfrac{1}{-2}, \dfrac{-6}{7}, \dfrac{3}{-4}$ in ascending as well as descending order.

33. Represent $\dfrac{2}{3}$ and $\dfrac{-2}{3}$ on the number-line.

34. What number should be added to $\dfrac{4}{9}$ to get $\dfrac{-7}{8}$?

35. Verify that $\left(\dfrac{-4}{5} \times \dfrac{-3}{7}\right) + \left(\dfrac{-4}{5} \times \dfrac{-9}{13}\right) = \dfrac{-4}{5} \times \left(\dfrac{-3}{7} + \dfrac{-9}{13}\right)$.

36. Find three rational numbers between $\dfrac{-2}{3}$ and $\dfrac{2}{3}$.

37. Verify $|x \times y| = |x| \times |y|$ for $x = \dfrac{7}{8}$ and $y = \dfrac{1}{-4}$

38. Express in decimal form : (a) $\dfrac{3147}{256}$ (b) $\dfrac{1}{7}$ up to 4 decimal places

39. Express as rational numbers : (a) $0 \cdot 2\overline{1}$ (b) $0 \cdot 12\overline{63}$

40. Find the value of $0 \cdot \overline{1} + 0 \cdot \overline{2} + 0 \cdot \overline{16}$.

41. Find the product of the cube of $\dfrac{4}{-7}$ and square of $\dfrac{-7}{8}$.

42. Prove that $\left(\dfrac{-4}{5}\right)^3 \times 5^2 \times \left(\dfrac{-1}{2}\right)^5 \times \left(\dfrac{1}{2}\right)^3 = \dfrac{1}{20}$

43. A jet aeroplane has a speed of $8 \cdot 0 \times 10^5$ kilometres an hour. How long will it take to cover $4 \cdot 0 \times 10^5$ kilometres ?

D. 44. A worker is paid Rs. 213 after working for 6 days. His total wages for the month were Rs. 923. How many days did he work during the month ?

45. A contractor promises to construct a house in 9 months with a work-force of 560 men. How many extra men should he employ to complete the building in 7 months ?

46. A regiment of 600 soldiers has food-stuffs to last 35 days at a certain rate of ration per head. How long will the food-stuffs last if the soldiers increase to be 900 and the rate of ration is reduced in the ratio 5 : 6 ?

47. A, B and C can do a job in 6, 8 and 12 days respectively. B and C work together for 2 days and then A replaces C. In how many days will the total work be finished ?

48. A train is 130 metres long and it is running at 65 km. per hour. How long will it take the train to pass an electric pole ?

49. Two trains are running on parallel lines in the same direction at 46 km. and 39 km. per hour. If they are 110 metres and 100 metres long respectively, how long will it take the faster train to pass the other train ?

50. 30% of a number is 9. Find the number.

51. In a test 72% candidates passed. If the number of failed candidates be 392. Find the total number of the examinees.

52. A trader allows a discount of 20% on the marked price of his articles. How much above the cost should he mark an item so as to gain 20% on it after allowing the discount ?

53. The selling price of 10 articles is equal to the cost price of 11 articles. Find the gain per cent.

54. Some marbles were bought at 11 for a rupee and the same number at 9 for a rupee. The whole lot was sold at 10 for a rupee. What will be the gain or loss per cent ?

55. Divide Rs. 6000 into two parts so that the S.I. on one part for 9 months at 16% per annum may be equal to the S.I. on the other part for 1·5 years at 12% per annum.

E. 56. Multiply : $x^2 - 3x + 7$ by $2x + 3$

57. Simplify : $\dfrac{2\cdot734 \times 2\cdot734 - 1\cdot266 \times 1\cdot266}{2\cdot734 + 1\cdot266}$

58. Factorise : $a^2 - 2ab + b^2 - 9$

59. Solve : $0\cdot5x + \dfrac{x}{5} = 0\cdot25x + 7$

60. The sum of four consecutive numbers is 266. Find the numbers.

F. Answer :

61. (a) How many elements does a triangle have ? ....

(b) How many sides of a scalene triangle are equal ? ....

(c) Write the value of the ∠s of an isosceles rt. Δ. ....

(d) Find the hypotenuse of a right triangle whose other two sides are 3 cm. and 4 cm. ....

G. Write the correct word in each blank :

62. (a) line-segment from the vertex of a Δ bisecting the opposite side. ....

(b) line-segments passing through the same point. ....

(c) point where bisectors of angles of a Δ meet. ....

(d) three common cases of congruency : ...., ..., ...

H. Fill up each blank :

63. (a) A quadrilateral has .... sides and .... angles.

(b) A convex quadrilateral has each of its angles less than ....

(c) Two adjacent angles of a quadrilateral are at the ends of a ....side.

(d) The sum of the angles of a quadrilateral is equal to ....

I. Say whether *true* or *false* :

64. (a) All the sides of a rectangle are equal.

(b) The diagonals of a rhombus are equal.

(c) The diagonals of a square are equal.

(d) A square is a rt. rhombus.

(e) A chord divides a circle into two segments.

(f) A sector is bounded by two radii and an arc.

(g) The diameter of a circle is twice its radius.

(h) Diameter is the shortest chord of a circle.

J. 65. (a) Draw angles of 45°, 60° and 120°.   (b) Bisect the angle of 60°.

66. Draw a rt. triangle whose side BC = 4 cm. and altitude CA = 3 cm. using a scale and compasses.

67. Draw CD parallel to AB through a given point P outside it.

K. 68. A parallelogram has its longer side = 25 cm. and both its altitudes are 20 cm. and 16 cm. respectively. Find its shorter side.

69. A wall is 4·5 m long and 3 m high. It has two equal windows with *form* and *measurements* as shown in front. Find the cost of plastering the remaining wall at Rs. 15 per sq. metre.

70. The diagonals of a rhombus are 12 m and 8 m. Find its area.

71. The area of a trapezium is 475 sq. cm. The distance between its parallel sides is 19 cm. If one of the parallel sides = 27 cm, find the other side.

72. A room is thrice as long as it is wide. It can contain 60 cu. m of air. Find the cost of plastering its floor at Rs. 10 per sq. m. if its height be 5 metres.

NUMBER SYSTEMS

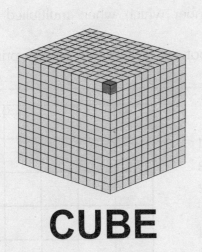

CUBE

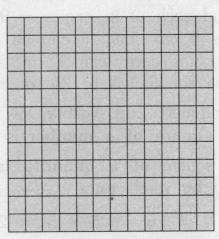

$$\sqrt[3]{12^3} = 12$$

(CUBE ROOT)

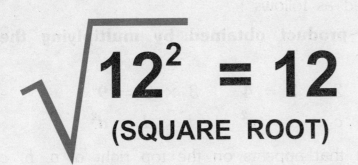

$$\sqrt{12^2} = 12$$

(SQUARE ROOT)

SQUARE

IN THIS UNIT—
1. Squares and Square Roots
2. More About Square Roots
3. Real Numbers
4. Cubes and Cube Roots
5. Exponents or Indices
6. Radicals or Surds

1 SQUARES AND SQUARE ROOTS

> *KNOW THESE TERMS :*
> 1. **square**—product obtained by multiplying a number by itself
> 2. **square root**—square root of a given number is the number which when multiplied by itself gives the given number
> 3. **perfect square**—number that has an integral square root or a number whose prime factors exist in pairs

WHAT IS A SQUARE ?

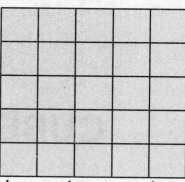

In geometry, a square is a plane quadrilateral that is *equilateral* as well as *equiangular, i.e.* its sides are equal and each of its angles = 90°. If the side of the square is 5 cm. long, it can be divided in 25 smaller equal squares each with 1 cm. side. So, the area of the bigger square will be 25 *square centimetres.*

In Arithmetic and Algebra, this very idea of a square has been taken as a base and the **square of a number** is defined as follows :

The *square* **of a quantity is the product obtained by multiplying the quantity by itself once** ; as—

$$4 \times 4 = \mathbf{16} \qquad 5 \times 5 = \mathbf{25} \qquad 2 \times 2 = \mathbf{4} \qquad 3 \times 3 = \mathbf{9}$$
$$a \times a = \mathbf{a^2} \qquad b \times b = \mathbf{b^2} \qquad c \times c = \mathbf{c^2} \qquad d \times d = \mathbf{d^2}$$

We know that the small number $2(^2)$ that appears on the top right of a, b, c and d is called the **index** or **exponent**. It shows that the quantity is to be taken *twice* while finding the product. The plural of the word—*index*—is **indices**.

PERFECT SQUARES

Observe the table given in front. It gives the squares of natural numbers from 1 to 20.

The numbers printed in normal type are whole numbers while those printed in **bold type** are their **squares**. Such numbers are called **perfect squares** because they are exact *square numbers* and do not involve any *decimals* or *fractions*.

Number	Square	Number	Square
1	$1^2 = $ **1**	11	$11^2 = $ **121**
2	$2^2 = $ **4**	12	$12^2 = $ **144**
3	$3^2 = $ **9**	13	$13^2 = $ **169**
4	$4^2 = $ **16**	14	$14^2 = $ **196**
5	$5^2 = $ **25**	15	$15^2 = $ **225**
6	$6^2 = $ **36**	16	$16^2 = $ **256**
7	$7^2 = $ **49**	17	$17^2 = $ **289**
8	$8^2 = $ **64**	18	$18^2 = $ **324**
9	$9^2 = $ **81**	19	$19^2 = $ **361**
10	$10^2 = $ **100**	20	$20^2 = $ **400**

In order to find whether a given number is a perfect square or not, write the number as a product of its prime factors. *If these factors exist in pairs, the number is a perfect square.* Let us now solve some examples.

Example 1. Which of the following numbers are perfect squares ?

(a) **256** (b) **154** (c) **225**

2	256
2	128
2	64
2	32
2	16
2	8
2	4
	2

Solution : (a) $256 = 2 \times 2 \times 2 \times 2 \times 2 \times 2 \times 2 \times 2$

$= (2 \times 2) \times (2 \times 2) \times (2 \times 2) \times (2 \times 2)$

∴ prime factors of 256 exist in pairs

∴ **256 is a perfect square** Ans.

(b) $154 = 2 \times 7 \times 11$

2	154
7	77
	11

∵ No prime factor exists in pairs

∴ **154 is not a perfect square** Ans.

(c) $225 = 5 \times 5 \times 3 \times 3 = (5 \times 5) \times (3 \times 3)$

5	225
5	45
3	9
	3

∵ its prime factors exist in pairs

∴ **225 is a perfect square** Ans.

SOME FACTS ABOUT PERFECT SQUARES

FACT 1

Squares of the digits (0 to 9) have 0, 1, 4, 5, 6 or 9 in their unit's place. The numbers ending in 2, 3, 7 and 8 are not perfect squares ; as—

(a) 100, 121, 144, 225, 256 and 289 are perfect squares.

(b) 112, 133, 187, 208 are not perfect squares.

FACT 2

A perfect square has an even number of zeroes at its end ; as—

(a) 100, 400, 1600, 2500, 10000 are perfect squares.

(b) 180, 220, 310, 480 are not perfect squares.

FACT 3

Squares of even numbers are always even ; as—

$8^2 = \mathbf{64}$ $18^2 = \mathbf{324}$ $24^2 = \mathbf{576}$

FACT 4

Squares of odd numbers are always odd ; as—

$9^2 = \mathbf{81}$ $17^2 = \mathbf{289}$ $23^2 = \mathbf{529}$

FACT 5

The square of a number other than 0 and 1, is either a multiple of 3 or exceeds the multiple of 3 by 1 ; as—

(a) $3^2 = \mathbf{9}$ $9^2 = \mathbf{81}$ $12^2 = \mathbf{144}$ *(all multiples of 3)*

(b) $4^2 = \mathbf{16} = (15 + 1)$, $13^2 = \mathbf{169} = (168 + 1)$, $17^2 = \mathbf{289} = (288 + 1)$

FACT 6

The square of a number other than 0 and 1, is either a multiple of 4 or exceeds a multiple of 4 by 1 ; as—

(a) $6^2 = \mathbf{36}$ $8^2 = \mathbf{64}$ $10^2 = \mathbf{100}$ *(all multiplies of 4)*

(b) $7^2 = \mathbf{49} = (48 + 1)$, $9^2 = \mathbf{81} = (80 + 1)$, $11^2 = \mathbf{121} = (120 + 1)$

FACT 7

There are no natural numbers p, q **such that** $p^2 = 2q^2$

p, q are natural numbers. So, one of them is **odd** and the other **even**.

∵ Square of an odd number cannot be even ; nor can the square of an even number be odd.

∴ $2q^2$ is an even number and p^2 is an odd one. So p^2 can never be equal to $2q^2$

FACT 8

Finding squares by observing some regular definite patterns ; as—

$1^2 = 1$	$5^2 = 0 \times 1$ hundred $+ 5^2 = 25$
$11^2 = 121$	$15^2 = 1 \times 2$ hundred $+ 5^2 = 225$
$111^2 = 12321$	$25^2 = 2 \times 3$ hundred $+ 5^2 = 625$
$1111^2 = 1234321$	$35^2 = 3 \times 4$ hundred $+ 5^2 = 1225$
$11111^2 = 123454321$	$45^2 = 4 \times 5$ hundred $+ 5^2 = 2025$
$111111^2 = 12345654321$	$55^2 = 5 \times 6$ hundred $+ 5^2 = 3025$

FACT 9

If the sum of the squares of two quantities equals the square of a third quantity, the three quantities make a *Pythagorean Triplet* **;** as—

$\mathbf{3^2 + 4^2} = 9 + 16 = 25 = \mathbf{5^2}$,   ∴ 3, 4, 5 are a Pythagorean Triplet.

$\mathbf{6^2 + 8^2} = 36 + 64 = 100 = \mathbf{10^2}$,   ∴ 6, 8, 10 are a Pythagorean Triplet.

FACT 10

Twice any natural number (other than 1), its square decreased by 1 and its square increased by 1 are a Pythagorean Triplet ; as—

(a) (2×2), $(2^2 - 1)$, $(2^2 + 1) = 4$, $(4 - 1)$, $(4 + 1)$ or **4, 3, 5**

∵ $\mathbf{4^2 + 3^2} = 16 + 9 = 25 = \mathbf{5^2}$

∴ **4, 3, 5 are a Pythagorean Triplet**

(b) (2×5), $(5^2 - 1)$, $(5^2 + 1)$ = 10, $(25 - 1)$ $(25 + 1)$ or **10, 24, 26**

because $10^2 + 24^2 = 100 + 576 = 676 = 26^2$

∴ **10, 24 and 26 are a Pythagorean Triplet.**

FACT 11

Any odd natural number, $\frac{1}{2}$ (its square decreased by 1) and $\frac{1}{2}$ (its square increased by 1) are a Pythagorean Triplet ; as—

(a) 3, $\frac{1}{2}$ $(3^2 - 1)$ and $\frac{1}{2}$ $(3^2 + 1)$ = 3, $\left(\frac{1}{2} \times 8\right)$ and $\left(\frac{1}{2} \times 10\right)$

= or **3, 4, 5**

because $3^2 + 4^2 = 9 + 16 = 25 = 5^2$

∴ **3, 4 and 5 are a Pythagorean Triplet.**

(b) 7, $\frac{1}{2}$ $(7^2 - 1)$ and $\frac{1}{2}$ $(7^2 + 1)$ = 7, $\left(\frac{1}{2} \times 48\right)$ and $\left(\frac{1}{2} \times 50\right)$

= **7, 24, 25**

because $7^2 + 24^2 = 49 + 576 = 625 = 25^2$

∴ **7, 24 and 25 are a Pythagorean Triplet.**

FACT 12

To find the square of any natural number, find the sum of as many first odd numbers as the numerical value of the natural number is ; as—

(a) *To find the square of 1*

We shall take the **first one odd number,** *i.e.* $1^2 = 1$

(b) *To find the square of 2*

We shall add up the **first two odd numbers,** *i.e.* $2^2 = 1 + 3 = 4$

(c) *To find the square of 3*

We shall add up the **first three odd numbers,** *i.e.* $3^2 = 1 + 3 + 5 = 9$

We can generalise this fact as under :

To find the square of a natural number *n*, *find the sum of the first n natural odd numbers.*

FACT 13

The difference between the squares of two consecutive natural numbers is equal to the sum of both the natural numbers ; as—

(a) $5^2 - 4^2$ = 25 – 16 = 9 = **5 + 4**

(b) $7^2 - 6^2$ = 49 – 36 = 13 = **7 + 6**

(c) $15^2 - 14^2$ = 225 – 196 = 29 = **15 + 14**

We can generalise this fact as under :

If n is a natural number and $n+1$ its conjectives successor, then—
$$(n+1)^2 - n^2 = n + (n+1)$$

Example 1. Observe the unit's and ten's digits in the following numerals and say which of them are perfect squares :

(a) **16**   (b) **14**   (c) **19**   (d) **25**

Solution : (a) 16 is divisible by 4 but not by 3

but $16 - 1 = 15$ is not a multiple of $(3 + 1)$ but it is a multiple of $(4 + 1)$, i.e. 5. So, **It is a perfect square** Ans.

(b) 14 is neither a multiple of 3 nor of 4

$14 - 1 = 13$ is also neither a multiple of $(3 + 1)$ nor of $(4 + 1)$

So, it is not a perfect square. Ans.

(c) 19 is not divisible by 3 or 4

Also, $19 - 1 = 18$ is neither a multiple of 4 nor of 5

So, it is not a perfect square. Ans.

(d) 25 is not divisible by 3 or 4

But $25 - 1 = 24$ is divisible by $3 + 1$, i.e. by 4

So, it is a perfect square. Ans.

Example 2. Which of the following perfect squares are squares of even numbers and which of odd numbers ?

(a) **121**   (b) **144**   (c) **225**   (d) **4900**

Solution : (a) 121 is a perfect square with its unit's digit being odd

So, it is the perfect square of an odd number. Ans.

(b) 144 is a perfect square with an even digit in its unit's place

So, it is the square of an even number. Ans.

(c) 225 is a perfect square with an odd digit in its unit's place

So, it is the square of an odd number. Ans.

(d) 4900 is a number with 49 as the perfect square and it has an even number of zeroes (two) on its right.

∴ **4900 is the perfect square of an even number.** Ans.

Example 3. Find the smallest square number that is exactly divisible by 6, 9, 15 and 20.

Solution : The number divisible by 6, 9, 15 and 20 must be divisible by their LCM.

LCM of 6, 9, 15, 20 = 180

$= 2 \times 2 \times 3 \times 3 \times 5$

$= (2 \times 2) \times (3 \times 3) \times 5$

2	6–9–15–20
3	3–9–15–10
5	1–3–5–10
	1–3–1–2

So, to make 180 a perfect square, it must be multiplied by 5

Hence the Reqd. No. = $180 \times 5 = $ **900** *Ans.*

PRACTICE EXERCISES 1

A. Using prime factors, find which of the following are perfect squares ?

1. 196   **2.** 189   **3.** 343   **4.** 3549   **5.** 6561

B. Which of the following numbers are perfect squares of even numbers ?

6. 324   **7.** 169   **8.** 784   **9.** 841   **10.** 576

C. Find the squares of the following numbers using *Fact 12* given on page 14.

11. 5   **12.** 7   **13.** 3   **14.** 9

D. Write down the correct number in each blank :

15. $27^2 - 26^2$ = ... = ...

16. $103^2 - 102^2$ = ... = ...

17. $569^2 - 568^2$ = ... = ...

E. Which of the following triplets are Pythagorean ?

18. (3, 4, 5)   **19.** (1, 2, 3)   **20.** (6, 7, 8)   **21.** (2, 3, 4)

F. Observe the pattern closely, follow it and then fill up the blanks :

Pattern : $1^2 + 2^2 + 2^2 = 3^2$ $2^2 + 3^2 + 6^2 = 7^2$

           $4^2 + 5^2 + 20^2 = 21^2$ $8^2 + 9^2 + 72^2 = 73^2$

22. $3^2 + 4^2 + 12^2 = (.......)^2$ **23.** $5^2 + 6^2 + (......)^2 = (31)^2$

24. $6^2 + 7^2 + (.......)^2 = (.......)^2$ **25.** $10^2 + 11^2 + (......)^2 = (......)^2$

G. Observe the pattern closely, follow it and then fill up the blanks :

Pattern : $121 = \dfrac{(22)^2}{1+2+1}$ and $12321 = \dfrac{(333)^2}{1+2+3+2+1}$

26. $1234321 = \dfrac{(............)^2}{.....+.....+.....+.....+.....+.....+.....}$

27. $123454321 = \dfrac{(.................)^2}{.....+.....+.....+.....+.....+.....+.....+.....+.....}$

17

H. Find the sum without adding :

28. $1 + 3 = $ ....

29. $1 + 3 + 5 = $ ....

30. $1 + 3 + 5 + 7 = $ ....

31. $1 + 3 + 5 + 7 + 9 = $ ....

32. Express each of the following numbers as sum of natural odd numbers :

$49 = $ ....

$64 = $ ....

$36 = $ ....

33. One number of each Pythagorean Triplet is given. Find the other two :

(a) 4, ..., ...   *(b)* 6, ..., ...   *(c)* 12, ..., ...

I. Do as directed :

34. What is meant by a *Pythagorean Triplet*. Give four example.

....

....

Examples : ....

35. Show that 1200 is not a perfect square.

36. Show that 11025 is a perfect square.

SQUARE ROOTS

The *square root* **of a given number is the number that, when multiplied by itself, gives the given number ;** as—

$\sqrt{4} = 2$ $\sqrt{9} = 3$ $\sqrt{16} = 4$ $\sqrt{25} = 5$

Observe the above examples. You will notice the following facts :

(a) the square root of an *even number* is even.

(b) the square root of an *odd number* is odd.

(c) If 2 is the *square root* of 4 then 4 is the **square** of 2.

(d) the symbol for the square root is $\sqrt{}$.

2	1156
2	576
17	289
	17

FINDING SQUARE ROOT BY FACTORISATION

Example 4. Find the square root of 1156.

Solution : $1156 = 2 \times 2 \times 17 \times 17 = (2 \times 2) \times (17 \times 17)$

$\therefore \sqrt{1156} = 2 \times 17 = \mathbf{34}$ *Ans.*

Example 5. Find the square root of 47089.

Solution : $47089 = 7 \times 7 \times 31 \times 31 = (7 \times 7) \times (31 \times 31)$

$\therefore \sqrt{47089} = 7 \times 31 = \mathbf{217}$ *Ans.*

7	47089
7	6727
31	961
	31

Example 6. Find the smallest square number that is divisible by each of the numbers 8, 12, 15, 20.

Solution :   A square number divisible by 8, 12, 15, 20 is divisible by their LCM

LCM of 8, 12, 15, 20   = 2 × 2 × 3 × 5 × 2

= (2×2) × 3 × 5 × 2

Clearly, pairs of 3, 5, 2 are to be completed

∴ Reqd No.   = 2 × 2 × 3 × 3 × 5 × 5 × 2 × 2

= 16 × 9 × 25 = **3600** Ans.

2	8–12–15–20
2	4–6–15–10
3	2–3–15–5
5	2–1–5–5
	2–1–1–1

PRACTICE EXERCISES 2

A. **1.** What is meant by *square root* ?

B. **Find the square root by factorisation :**

2. 1296   **3.** 1764   **4.** 841   **5.** 7056

6. 53361   **7.** 298116   **8.** 2601   **9.** 1000000

C. **10.** By what smallest number must 180 be multiplied so that it may become a perfect square ? Also find the square root of the number thus obtained.

11. By what smallest number should 3125 be divided so that it may become a perfect square. Also find the square root of the number thus obtained.

12. A gardener planted 1521 trees in rows such that the number of rows was equal to the number of plants in each row. Find the number of rows.

13. By what least number should 9900 be multiplied to make it a perfect square ?

14. By what smallest number should 117600 be divided so that it may become a perfect square. Also find the square root of the number thus obtained.

D. **Find the square root of each of the following :**

15. $\dfrac{1}{9}$ **16.** $\dfrac{121}{169}$ **17.** $\dfrac{256}{361}$ **18.** $\dfrac{729}{225}$

19. 121 × 144   **20.** 196 × 169   **21.** 1024 × 81

22. 32 × 8 × 9   **23.** 27 × 24 × 8   **24.** 50 × 8 × 9

E. **25.** Write the lowest number of 6 digits. By what smallest number should it be divided so that it becomes a perfect square. Also write its square root.

26. By what should 267696 be multiplied so that it may become a perfect square ?

27. By what must 46875 be divided so that it may become a perfect square ?

28. Write the lowest and the largest numbers of four digits. By which numbers must they be respectively multiplied so that they may become perfect squares ?

29. By which smallest number must 9408 be multiplied to make it a perfect square ?

2 MORE ABOUT SQUARE ROOTS

We studied how to find the square roots of small and medium numbers using *factorisation method*. In this chapter, we shall learn how to find square roots of large numbers. The method used for finding square roots of large number involves **long division**. This method is carried out as below :

STEPS :
1. Write the given number as dividend separating its digits in pairs from the right.
2. Observe the first pair on the left and think of the largest digit whose square is equal to or just near this first pair.
3. Put this digit in the divisor's place as well as in the quotient's place.
4. Write the square of the divisor under the first pair and find the remainder.
5. Bring down the next pair of digits from the original dividend and make a new *sub-dividend*.
6. Write twice the previous quotient in place of the new divisor.
7. Think of a digit that when multiplied by the new divisor will make the product reach near the sub-dividend.
8. Write this digit to the right of the divisor and also make it the next digit in the quotient.
9. Go on repeating the steps 5, 6, 7, 8 till all the pairs have been brought down. The quotient obtained in this way will be the square root of the given number.

Example 1. Find the square root of 848241.

Solution :
1. Writing the number in three pairs : 41, 82, 84
2. Square of **9** is **81** and it reaches near 84. So, we write 9 as the divisor and as the first digit in the quotient.
3. Subtracting 81 from 84, we get 3.
4. Bringing down the next pair 82, we get 382 as the new sub-divisdend.

		921
9		$\overline{84}\ \overline{82}\ \overline{41}$
		81
182		382
		364
1841		1841
		1841
		0

5. Writing $9 \times 2 = 18$ in the divisor's place, we think of the digit **2** that when multiplied by 18 takes it near **38** of 382.

6. So, we write 2 to the right of 18 and also in the quotient.

7. Multiplying 182 by 2, we get 364 and write it under 382.

8. Getting the remainder 18, we bring down the last pair (41) to get the last sub-dividend 1841.

9. Repeating the process, we get **1** as the next digit in the quotient.

∴ **Reqd. square root = 921** *Ans.*

Example 2. Find the square root of 1234321

Solution :

1. While making pairs from the right, only one digit (1) is left at the left end.

2. So, we start by thinking of a digit that can have its square equal to or nearest 1.

3. The remaining process is the same.

∴ $\sqrt{1234321}$ = **1111** *Ans.*

```
            1 1 1 1
   1 | 1 23 43 21
       1
  21 |   23
         21
 221 |   243
         221
2221 |   2221
         2221
            0
```

Example 3. Find the square root of 4401604.

Solution :

1. In this solution, the **second** and the **third** steps need special attention.

2. In the **second step**, the divisor is 4 and the dividend is 40. So, we cannot complete the divisor as 41. So, we put **0** in the divisor and the quotient.

3. In the **third step**, the dividend is 4016 and the divisor 40, the additional digit can be 10, but it is not possible. So, we take this digit to be **9**. The final step is normal.

∴ Reqd. sq. root = $\sqrt{4401604}$ = **2098** *Ans.*

```
            2 0 9 8
    2 | 4 40 16 04
        4
   40 | 40
        00
  409 | 4016
        3681
 4188 | 33504
        33504
            0
```

SQUARE ROOT OF DECIMALS AND FRACTIONS

Example 4. Find the square root of 447·4225.

Solution :

1. In the integral part, make pairs from the right. But in the decimal part, make pairs from the left.

2. Place the decimal point as soon as the integral part comes to an end.

∴ Reqd. sq. root = $\sqrt{447·4225}$ = **21·15** *Ans.*

```
            21 · 15
    2 | 4 47·32 25
        4
   41 |   47
          41
  421 |   632
          421
 4225 |   21125
          21125
              0
```

21

Example 5. Find the square root of $\cdot00008281$.

Solution :

1. The first pair of decimal part has two zeroes.
2. The second pair also has two zeroes.
3. So, the first two digits in the quotient after the decimal point will be two zeroes.
4. Next we bring down 82 and complete the solution.

```
                    ·0091
  0  | ·00  00  82  81
       00
 00  |      00
            00
  9  |          82
               81
 181 |          181
               181
                 0
```

$\therefore$ Reqd. sq. root $= \sqrt{\cdot00008281} = \cdot\textbf{0091}$ *Ans.*

Example 6. Find the square root of :

(a) $\dfrac{361}{625}$ (b) $34\dfrac{15}{49}$ (c) $332\dfrac{61}{169}$

Solution :

(a) $\dfrac{361}{625} = \dfrac{19 \times 19}{25 \times 25}$ or $\sqrt{\dfrac{361}{625}} = \dfrac{\sqrt{19 \times 19}}{\sqrt{25 \times 25}} = \dfrac{\textbf{19}}{\textbf{25}}$ *Ans.*

(b) $34\dfrac{15}{49} = \dfrac{(34 \times 49) + 15}{49} = \dfrac{1681}{49}$

$\therefore \sqrt{34\dfrac{15}{49}} = \sqrt{\dfrac{1681}{49}} = \dfrac{\sqrt{1681}}{\sqrt{49}} = \dfrac{41}{7} = 5\dfrac{\textbf{6}}{\textbf{5}}$ *Ans.*

```
           41
  4  | 16  81
       16
 81  |     81
          81
           0
```

(c) $332\dfrac{61}{169} = \dfrac{56169}{169}$

$\therefore \sqrt{332\dfrac{61}{169}} = \sqrt{\dfrac{56169}{169}} = \dfrac{\sqrt{56169}}{\sqrt{169}} = \dfrac{237}{13} = \textbf{18}\dfrac{\textbf{3}}{\textbf{13}}$ *Ans.*

Remember :

1. If a perfect square has 1 or 2 digits, its square root has only **1 digit**.
2. If a perfect square has 3 or 4 digits, its square root has **2 digits**.
3. If a perfect square has 5 or 6 digits, its square root has **3 digits**.
4. If a, b are two different whole numbers, $\sqrt{\dfrac{a}{b}} = \dfrac{\sqrt{a}}{\sqrt{b}}$ and $\sqrt{ab} = \sqrt{a} \times \sqrt{b}$

PRACTICE EXERCISES 3

A. find the square root by long division method :

1. 529	**2.** 6561	**3.** 531441	**4.** 108241
5. 363609	**6.** 4401604	**7.** 306916	**8.** 1471369
9. 290521	**10.** 57121	**11.** 82264900	**12.** 64432729
13. 1734489	**14.** 998001	**15.** 100489	**16.** 20421361
17. 13010449	**18.** 174345616	**19.** 18464209	**20.** 1157428441

B. Find the square root of the following decimal fractions :

21. 610·09   **22.** 84·8241   **23.** 147·1369

24. ·564001   **25.** 1532·7225   **26.** ·00059049

27. ·565504   **28.** 176·252176   **29.** ·00038809

30. ·00367236   **31.** 1218·7081   **32.** ·00139876

33. ·374544   **34.** 99·8001   **35.** 5·774409

C. Find the square root of each of the following fractions :

36. $\dfrac{529}{841}$ **37.** $\dfrac{441}{961}$ **38.** $\dfrac{5625}{441}$ **39.** $\dfrac{73441}{3364}$

40. $21\dfrac{51}{169}$ **41.** $5\dfrac{19}{25}$ **42.** $23\dfrac{394}{729}$ **43.** $7\dfrac{18}{49}$

44. $37\dfrac{212}{841}$ **45.** $\dfrac{5329}{95481}$ **46.** $34\dfrac{111}{121}$ **47.** $\dfrac{81796}{41209}$

48. $1125\dfrac{711}{729}$ **49.** $35\dfrac{85}{1444}$ **50.** $\dfrac{25·6}{52·9}$ **51.** $\dfrac{243}{867}$

D. Simplify :

52. $\sqrt{156·25} - \sqrt{1·5625}$ **53.** $\dfrac{\sqrt{·0441}}{\sqrt{·000441}}$

54. The area of a square field is 256·6404 sq. metres. Find the length of its side.

55. Find the fraction which when multiplied by itself gives 251953·8025.

SQUARE ROOTS OF NON-PERFECT SQUARES

Example 1. Find the square root of 2 up to 3 decimal places.

Solution :   We know that $1^2 = 1$ which is less than 2

and $2^2 = 4$ which is more than 2

In other words, $1 < \sqrt{2} < 2$

we cannot have a natural number as square root of 2.

So, we must use division method to find the square root of 2.

Square root of 2 = 1·414

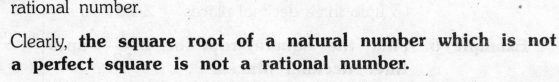

We see that the square root of 2 is not a rational number.

Clearly, **the square root of a natural number which is not a perfect square is not a rational number.**

Example 2. $\sqrt{}$ **Find the square root of 0·9 up to three decimal places.**

Solution : 0·9 = ‘**0·948** and it is greater than 0·9

So, remember that **the square root of a number less than 1 > the given number.**

```
         0.948
    9 | 0·90 00 00
      |   81
  184 |   900
      |   736
 1888 | 16400
      | 15104
      |  1296
```

Example 3. **Find the square root of $\frac{1}{3}$.**

Solution : In such cases, we first make the denominator a perfect square

$$\sqrt{\frac{1}{3}} = \sqrt{\frac{1 \times 3}{3 \times 3}} = \sqrt{\frac{3}{9}} = \frac{\sqrt{3}}{3}$$

Now $\sqrt{3} = 1·732$

$$\therefore \sqrt{\frac{1}{3}} = \frac{\sqrt{3}}{3} = \frac{1·732}{3} = ·\textbf{577} \; Ans.$$

```
         1·732
    1 | 3·00 00 00
      | 1
   27 |  200
      |  189
  343 | 1100
      | 1029
 3462 | 7100
      | 6924
      |  276
```

APPROXIMATE SQUARE ROOTS

Long division method of finding square roots is also used to find approximate square roots of numbers or decimal fractions upto certain decimal places. These numbers are not perfect squares. So, their square roots are not exact numbers but they are decimal fractions. Let us have some examples.

Example 4. **Find the square root of 0·019 upto three decimal places.**

Solution : Using the division method

Sq. root of 0·019 upto four decimal places = 0·1378

But the last decimal digit is more than 5

∴ Sq. root up to 3 decimal places = **0·138** *Ans.*

```
         0.1378
    1 | 0·01 90 00 00
      | 1
   23 |   90
      |   69
  267 |  2100
      |  1869
 2748 | 23100
      | 21984
      |  1116
```

Example 5. **Find the square root of 5 upto three decimal places.**

Solution : By long division method, we find that

$\sqrt{5}$ upto 4 decimal places = 2·2366

∴ 4th decimal figure is more than 5

∴ $\sqrt{5}$ upto three decimal places = **2·237** *Ans.*

```
          2.2366
     2 | 5·00 00 00 00
       | 4
    42 | 100
       |  84
   443 | 1600
       | 1329
  4466 | 27100
       | 26796
 44726 | 30400
       | 26832
       |  3568
```

Example 6. **Find the square root of $2\frac{1}{12}$ upto three decimal places.**

24

Solution : $2\dfrac{1}{12} = \dfrac{25}{12} = \dfrac{25 \times 12}{12 \times 12}$

$\therefore \sqrt{2\dfrac{1}{12}} = \sqrt{\dfrac{25 \times 12}{12 \times 12}} = \dfrac{\sqrt{300}}{12}$

Now $\sqrt{300} = 17\cdot320$

$\therefore \dfrac{\sqrt{300}}{12} = \dfrac{17\cdot320}{12} = 1\cdot443$

$\therefore \sqrt{2\dfrac{1}{12}} = \dfrac{\sqrt{300}}{12} = \textbf{1·443}$ Ans.

```
              17·3202
    1 │ 3̄0̄0̄·0̄0̄ 0̄0̄ 0̄0̄
      │ 1
   27 │ 200
      │ 189
  343 │ 1100
      │ 1029
 3462 │   7100
      │   6924
346402│      760000
      │      692804
```

USE OF SQUARE ROOT TABLES

We have seen that square roots of non-perfect squares are not rational numbers. In such cases, a rational number is found whose square is nearly equal to the number whose square root is to be found. Such square roots are approximate, not exact.

We learnt to find approximate square roots by long division. But it is very time-consuming as well as cumbersome. So, tables have been prepared that list the approximate square roots of different numbers. These tables can be used as a help. Two such tables have been given on the next page.

Example 7.   Find the sq. root of 5 with the help of the sq. root table.

Solution :   Observe the row containing 5 in the table.

The value of the sq. root of 5 given in the table is 2·236.

$\therefore \sqrt{5} = \textbf{2·236}$ Ans.

Example 8. Find the value of $\sqrt{14\cdot58}$.

Solution :   We know that—

$14 < 14\cdot58 < 15$

$\therefore \sqrt{14} < \sqrt{14\cdot58} < \sqrt{15}$

From the square root table, $\sqrt{14} = \textbf{3·742}$

and $\sqrt{15} = \textbf{3·873}$

$\therefore \sqrt{15} - \sqrt{14} = 3\cdot873 - 3\cdot742 = \textbf{·131}$

Now difference between 15 and 14 is 1 and difference between 14 and 14·58 is ·58

By Unitary Method—

If the difference is 1, the difference in square roots = ·131

If the difference is ·58, the difference in sq. roots.   = ·131 × ·58

$= \cdot07598 = \textbf{·076}$ (up to 3 decimal places)

$\therefore \sqrt{14\cdot58} = \sqrt{14} + \cdot076 = 3\cdot742 + \cdot076 = \textbf{3·818}$ Ans.

SQUARE ROOT TABLES

TABLE I

x	1	1·1	1·2	1·3	1·4	1·5	1·6	1·7	1·8	1·9
x^2	1	1·21	1·44	1·69	1·96	2·25	2·56	2·89	3·24	3·61

TABLE II

Number	Square Root	Number	Square Root	Number	Square Root
1	1·000	34	5·831	67	8·185
2	1·414	35	5·916	68	8·246
3	1·732	36	6·000	69	8·307
4	2·000	37	6·083	70	8·367
5	2·236	38	6·164	71	8·426
6	2·449	39	6·245	72	8·485
7	2·646	40	6·325	73	8·544
8	2·828	41	6·403	74	8·602
9	3·000	42	6·481	75	8·660
10	3·162	43	6·557	76	8·718
11	3·317	44	6·633	77	8·775
12	3·464	45	6·708	78	8·832
13	3·606	46	6·782	79	8·888
14	3·742	47	6·856	80	8·944
15	3·873	48	6·928	81	9·000
16	4·000	49	7·000	82	9·055
17	4·123	50	7·071	83	9·110
18	4·243	51	7·141	84	9·165
19	4·359	52	7·211	85	9·220
20	4·472	53	7·280	86	9·274
21	4·583	54	7·348	87	9·327
22	4·690	55	7·416	88	9·381
23	4·796	56	7·483	89	9·434
24	4·899	57	7·550	90	9·487
25	5·000	58	7·616	91	9·539
26	5·099	59	7·681	92	9·592
27	5·196	60	7·746	93	9·644
28	5·292	61	7·810	94	9·695
29	5·385	62	7·874	95	9·747
30	5·477	63	7·937	96	9·798
31	5·568	64	8·000	97	9·849
32	5·657	65	8·062	98	9·899
33	5·745	66	8·124	99	9·950

Example 9. Find the square root of 4955 with the help of the square root table.

Solution : $4955 = 49 \cdot 55 \times 100$

∴ $\sqrt{4955} = \sqrt{49 \cdot 55} \times \sqrt{100} = \sqrt{49 \cdot 55} \times 10$

Now $49 < 49 \cdot 55 < 50$ or $\sqrt{49} < \sqrt{49 \cdot 55} < \sqrt{50}$

From the table, $\sqrt{49} = 7$ and $\sqrt{50} = \textbf{7·071}$

∴   Difference in both the square roots $= (7 \cdot 071 - 7) = \textbf{·07}$

For a difference $(50 - 49)$, *i.e.* 1, difference in sq. roots $= ·071$

For a difference of $·55$, difference in sq. roots $= ·55 \times ·071$

$= ·03905 = \textbf{·0391}$

∴ $\sqrt{49 \cdot 55} = 7 + ·0391 = 7 \cdot 0391$

and $\sqrt{4955} = \sqrt{49 \cdot 55} \times 10 = 7 \cdot 0391 \times 10 = \textbf{70·391}$ *Ans.*

Example 10. Find the diagonal of a rectangle whose sides are 8 cm. and 5 cm.

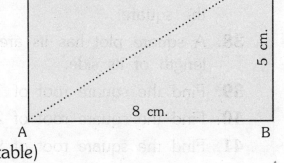

Solution : Side AB = 8 cm.

Side BC = 5 cm.

∵ ABC is a rt. Δ

∴ $AC^2 = AB^2 + BC^2$

$= 8^2 + 5^2$

$= 64 + 25 = 89$

∴ $AC = \sqrt{89} = 9 \cdot 434$ (From the table)

Hence AC = **9·434 cm.** *Ans.*

Example 11. Find the square root of 25725.

Solution : $25725 = 5^2 \times 7^2 \times 21$

∴ $\sqrt{25725} = \sqrt{5^2 \times 7^2 \times 21} = 5 \times 7 \times \sqrt{21} = 35 \times \sqrt{21}$

$= 35 \times 4 \cdot 583$ $(\because \sqrt{21} = 4 \cdot 583,$ *from the table)*

$= 160 \cdot 405 = \textbf{160·41}$ *Ans.*

PRACTICE EXERCISES 4

A. Find the square roots up to three decimal places : :

1. 3	2. 7	3. 6	4. 2	5. 8
6. 0·9	7. 2·8	8. 0·4	9. 0·8	10. 5·6
11. 1·6	12. 0·2	13. 19·2	14. 0·016	15. 3·6
16. $\frac{5}{8}$	17. $\frac{2}{9}$	18. $\frac{2}{3}$	19. $\frac{1}{9}$	20. $\frac{7}{12}$

B. Find the square roots up to three decimal places :

21. $10\frac{2}{3}$ **22.** $29\frac{4}{25}$ **23.** $39\frac{1}{16}$ **24.** $10\frac{1}{36}$

25. $\frac{25\cdot6}{52\cdot9}$ **26.** $\frac{3}{7}$ **27.** $2\frac{11}{18}$ **28.** $\frac{1}{2}$

29. 99×396 **30.** $\frac{243}{867}$ **31.** $\frac{1\cdot44}{2\cdot25}$ **32.** $\frac{2023}{1183}$

C. 33. A decimal fraction when multiplied by itself results in $6\cdot4009$. Find the fraction.

34. A decimal fraction is multiplied by itself. The product so obtained is $0\cdot00037249$. Find the decimal fraction.

35. The area of a square field is $27\cdot6676$ sq. m. Find the length of its side.

36. The area of a rectangular field with sides $61\cdot2$ metres and $6\cdot8$ metres is equal to the area of a square field. Find the side of the square field.

37. The area of a square field is equal to the area of a rectangular field with sides 24 metres and 15 metres. Find the approximate length of the side of the square.

38. A square plot has its area to be $6\cdot50$ square metres. Find the approximate length of its side.

39. Find the square root of 13 correct to four decimal places.

40. Find the square root of $237\cdot615$ up to four decimal places.

41. Find the square root of 96 up to three decimal places.

42. The square root $14 = 3\cdot7416$. Write it as a square root up to—

   (a) three decimal places   *(b) two decimal places*

E. Write yes or no :

43. (a) The square root of a two-digit number is a single-digit number.

   (b) The square root of a single-digit number is a single-digit number.

   (c) The square root of a three-digit or four-digit number has three digits.

   (d) If a square root has three digits, its square must have five or six digits.

F. 44. Pair off the digits of the following numbers for finding their square roots.

   (a) $\cdot848241$ *(b)* 4401604 *(c)* 82264900

   (d) $84321\cdot167$ *(e)* $0\cdot00008281$ *(f)* $0\cdot07176$

3 REAL NUMBERS

KNOW THESE TERMS :
1. **natural numbers**— numbers used for counting and beginning from one
2. **whole numbers**— numbers used for writing numerals and beginning from 0
3. **integers**— *negative* and *positive* whole numbers are collectively called integers
4. **real numbers**— numbers including *natural* and *whole* numbers, *integers* and *rational* numbers

---

We have read about various number-systems in the previous two books of this series. We know that—

1. Numbers 1, 2, 3, 4, 5, 6............. are called **Natural Numbers** (N) for counting numbers.

2. Numbers 0, 1, 2, 3, 4, 5, 6.......... are called **Whole Numbers** (W)

   It is clear that every natural number is a whole number but 0 is a whole number, not a natural number.

3. All *whole numbers* together with their *negatives* are called **integers** ; as—

   – 4, – 3, – 2, – 1, 0, 1, 2, 3, 4..........

   Remember that—

   (a) – 4, – 3, – 2, – 1 are *negative integers.*

   (b) 0 is *neither* a *positive integer* nor a *negative integer.*

   (c) 1, 2, 3, 4....... are *positive integers.*

4. Numbers of the form $\dfrac{p}{q}$ where p, q are natural numbers are called **fractions** ; as : $\dfrac{3}{4}, \dfrac{5}{6}, \dfrac{2}{3}, \dfrac{7}{8}$ etc.

5. Numbers of the form $\dfrac{p}{q}$ where p and q are integers and q is not equal to 0 are called **rational numbers** ; as—

   $\dfrac{-3}{5}, \dfrac{7}{-9}, \dfrac{-11}{-13}, \dfrac{13}{16}$ etc.

Form the above details, the following facts are quite clear—

(a) Every natural number is a rational number.

(b) Every whole number is a rational number.

(c) Every integer is a rational number.

(d) Every fraction is a rational number.

Moreover—

(a) Every rational number has its equivalents ; as—

$$\frac{p}{q} = \frac{2p}{2q} = \frac{3p}{3q} \ldots\ldots\ldots$$

(b) All properties of *addition, subtraction, multiplication* and *division* hold good for rational numbers.

(c) Every rational number has its *additive inverse* ; as—

$\frac{p}{q}$ has its additive inverse $\frac{-p}{q}$

(d) Every non-zero rational number has its *reciprocal*.

$\frac{p}{q}$ has its reciprocal $\frac{q}{p}$

(e) Every rational number has its decimal form. This form is either terminating or recurring ; as—

1. Rational number $\frac{3}{4} = 0.75$ ....   *(a terminating decimal)*

2. Rational number $\frac{1}{3} = 0.\overline{3}$ ....   *(a recurring decimal)*

(f) Every rational number can be represented on a number-line.

LIMITATION OF RATIONAL NUMBERS

We have just read that every rational number can be represented on a number-line. In other words, there is certainly a point on the number-line for every rational number.

It was held that all points making a number-line stand for rational numbers and that irrational numbers have no place on the number-line. But it is not so. There are points that stand for irrational numbers also. These points cannot be represented by rational numbers though they exist on the number-line quite densely. Let us have a few examples.

A. Suppose the point O shown on the number-line given in front stands for the rational number 0. Clearly. OA = 1 unit.

If we draw a rt. $\triangle$ OAB with its side AB = OA = 1, we get

$$OB^2 = OA^2 + AB^2 = 1^2 + 1^2 = 1 + 1 = 2$$

$\therefore$ OB $= \sqrt{2}$ units

If we draw an arc with centre O and radius OB, it will cut the number-line at a point (say P).

Clearly, **OP = OA = $\sqrt{2}$**. Hence pt. P marks off $\sqrt{2}$ units.

But $\sqrt{2}$ is not a rational number. It is an **irrational number.**

B. If we draw a line-segment perpendicular to the number-line at P, then cut off PD = AB = 1 and then join OD, we shall get a rt. Δ OPD.

In rt. Δ OPD

$OD^2 = OP^2 + PD^2$

$\qquad = (\sqrt{2})^2 + (1)^2 = 2 + 1 = 3$

$\therefore$ OD = $\sqrt{3}$, *i.e.* if we draw an arc with centre O and radius OD, it will cut the number-line at Q.

$\therefore$ OQ = $\sqrt{3}$ or point Q will mark off $\sqrt{3}$ units

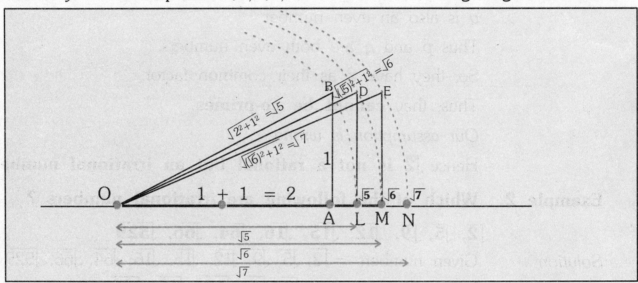

Similarly we can represent $\sqrt{5}, \sqrt{6}, \sqrt{7}$ as shown in the figure given below.

From the above explanation, it clearly follows that **irrational numbers** are as meaningful as **rational numbers** which include *natural numbers, whole numbers,* integers as well. Thus a new number-system is their and it has been named **Real Numbers**. This number-system is denoted by the letter R.

REAL NUMBERS

Real numbers refer to the number-system that includes natural numbers, whole numbers, integers and rational numbers. Thus we see that—

1. *Every point on a number-line stands for a real number.*
2. *Every number whether +ve or –ve, has its square root that can be represented on a number-line.*
3. *Real numbers do not make the final system of numbers. Researches are going on and any new number-system may follow it.*

Example 1. **Prove that $\sqrt{2}$ is an irrational number.**

Solution : Assume that $\sqrt{2}$ is a rational number

∴ it can be expressed in the form $\frac{p}{q}$ where $q \neq 0$ and p, q are co-primes

Now $\sqrt{2} = \frac{p}{q}$ or $2 = \frac{p^2}{q^2}$ or $2q^2 = p^2$

∵ $2q^2$ is certainly an even number   (∵ *it is a multiple of 2*)

∴ p^2 is also an even number

Hence p is also an even number   (∵ $p = \sqrt{p^2}$)

Now suppose $p = 2a$, then

$p^2 = (2a)^2 = 4a^2$ or $2q^2 = 4a^2$ (∵ $p^2 = 2q^2$)

∴ $q^2 = 2a^2$ and so q^2 is an even number.

∴ q is also an even number.

Thus p and q are both even numbers.

So, they have 2 as their common factor.

Thus, they **cannot be co-primes**.

∴ *Our assumption is wrong.*

Hence $\sqrt{2}$ **is not a rational but an irrational number.**

Example 2. **Which of the following are irrational numbers ?**

$\sqrt{2}, \sqrt{5}, \sqrt{9}, \sqrt{12}, \sqrt{15}, \sqrt{16}, \sqrt{64}, \sqrt{66}, \sqrt{529}$

Solution : Given numbers $= \sqrt{2}, \sqrt{5}, \sqrt{9}, \sqrt{12}, \sqrt{15}, \sqrt{16}, \sqrt{64}, \sqrt{66}, \sqrt{529}$

∴ Irrational numbers $= \sqrt{2}, \sqrt{5}, \sqrt{12}, \sqrt{15}, \sqrt{66}$ *Ans.*

Example 3. **Represent $\sqrt{10}$ on a number line.**

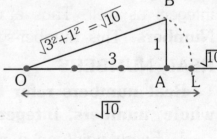

Solution : $10 = 9 + 1 = 3^2 + 1$

So, we shall take the following steps :

1. Take a point O on the number-line

2. Mark off 3 units on it such that
   OA = 3

3. Draw a perpendicular AB on the number-line at A = 1 unit

4. Join OB which is equal to $\sqrt{3^2 + 1^2} = \sqrt{9 + 1} = \sqrt{10}$

5. With O as centre and OB as radius, draw an arc that cuts the number-line at L.
   Then OL = OB = $\sqrt{10}$ *Ans.*

Example 4. Solve : (a) $\dfrac{1}{\sqrt{3}} + \sqrt{2}$ (b) $\dfrac{\sqrt{3} + 1}{\sqrt{3} - 1}$ (c) $\dfrac{3}{\sqrt{5} - 1}$

Solution : (a) $\dfrac{1}{\sqrt{3}} + \sqrt{2} = \left(\dfrac{1}{\sqrt{3}} \times \dfrac{\sqrt{3}}{\sqrt{3}} \right) + \sqrt{2}$

$$= \dfrac{\sqrt{3}}{\sqrt{3} \times \sqrt{3}} + \sqrt{2} = \dfrac{\sqrt{3}}{3} + \sqrt{2}$$

$$= \dfrac{1 \cdot 732}{3} + 1 \cdot 414 = 0 \cdot 577 + 1 \cdot 414$$

$$= \mathbf{1 \cdot 991} \; Ans.$$

(b) $\dfrac{\sqrt{3} + 1}{\sqrt{3} - 1} = \dfrac{(\sqrt{3} + 1)\,(\sqrt{3} + 1)}{(\sqrt{3} - 1)\,(\sqrt{3} + 1)}$

$$= \dfrac{(\sqrt{3} + 1)^2}{(\sqrt{3})^2 - (1)^2} = \dfrac{3 + 1 + 2\sqrt{3} \times 1}{3 - 1}$$

$$= \dfrac{4 + 2\sqrt{3}}{2} = \dfrac{4 + 1 \cdot 732 \times 2}{2}$$

$$= \dfrac{4 + 3 \cdot 464}{2} = \dfrac{7 \cdot 464}{2} = \mathbf{3 \cdot 732} \; Ans.$$

(c) $\dfrac{3}{\sqrt{5} - 1} = \dfrac{3\,(\sqrt{5} + 1)}{(\sqrt{5} - 1\,(\sqrt{5} + 1)} = \dfrac{3\sqrt{5} + 3}{(\sqrt{5})^2 - (1)^2}$

$$= \dfrac{3\sqrt{5} + 3}{5 - 1} = \dfrac{3\sqrt{5} + 3}{4}$$

$$= \dfrac{(3 \times 2 \cdot 236) + 3}{4} = \dfrac{6 \cdot 708 + 3}{4}$$

$$= \dfrac{9 \cdot 708}{4} = \mathbf{2 \cdot 427} \; Ans.$$

REMEMBER THESE FACTS ABOUT REAL NUMBERS :

1. The sum of two real numbers is always a real number.
2. All properties of rational numbers hold good for real numbers.
3. Every real number has its *additive inverse*.
4. The product of two real numbers is a real number.
5. Every real number has its *reciprocal*.
6. The negative of an irrational number is an irrational number.
7. The sum of a rational and an irrational number is an irrational number.
8. The product of a rational number and an irrational number is an irrational number.
9. The *sum, difference, product* or *quotient* obtained from two irrational numbers is not always irrational.

33

PRACTICE EXERCISES 5

A. Which of the following are irrational numbers ?

    1. $\sqrt{15}$ **2.** $\sqrt{16}$ **3.** $\sqrt{31}$ **4.** $\sqrt{32}$ **5.** $\sqrt{49}$

    6. $\sqrt{25}$ **7.** $\sqrt{125}$ **8.** $\sqrt{12}$ **9.** $\sqrt{72}$ **10.** $\sqrt{2 \cdot 3145}$

B. 11. Calculate the square roots of 6 and 11 to prove that they are irrational numbers.

C. Write—

    12. two irrational numbers whose sum is a rational number.

    13. two irrational numbers whose difference is a rational number.

    14. two irrational numbers whose product is a rational number.

    15. two irrational numbers whose quotient is a rational number.

    16. a real number that is not rational.

D. Represent the following irrational numbers on the number-line.

    17. $\sqrt{7}$ **18.** $\sqrt{5}$ **19.** $\sqrt{3}$ **20.** $\sqrt{10}$

E. Write yes or no :

    21. $\sqrt{5} \times \sqrt{5}$ is an irrational number.

    22. All integers are rational numbers.

    23. 0 is neither positive nor negative.

    24. Every point on a number-line marks a real number.

    25. All rational numbers are real numbers too.

    26. Every real number has its *additive inverse.*

    27. Every real number has its *multiplicative inverse.*

    28. Irrational numbers can be shown on the number-line.

    29. Real numbers make the final number-system.

    30. $\sqrt{3}$ is an irrational number.

F. Simplify :

    31. $\dfrac{1}{\sqrt{2}} + \sqrt{5}$ **32.** $\dfrac{1}{3} + \sqrt{2}$ **33.** $(\sqrt{5} - 3)^2$

    34. $\dfrac{1}{\sqrt{5} + \sqrt{3}}$ **35.** $(\sqrt{2} + 1)(\sqrt{2} - 1)$ **36.** $\dfrac{\sqrt{3} - \sqrt{2}}{\sqrt{3} + \sqrt{2}}$

    37. Represent a point on a number line that stands for $\sqrt{5}$.

4 CUBES AND CUBE ROOTS

KNOW THESE TERMS :
1. **cube**—product obtained by multiplying a number by itself twice
2. **cube root**—cube root of a given number is a number which, when multiplied by itself twice, gives the given number.
3. **perfect cube**—a number that has an integral cube root or a number whose prime factors exist in triplets

WHAT IS A CUBE ?

We know that in geometry, a cube is a solid figure with six surfaces of equal area. Each of its vertices forms a right angle and all of its 12 edges are of equal length.

If the edge of a cube is 12 cm., the total space occupied by the cube can be divided into 12 × 12 × 12 = 1728 smaller cubes. So, the volume of the bigger cube will be *1728 cubic centimetres.*

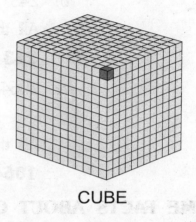

CUBE

In Arithmetic and Algebra, this very idea of a cube has been taken as a base and the **cube of a number** is defined as follows :

The *cube* of a quantity is the product obtained by multiplying the quantity by itself twice ; as—

$2 \times 2 \times 2 = \mathbf{8}$ $3 \times 3 \times 3 = \mathbf{27}$ $4 \times 4 \times 4 = \mathbf{64}$ $5 \times 5 \times 5 = \mathbf{125}$

$a \times a \times a = \mathbf{\textit{a}^3}$ $b \times b \times b = \mathbf{\textit{b}^3}$ $c \times c \times c = \mathbf{\textit{c}^3}$ $d \times d \times d = \mathbf{\textit{d}^3}$

We already know that the small number $3^{(3)}$ that appears on the top right of a, b, c and d is called the **index** or **exponent**. It shows that the quantity is to be taken *thrice* while finding its product.

PERFECT CUBES

Observe the table given in front. It gives the cubes of natural numbers from 1 to 20

The numbers printed in normal type are whole numbers while those printed in bold type are their cubes. Such numbers are called **perfect cubes** because they are exact cubic numbers and do not involve any *decimals* or *fractions.*

Number	Cube	Number	Cube
1	$1^3 = \mathbf{1}$	11	$11^3 = \mathbf{1331}$
2	$2^3 = \mathbf{8}$	12	$12^3 = \mathbf{1728}$
3	$3^3 = \mathbf{27}$	13	$13^3 = \mathbf{2197}$
4	$4^3 = \mathbf{64}$	14	$14^3 = \mathbf{2744}$
5	$5^3 = \mathbf{125}$	15	$15^3 = \mathbf{3375}$
6	$6^3 = \mathbf{216}$	16	$16^3 = \mathbf{4096}$
7	$7^3 = \mathbf{343}$	17	$17^3 = \mathbf{4913}$
8	$8^3 = \mathbf{512}$	18	$18^3 = \mathbf{5832}$
9	$9^3 = \mathbf{729}$	19	$19^3 = \mathbf{6851}$
10	$10^3 = \mathbf{1000}$	20	$20^3 = \mathbf{8000}$

In order to find whether a given number is a perfect cube or not, write the number as a product of its prime factors. If *these factors exist in triplets, the number is a perfect cube.* Let us now solve some examples :

Example 1. Which of the following are perfect cubes ?
   (a) **216**   (b) **243**   (c) **10648**

Solution :   (a) $216 = 2 \times 2 \times 2 \times 3 \times 3 \times 3 = (2 \times 2 \times 2) \times (3 \times 3 \times 3)$

$\because$ All the prime factors of 216 exist in triplets

$\therefore$ **216 is a perfect cube.** *Ans.*

(b) $243 = 3 \times 3 \times 3 \times 3 \times 3 = (3 \times 3 \times 3) \times 3 \times 3$

$\because$ All the prime factors of 243 do not exist in triplets.

$\therefore$ **243 is not a perfect cube.** *Ans.*

(c) $10648 = 2 \times 2 \times 2 \times 11 \times 11 \times 11$

$= (2 \times 2 \times 2) \times (11 \times 11 \times 11)$

$\because$ All the prime factors of 10648 exist in triplets

$\therefore$ **10648 is a perfect cube.** *Ans.*

SOME FACTS ABOUT CUBES

FACT 1

The cube of an even number is always even ; as—
(a) cube of $2 = 2 \times 2 \times 2 = $ **8**   (b) cube of $12 = 12 \times 12 \times 12 = $ **1728**

FACT 2

The cube of an odd number is always odd ; as—
(a) cube of $3 = 3 \times 3 \times 3 = $ **27**   (b) cube of $9 = 9 \times 9 \times 9 = $ **729**

FACT 3

The cube of any multiple of 2 is divisible by 8 ; as—
cube of $4 = 4 \times 4 \times 4 = $ **64** which is divisible by 8.
cube of $10 = 10 \times 10 \times 10 = $ **1000** which is divisible by 8.

FACT 4

The cube of any multiple of 3 is divisible by 27 :
cube of $9 = 9 \times 9 \times 9 = $ **729** which is divisible by 27.
cube of $12 = 12 \times 12 \times 12 = $ **1728** which is divisible by 27.

FACT 5

The cube of a natural number of the form $(3x + 1)$ is a number with the same form ; as—

$(3 \times 1 + 1)^3, = 4^3 = 4 \times 4 \times 4 = 64 = (3 \times 21 + 1)$

$(3 \times 2 + 1)^3, = 7^3 = 7 \times 7 \times 7 = 343 = (3 \times 114 + 1)$

FACT 6

The cube of a natural number of the form $(3x + 2)$ is a number with the same form ; as—

$(3 \times 1 + 2)^3, = 5^3 = 5 \times 5 \times 5 = 125 = (3 \times 41 + 2)$

$(3 \times 2 + 2)^3, = 8^3 = 8 \times 8 \times 8 = 512 = (3 \times 170 + 2)$

FACT 7

The cube of a negative number is always negative ; as—

$(-1)^3 = (-1) \times (-1) \times (-1) = 1 \times (-1) = -1$ which is negative.

$(-2)^3 = (-2) \times (-2) \times (-2) = 4 \times (-2) = -8$ which is negative.

FACT 8

The cube of a positive number is always positive ; as—

$(2)^3 = 2 \times 2 \times 2 = 8$ which is positive.

$(5)^3 = 5 \times 5 \times 5 = 125$ which is positive.

FACT 9

The cube of a rational number is equal to the cube of its numerator divided by the cube of its denominator ; as—

$$\left(\frac{3}{4}\right)^3 = \frac{3^3}{4^3} = \frac{27}{64} \text{ and } \left(\frac{a}{b}\right)^3 = \frac{a^3}{b^3}$$

Example 2. Show that 2744 is a perfect cube. Also find the number whose cube it is.

Solution : $\quad 2744 = 2 \times 2 \times 2 \times 7 \times 7 \times 7 = (2 \times 2 \times 2) \times (7 \times 7 \times 7)$

$\because$ All the factors of 2744 exist in triplets

$\therefore$ **2744 is a perfect cube of $2 \times 7 = 14$** *Ans.*

Example 3. Find the smallest number by which 1323 be multiplied so that it may become a perfect cube.

Solution : $\quad 1323 \quad = 3 \times 3 \times 3 \times 7 \times 7 \quad\quad = (3 \times 3 \times 3) \times 7 \times 7$

As factor 7 is only a pair, the required number = **7** *Ans.*

Example 4. Find the smallest number by which 8788 be divided so that the quotient is a perfect cube.

Solution : $8788 = 13 \times 13 \times 13 \times 2 \times 2 = (13 \times 13 \times 13) \times 2 \times 2$

∵ The factor 2 is only a pair, not a triplet

∴ 8788 must be divided by 2×2, *i.e.* by **4 Ans.**

PRACTICE EXERCISES 6

A. Find the cubes of the following numbers :

1. 9	**2.** 17	**3.** 19	**4.** 14	**5.** 16
6. 10	**7.** 20	**8.** 30	**9.** 40	**10.** 50
11. 0·5	**12.** 1·2	**13.** 0·8	**14.** 0·06	**15.** 2·5
16. $\frac{2}{3}$	**17.** $\frac{4}{5}$	**18.** $1\frac{3}{14}$	**19.** $\frac{1}{17}$	**20.** $\frac{11}{14}$
21. –7	**22.** –p	**23.** $-1\frac{2}{3}$	**24.** $\frac{-x}{y}$	**25.** $\frac{c}{-d}$

B. Which of the following are perfect cubes ?

26. 128	**27.** 432	**28.** 392	**29.** 27000	**30.** 675
31. 125	**32.** 15625	**33.** 4096	**34.** 108	**35.** 10976

C. 36. By which smallest number should we multiply 5400 so that the product may be a perfect cube.

37. Find the smallest number by which 6655 be divided so that the quotient is a perfect cube.

38. One side of a cube is 11 metres. What is its volume ?

39. Verify each of the following by three examples :

(a) The cube of a natural number of the form $3x + 1$ is of the same form.

(b) The cube of a natural number of the form $3x + 2$ of the same form.

B. CUBE ROOTS

The *cube root* of a given number is the number which when multiplied by itself twice gives the given number ; as—

(a) $\sqrt[3]{1} = \mathbf{1}$ because $1 \times 1 \times 1 = 1$ (b) $\sqrt[3]{8} = \mathbf{2}$ because $2 \times 2 \times 2 = 8$

(b) $\sqrt[3]{27} = \mathbf{3}$ because $3 \times 3 \times 3 = 27$ (d) $\sqrt[3]{a^3} = \mathbf{a}$ because $a \times a \times a = a^3$

Remember that—

1. The symbol for **cube root** is $\sqrt[3]{}$.
2. The cube root of an even number is even.
3. The cube root of a negative number is negative.
4. The number whose cube root is found is called the **radicand**
5. The symbol $\sqrt{}$ is called the **radical sign** or **surd**.
6. The small number written in the bend of the radical sign is called **root index**.
7. The symbol for cube root ($\sqrt[3]{}$) is almost similar to the symbol for square root. But while using the symbol $\sqrt{}$ for square root, we should actually use 2 with the radical sign as $\sqrt[2]{}$. But because square root is the lowest root, *i.e.* there is no root below it. So, we generally omit the small figure (^{2}).

FINDING CUBE ROOTS THROUGH FACTORS

Example 1. Find the cube root of 74088.

Solution :

$$74088 = 2 \times 2 \times 2 \times 3 \times 3 \times 3 \times 7 \times 7 \times 7$$
$$= (2\times2\times2) \times (3\times3\times3) \times (7\times7\times7)$$
$$\therefore \ \sqrt[3]{74088} = 2 \times 3 \times 7 = \textbf{42 } Ans.$$

2	74088
2	37044
2	18522
3	9261
3	3087
3	1029
7	343
7	49
	7

From this example, the rule for finding cube root by factorization is clear as under :

1. Resolve the given perfect cube into its prime factors.
2. Group the factors into triplets.
3. Take one factor out of each triplet.
4. Multiply all the factors taken from the triplets. Their product will be the required cube root of the given number.

Example 2. Find the cube root of – 5832

Solution :

$$-5832 = 2 \times 2 \times 2 \times 3 \times 3 \times 3 \times 3 \times 3 \times 3$$
$$= (2\times2\times2) \times (3\times3\times3) \times (3\times3\times3)$$
$$\therefore \ \sqrt[3]{5832} = 2 \times 3 \times 3 = 18$$

Hence cube root of – 5832 = **–18** *Ans.*

2	5832
2	2916
2	1458
3	729
3	243
3	81
3	27
3	9
	3

The following rule is clear from this example :

1. Resolve the negative perfect cube into its prime factors without its minus (–).
2. Group the factors into triplets and find the cube root of the positive number.
3. Put minus (–) before the cube root found in this way.

Example 3. Find the values of :

(a) $\sqrt[3]{343 \times 216}$ (b) $\sqrt[3]{343} \times \sqrt[3]{216}$

Solution : (a) 343×216

$$= (7 \times 7 \times 7) \times (2 \times 2 \times 2) \times (3 \times 3 \times 3)$$

$$\therefore \sqrt[3]{343 \times 216} = 7 \times 2 \times 3 = \textbf{42} \text{ Ans.}$$

(b) $343 = 7 \times 7 \times 7$ and $216 = (2 \times 2 \times 2) \times (3 \times 3 \times 3)$

$$\therefore \sqrt[3]{343} = \textbf{7} \text{ and } \sqrt[3]{216} = 2 \times 3 = \textbf{6}$$

$$\therefore \sqrt[3]{343} \times \sqrt[3]{216} = 7 \times 6 = \textbf{42} \text{ Ans.}$$

7	343
7	49
	7

2	216
2	108
2	54
3	27
3	9
	3

If we observe this example with care we shall come to know that—

The product of the cube roots of two perfect cubes is equal to the cube root of their product ; *i.e.*

$$\sqrt[3]{343} \times \sqrt[3]{216} = \sqrt[3]{343 \times 216}$$

Example 4. Prove that $\sqrt[3]{8} \times \sqrt[3]{729} = \sqrt[3]{8 \times 729}$

Solution : $\sqrt[3]{8} = \sqrt[3]{2 \times 2 \times 2} = \textbf{2}$

$\sqrt[3]{729} = \sqrt[3]{(3 \times 3 \times 3) \times (3 \times 3 \times 3)} = 3 \times 3 = \textbf{9}$

$$\therefore \sqrt[3]{8} \times \sqrt[3]{729} = 2 \times 9 = \textbf{18} \dots\dots\dots\dots \text{ (i)}$$

$\sqrt[3]{8 \times 729} = \sqrt[3]{2 \times 2 \times 2 \times 3 \times 3 \times 3 \times 3 \times 3 \times 3}$

$$= \sqrt[3]{(2 \times 2 \times 2) \times (3 \times 3 \times 3) \times (3 \times 3 \times 3)}$$

$$= 2 \times 3 \times 3 = \textbf{18} \dots\dots\dots\dots \text{ (ii)}$$

From (i) and (ii)

$$\sqrt[3]{8} \times \sqrt[3]{729} = \sqrt[3]{8 \times 729} \text{ Ans.}$$

Example 5. Find the values of : (a) $\sqrt[3]{\dfrac{8}{125}}$ (b) $\sqrt[3]{\dfrac{-64}{1331}}$

Solution : (a) $\dfrac{8}{125} = \dfrac{2 \times 2 \times 2}{5 \times 5 \times 5} = \dfrac{2}{5} \times \dfrac{2}{5} \times \dfrac{2}{5} = \left(\dfrac{2}{5}\right)^3$

$$\sqrt[3]{\dfrac{8}{125}} = \sqrt[3]{\left(\dfrac{2}{5}\right)^3} = \dfrac{\textbf{2}}{\textbf{5}} \text{ Ans.}$$

(b) $\dfrac{-64}{1331} = \dfrac{-(2 \times 2 \times 2 \times 2 \times 2 \times 2)}{11 \times 11 \times 11} = \dfrac{-(4 \times 4 \times 4)}{11 \times 11 \times 11} = \left(\dfrac{-4}{11}\right)^3$

$$\sqrt[3]{\dfrac{-64}{1331}} = \sqrt[3]{\left(\dfrac{-4}{11}\right)^3} = \dfrac{\textbf{-4}}{\textbf{11}} \text{ Ans.}$$

Example 6. Prove that $\dfrac{\sqrt[3]{729}}{\sqrt[3]{1000}} = \sqrt[3]{\dfrac{729}{1000}}$

Solution :
$$\sqrt[3]{729} = \sqrt[3]{3 \times 3 \times 3 \times 3 \times 3 \times 3}$$
$$= \sqrt[3]{(3 \times 3 \times 3) \times (3 \times 3 \times 3)}$$
$$= 3 \times 3 = \mathbf{9} \quad .... \text{(i)}$$
$$= \sqrt[3]{1000} = \sqrt[3]{10 \times 10 \times 10} = \mathbf{10} \quad .... \text{(ii)}$$

From (i) and (ii)

$$\frac{\sqrt[3]{729}}{\sqrt[3]{1000}} = \frac{\mathbf{9}}{\mathbf{10}} \quad .... \text{(A)}$$

Again $\sqrt[3]{\dfrac{729}{1000}} = \sqrt[3]{\dfrac{3 \times 3 \times 3 \times 3 \times 3 \times 3}{10 \times 10 \times 10}} = \sqrt[3]{\dfrac{(3\times3\times3) \times (3\times3\times3)}{10 \times 10 \times 10}}$

$$= \frac{3 \times 3}{10} = \frac{\mathbf{9}}{\mathbf{10}} \quad .... \text{(B)}$$

From A and B, $\quad \dfrac{\sqrt[3]{729}}{\sqrt[3]{1000}} = \sqrt[3]{\dfrac{729}{1000}}$ *Ans.*

Example 7. By which smallest number should 26244 be multiplied so that the product is a perfect cube. Find that number and also its cube root.

Solution :
$$26244 = (2 \times 2) \times (3 \times 3) \times (3 \times 3 \times 3) \times (3 \times 3 \times 3)$$

Clearly, 2 and 3 have incomplete triplets *(only pairs)*.

So, Reqd. smallest No. $= 2 \times 3 = \mathbf{6}$ *Ans.*

∴ Reqd. perfect cube $= 26244 \times 6 = \mathbf{157464}$ *Ans.*

$157464 = (2\times2\times2) \times (3\times3\times3) \times (3\times3\times3) \times (3\times3\times3)$

∴ Reqd. cube root $= 2 \times 3 \times 3 \times 3 = \mathbf{54}$ *Ans.*

CUBE ROOT OF A DECIMAL NUMBER

Example 8. Find the cube root of 32·768.

Solution :
$$32 \cdot 768 = \frac{32768}{1000} \quad \therefore \quad \sqrt[3]{32 \cdot 768} = \frac{\sqrt[3]{32768}}{\sqrt[3]{1000}}$$

Now $32768 = 2^3 \times 2^3 \times 2^3 \times 2^3 \times 2^3$

∴ $\sqrt[3]{32768} = 2 \times 2 \times 2 \times 2 \times 2 = \mathbf{32}$

And $\sqrt[3]{1000} = \sqrt[3]{10 \times 10 \times 10} = \mathbf{10}$

∴ $\sqrt[3]{\dfrac{32768}{1000}} = \dfrac{32}{10} = \mathbf{3 \cdot 2}$ *Ans.*

2	26244
2	13122
3	6561
3	2187
3	729
3	243
3	81
3	27
3	9
	3

2	32768
2	16384
2	8192
2	4096
2	2048
2	1024
2	512
2	256
2	128
2	64
2	32
2	16
2	8
2	4
	2

Example 9. A metallic rectangular cuboid 25 cm. × 15 cm. × 9 cm. was melted to form a cube. Find the side of the cube.

Solution : Volume of the cuboid = 25 × 15 × 9 cu. cm. = 3375 cu. cm.

Volume of the cube = Volume of the cuboid = 3375 cu. cm.

∴ Side of the cube = $\sqrt[3]{3375}$ cm. = $\sqrt[3]{5 \times 5 \times 5 \times 3 \times 3 \times 3}$ cm.

= (5 × 3) cm. = **15 cm.** *Ans.*

PRACTICE EXERCISES 7

A. Find the cube root of :

1. 216   2. 1728   3. 343   4. 512   5. 729

6. 1157625   7. 157464   8. 216000   9. 21952   10. $5\frac{104}{125}$

11. 343   12. –343   13. ·343   14. ·027   15. ·000216

16. –1728   17. $\sqrt[3]{27} \times \sqrt[3]{64}$ 18. $\sqrt[3]{27 \times 64}$ 19. –287496   20. 21952

21. $\sqrt[3]{\dfrac{27}{125}}$ 22. $\sqrt[3]{\dfrac{-64}{1000}}$ 23. ·001331   24. – 5832

25. 3 × 2 × 2 × 3 × 2 × 3 × 5 × 5 × 5

26. 2 × 2 × 2 × 5 × 5 × 5 × 3 × 3 × 3 × 2 × 2 × 2

B. Show that—

27. $\sqrt[3]{64} \times \sqrt[3]{729} = \sqrt[3]{64 \times 729}$ 28. $\sqrt[3]{216} \times \sqrt[3]{-125} = \sqrt[3]{216 \times (-125)}$

29. $\sqrt[3]{343 \times 512} = \sqrt[3]{343} \times \sqrt[3]{512}$ 30. $\sqrt[3]{343} \times \sqrt[3]{-64} = \sqrt[3]{343 \times (-64)}$

31. $\sqrt[3]{\dfrac{729}{1000}} = \dfrac{\sqrt[3]{729}}{\sqrt[3]{1000}}$ 32. $\dfrac{\sqrt[3]{512}}{\sqrt[3]{-343}} = \sqrt[3]{\dfrac{512}{-343}}$

C. 33. By which smallest number must 5400 be multiplied to make it a perfect cube.

34. Find the smallest number by which 6655 be divided so that the quotient may be a perfect cube.

35. Find the smallest number by which 3087 may be divided to leave the quotient a perfect cube.

36. Find the smallest number by which 392 be multiplied so that the product may be a perfect cube.

37. Find the lowest number by which 36000 may be multiplied to make the product a perfect cube.

38. The volume of a cube is 32·768 m³. Find the length of its side.

39. The volume of a cubical box is 343000 cm³. Find the length of its side.

40. Three metallic cubes had their sides 5 cm. 10 cm. and 15 cm. respectively. They were melted and formed into a single cube. Find the side of the new cube .

TABLE OF CUBES AND CUBE ROOTS

x	$\sqrt[3]{x}$	$\sqrt[3]{10x}$	$\sqrt[3]{100x}$	x	$\sqrt[3]{x}$	$\sqrt[3]{10x}$	$\sqrt[3]{100x}$
1	1·000	2·154	4·642	51	3·708	7·990	17·21
2	1·260	2·714	5·848	52	3·733	8·041	17·32
3	1·442	3·107	6·694	53	3·756	8·093	17·44
4	1·587	3·420	7·368	54	3·780	8·143	17·54
5	1·710	3·684	7·937	55	3·803	8·193	17·65
6	1·817	3·915	8·434	56	3·826	8·243	17·76
7	1·913	4·121	8·879	57	3·849	8·291	17·86
8	2·000	4·309	9·283	58	3·871	8·340	17·97
9	2·080	4·481	9·655	59	3·893	8·387	18·07
10	2·154	4·642	10·00	60	3·915	8·434	18·17
11	2·224	4·791	10·32	61	3·936	8·481	18·27
12	2·289	4·932	10·63	62	3·958	8·527	18·37
13	2·351	5·066	10·91	63	3·979	8·573	18·47
14	2·410	5·192	11·19	64	4·000	8·618	18·57
15	2·466	5·313	11·45	65	4·021	8·662	18·66
16	2·520	5·429	11·70	66	4·041	8·707	18·76
17	2·571	5·540	11·93	67	4·062	8·750	18·85
18	2·621	5·646	12·16	68	4·082	8·794	18·95
19	2·668	5·749	12·39	69	4·102	8·837	19·04
20	2·714	5·848	12·60	70	4·121	8·879	19·13
21	2·759	5·944	12·81	71	4·141	8·921	19·22
22	2·802	6·037	13·01	72	4·160	8·963	19·21
23	2·844	6·127	13·20	73	4·179	9·004	19·40
24	2·884	6·214	13·39	74	4·198	9·045	19·49
25	2·924	6·300	13·57	75	4·217	9·086	19·57
26	2·962	6·383	13·75	76	4·236	9·126	19·66
27	3·000	6·463	13·92	77	4·254	9·166	19·75
28	3·037	6·542	14·09	78	4·273	9·205	19·83
29	3·072	6·619	14·26	79	4·291	9·244	19·92
30	3·107	6·694	14·42	80	4·309	9·283	20·00

x	$\sqrt[3]{x}$	$\sqrt[3]{10x}$	$\sqrt[3]{100x}$	x	$\sqrt[3]{x}$	$\sqrt[3]{10x}$	$\sqrt[3]{100x}$
31	3·141	6·768	14·58	81	4·327	9·322	20·08
32	3·175	6·840	14·74	82	4·344	9·360	20·17
33	3·208	6·910	14·89	83	4·362	9·398	20·25
34	3·240	6·980	15·04	84	4·380	9·435	20·33
35	3·271	7·047	15·18	85	4·397	9·473	20·41
36	3·302	7·114	15·33	86	4·414	9·510	20·49
37	3·332	7·179	15·47	87	4·431	9·546	20·57
38	3·362	7·243	15·60	88	4·448	9·583	20·65
39	3·391	7·306	15·74	89	4·465	9·619	20·72
40	3·420	7·368	15·87	90	4·481	9·655	20·80
41	3·448	7·429	16·01	91	4·498	9·691	20·88
42	3·476	7·489	16·13	92	4·514	9·726	20·95
43	3·503	7·548	16·26	93	4·531	9·761	21·03
44	3·530	7·606	16·39	94	4·547	9·796	21·10
45	3·557	7·663	16·51	95	4·563	9·830	21·18
46	3·583	7·719	16·63	96	4·579	9·865	21·25
47	3·609	7·775	16·75	97	4·595	9·899	21·33
48	3·634	7·830	16·87	98	4·610	9·933	21·40
49	3·659	7·884	16·98	99	4·626	9·967	21·47
50	3·684	7·937	17·10				

CUBE ROOT USING THE TABLE

Example 10. Using the cube root table, find the value of :

(a) $\sqrt[3]{37600}$ (b) $\sqrt[3]{73·8}$ (c) $\sqrt[3]{36}$ (d) $\sqrt[3]{384}$

Solution : (a) $37600 = 8 \times 100 \times 47$

$\therefore \sqrt[3]{37600} = \sqrt[3]{8 \times 100 \times 47} = \sqrt[3]{8} \times \sqrt[3]{100 \times 47}$

$= 2 \times 16·75 = \mathbf{33·50}$ *Ans. (using the table)*

(b) 73·8 is decimal number

$\because$ 73 < 73·8 < 74 and 73 < 73·8 by **·8**

$\therefore \sqrt[3]{73} < \sqrt[3]{73·8} < \sqrt[3]{74}$

From the cube root table

$\sqrt[3]{74} = 4·198$ and $\sqrt[3]{73} = 4·179$

44

Difference between the cube roots = 4·198 – 4·179 = **·019**

Difference between 74 and 73 = 1

Using unitary method—

If the difference is 1, the cube-root difference = ·019

If the difference is ·8, the cube-root difference = ·019 × ·8

$$= ·0152$$

$$\therefore \sqrt[3]{73·8} = \sqrt[3]{73} + 0.152 = 4·179 + ·0152 = \textbf{4·1942} \text{ Ans.}$$

(c) $\sqrt[3]{36} = \textbf{3·302}$ *Ans.*   (*using the table*)

(d) $\sqrt[3]{384} = \sqrt[3]{8 \times 48} = \sqrt[3]{8 \times 8 \times 6}$

$$= \sqrt[3]{8} \times \sqrt[3]{8} \times \sqrt[3]{6}$$

$$= 2 \times 2 \times \sqrt[3]{6} \text{ and the table gives } \sqrt[3]{6} = 1.817$$

$$\therefore \sqrt[3]{384} = 2 \times 2 \times 1·817 = 4 \times 1·817 = \textbf{7·268} \text{ Ans.}$$

Example 11. Find the cube root of $\sqrt[3]{\dfrac{85}{1728}}$

Solution : $\sqrt[3]{\dfrac{85}{1728}} = \dfrac{\sqrt[3]{85}}{\sqrt[3]{1728}} = \dfrac{\sqrt[3]{85}}{\sqrt[3]{12 \times 12 \times 12}} = \dfrac{\sqrt[3]{85}}{12} = \dfrac{1}{12} \times (\sqrt[3]{85})$

From the table $\sqrt[3]{85} = 4·397$

$$\therefore (\sqrt[3]{85}) \times \dfrac{1}{12} = 4·397 \times \dfrac{1}{12} = 0·366$$

$$\therefore \sqrt[3]{\dfrac{85}{1728}} = \textbf{0·366} \text{ Ans.}$$

PRACTICE EXERCISES 8

A. Find the cube root using the cube root table :

1. 6   **2.** 60   **3.** 600   **4.** 696

5. 29600   **6.** $\dfrac{32}{216}$ **7.** $\dfrac{23}{343}$ **8.** 752

9. 7344   **10.** 792   **11.** $\dfrac{31}{216}$ **12.** $\dfrac{26}{729}$

B.13. A cube has its volume equal to 99 cubic cm. Find the approximate length of its side.

14. The volume of a cube is 6400 cu. cm. Find the approximate length of its side.

15. The volume of a cube is 632 cubic cm. Find the approximate length of the side of the cube.

5 EXPONENTS OR INDICES

The word—**exponent**—means *a thing that expresses something stated.*

In mathematics, *an exponent is a symbol written at the top right of a number or letter to show how many times the quantity is to be multiplied by itself* ; as—

In a^4, *a* is the quantity and 4 is its exponent.

In 12^3, 12 is the quantity and 3 is its exponent.

Another word for an exponent is **index**. Its plural is **indices** (in-di-seez).

In this lesson, we shall study *indices, i.e. exponents* in detail.

RATIONAL NUMBERS AS EXPONENTS

We know that $a \times a \times a \times a \times a = a^5$

and $2 \times 2 \times 2 \times 2 \times 2 \times 2 = 2^6$

We read these quantities as *a* **raised to power 5** and *2* **raised to power 6**.

In a^5, *a* is called the **base** while **5** is called the **index** or **exponent**.

In 2^6, **2** is called the **base** while **6** is called the **index** or **exponent**.

In $\left(\dfrac{3}{4}\right)^{-4}$, $\dfrac{3}{4}$ is the **base** while **– 4** is the **index** or **exponent**

In the previous class, we learnt some important laws about exponents, *i.e.* indices. Let us review them.

1. $a^m \times a^n = a^{m+n}$ 2. $a^m \div a^n = a^{m-n}$ 3. $(a^m)^n = a^{mn}$ 4. $(ab)^n = a^n b^n$

5. $\left(\dfrac{a}{b}\right)^n = \dfrac{a^n}{b^n}$ 6. $a^{-2} = \dfrac{1}{a^2}$ 7. $a^0 = 1$ 8. $\left(\dfrac{a}{b}\right)^{-3} = \left(\dfrac{b}{a}\right)^3$

RECIPROCALS OF RATIONAL NUMBERS AS EXPONENTS

We have read about squares, square roots, cubes and cube roots in detail in the previous lesson. We know that—

$2^2 = 4$ and inversely $\sqrt[2]{4} = 2$

We read them as (a) **2 raised to the power 2 is 4.**

  (b) **square root of 4 is 2.**

Can we write $\sqrt[2]{4}$ in the form of an exponent ? Yes, we can write it as $4^{\frac{1}{2}}$, i.e. **4 raised to power half**. Let us try to understand it.

$4^{\frac{1}{2}} \times 4^{\frac{1}{2}} = 4^{\frac{1}{2}+\frac{1}{2}} = 4^1$ (*we have multiplied the factor $4^{\frac{1}{2}}$ twice to get 4^1*)

So, $4^{\frac{1}{2}}$ **is the square root of 4**

Similarly, $4^{\frac{1}{3}} \times 4^{\frac{1}{3}} \times 4^{\frac{1}{3}} = 4^{\frac{1}{3}+\frac{1}{3}+\frac{1}{3}} = 4^{\frac{3}{3}} = 4^1$

Clearly, we have multiplied the factor $4^{\frac{1}{3}}$ three times to get 4^1

So, $4^{\frac{1}{3}}$ is the cube root of 4

When a quantity has its exponent in the form of a fraction (rational number), its *numerator* **denotes the** *exponent (power)* **of the quantity while its** *denominator* **denotes the** *radical (root)* **of the quantity ; as —**

(a) $5^{\frac{2}{3}}$ means the cube root of 5^2

(b) $a^{\frac{m}{n}}$ means the *nth* root of a^m

(c) $y^{\frac{a}{b}}$ means *bth* root of y^a

We can generalise it as under :

If a be any positive real number and m be an integer while n be a natural number, then $a^{\frac{m}{n}} = \sqrt[n]{a^m}$

Let us solve some examples.

Example 1.   Express the following in the exponential form :

(a) $\sqrt{13}$ (b) $\sqrt[3]{41}$ (c) $\sqrt[4]{136}$

(d) $\sqrt[3]{8^2}$ (e) $\sqrt[3]{3^{-2}}$ (f) $\sqrt[6]{\dfrac{5}{8}}$

Solution :   (a) $\sqrt{13} = \sqrt[2]{13} = \sqrt[2]{13^1} = 13^{\frac{1}{2}}$ *Ans.*   (b) $\sqrt[3]{41} = \sqrt[3]{41^1} = 41^{\frac{1}{3}}$ *Ans.*

(c) $\sqrt[4]{136} = \sqrt[4]{136^1} = 136^{\frac{1}{4}}$ *Ans.*   (d) $\sqrt[3]{8^2} = 8^{\frac{2}{3}}$ *Ans.*

(e) $\sqrt[3]{3^{-2}} = 3^{\frac{-2}{3}}$ *Ans.*   (f) $\sqrt[6]{\dfrac{5}{8}} = \sqrt[6]{\left(\dfrac{5}{8}\right)^1} = \left(\dfrac{5}{8}\right)^{\frac{1}{6}}$ *Ans.*

Example 2.   Express the following as radicals :

(a) $3^{\frac{1}{5}}$ (b) $19^{\frac{-1}{3}}$ (c) $17^{\frac{3}{5}}$ (d) $\left(\dfrac{5}{6}\right)^{\frac{5}{8}}$

Solution :   (a) $3^{\frac{1}{5}} = \sqrt[5]{3^1} = \sqrt[5]{3}$ *Ans.*

(b) $19^{\frac{-1}{3}} = \sqrt[3]{19^{-1}} = \sqrt[3]{\dfrac{1}{19}}$ *Ans.* ....(as $19^{-1} = \dfrac{1}{19}$)

(c) $17^{\frac{3}{5}} = \sqrt[5]{17^3}$ *Ans.*   (d) $\left(\dfrac{5}{6}\right)^{\frac{5}{8}} = \sqrt[8]{\left(\dfrac{5}{6}\right)^5}$ *Ans.*

Let us now solve some examples on laws of exponents :

Example 3. **Simplify :** $\left[(64)^{\frac{1}{3}}\right]^{\frac{1}{2}}$

Solution : $\left[(64)^{\frac{1}{3}}\right]^{\frac{1}{2}} = \left(\sqrt[3]{64}\right)^{\frac{1}{2}} = (4)^{\frac{1}{2}} = \sqrt{4} = \mathbf{2}$ *Ans.*

Example 4. **Find the value of** $3 \times 16^{\frac{3}{4}}$

Solution : $3 \times 16^{\frac{3}{4}} = 3 \times \sqrt[4]{16^3} = 3 \times \sqrt[4]{16 \times 16 \times 16}$

$= 3 \times \sqrt[4]{2^4 \times 2^4 \times 2^4} = 3 \times 2 \times 2 \times 2 = \mathbf{24}$ *Ans.*

Example 5. **Solve** $2 \times 27^{\frac{-2}{3}}$

Solution : $2 \times 27^{\frac{-2}{3}} = 2 \times \dfrac{1}{27^{\frac{2}{3}}} = 2 \times \dfrac{1}{\sqrt[3]{27^2}} = 2 \times \dfrac{1}{\sqrt[3]{27 \times 27}}$

$= 2 \times \dfrac{1}{\sqrt[3]{3^3 \times 3^3}} = 2 \times \dfrac{1}{3 \times 3} = \dfrac{\mathbf{2}}{\mathbf{9}}$ *Ans.*

Example 6. **Evaluate** $27^{\frac{2}{3}} \times 27^{\frac{1}{3}} \times 27^{\frac{-4}{3}}$

Solution : $27^{\frac{2}{3}} \times 27^{\frac{1}{3}} \times 27^{\frac{-4}{3}} = (27)^{\frac{2}{3}+\frac{1}{3}-\frac{4}{3}} = 27^{1-\frac{4}{3}} = 27^{-\frac{1}{3}}$

$= \dfrac{1}{27^{\frac{1}{3}}} = \dfrac{1}{\sqrt[3]{27}} = \dfrac{1}{\sqrt[3]{3^3}} = \dfrac{\mathbf{1}}{\mathbf{3}}$ *Ans.*

Example 7. **Find the value of** *(a)* $(\cdot008)^{\frac{2}{3}}$ *(b)* $(\cdot000064)^{\frac{5}{6}}$

Solution :   *(a)* $(\cdot008)^{\frac{2}{3}} = \left(\dfrac{8}{1000}\right)^{\frac{2}{3}} = \dfrac{(8)^{\frac{2}{3}}}{(1000)^{\frac{2}{3}}} = \dfrac{\sqrt[3]{8^2}}{\sqrt[3]{1000^2}}$

$= \dfrac{\sqrt[3]{64}}{\sqrt[3]{1000 \times 1000}} = \dfrac{\sqrt[3]{4^3}}{\sqrt[3]{100^3}} = \dfrac{4}{100} = \mathbf{\cdot04}$ *Ans.*

(b) $(\cdot000064)^{\frac{5}{6}} = \left(\dfrac{64}{1000000}\right)^{\frac{5}{6}} = \dfrac{(64)^{\frac{5}{6}}}{(1000000)^{\frac{5}{6}}} = \dfrac{\sqrt[6]{(64)^5}}{\sqrt[6]{(1000000)^5}}$

$= \dfrac{\sqrt[6]{(2^6)^5}}{\sqrt[6]{(10^6)^5}} = \dfrac{\sqrt[6]{(2^5)^6}}{\sqrt[6]{(10^5)^6}} = \dfrac{2^5}{10^5} = \dfrac{2 \times 2 \times 2 \times 2 \times 2}{10 \times 10 \times 10 \times 10 \times 10}$

$= \dfrac{32}{100000} = \mathbf{0 \cdot 00032}$ *Ans.*

Example 8. **Simplify and express the answer with positive indices :**

(a) $\mathbf{2x^{\frac{1}{6}} \times 2x^{-\frac{7}{6}}}$ *(b)* $\left[\sqrt[4]{\left(\dfrac{1}{x}\right)^{-12}}\right]^{-\frac{2}{3}}$

Solution : (a) $2x^{\frac{1}{6}} \times 2x^{-\frac{7}{6}} = 2 \times 2\,(x)^{\frac{1}{6}-\frac{7}{6}} = 4(x^{-1}) = 4 \times \frac{1}{x} = \dfrac{4}{x}$ Ans.

(b) $\left[\sqrt[4]{\left(\dfrac{1}{x}\right)^{-12}}\right]^{\frac{-2}{3}} = \left(\sqrt[4]{x^{12}}\right)^{\frac{-2}{3}} = \left(x^{\frac{12}{4}}\right)^{\frac{-2}{3}} = (x^3)^{\frac{-2}{3}} = x^{3 \times \frac{-2}{3}} = x^{-2} = \dfrac{1}{x^2}$ Ans.

Example 9. Simplify : $\dfrac{(64)^{\frac{-1}{6}} \times (216)^{\frac{-1}{3}} \times (81)^{\frac{1}{4}}}{(512)^{\frac{-1}{3}} \times (16)^{\frac{1}{4}} \times (9)^{\frac{-1}{2}}}$

Solution : $\dfrac{(64)^{\frac{-1}{6}} \times (216)^{\frac{-1}{3}} \times (81)^{\frac{1}{4}}}{(512)^{\frac{-1}{3}} \times (16)^{\frac{1}{4}} \times (9)^{\frac{-1}{2}}} = \dfrac{(81)^{\frac{1}{4}} \times (512)^{\frac{1}{3}} \times (9)^{\frac{1}{2}}}{(64)^{\frac{1}{6}} \times (216)^{\frac{1}{3}} \times (16)^{\frac{1}{4}}}$

$= \dfrac{\sqrt[4]{81} \times \sqrt[3]{512} \times \sqrt{9}}{\sqrt[6]{64} \times \sqrt[3]{216} \times \sqrt[4]{16}} = \dfrac{\sqrt[4]{3^4} \times \sqrt[3]{8^3} \times 3}{\sqrt[6]{2^6} \times \sqrt[3]{6^3} \times \sqrt[4]{2^4}}$

$= \dfrac{3 \times 8 \times 3}{2 \times 6 \times 2} = \dfrac{72}{24} = 3$ Ans.

PRACTICE EXERCISES 9

A. Find the value of :

1. $4^2 \times 4^2 \times 4^2$ 2. $\left(\dfrac{1}{3}\right)^2 \times \left(\dfrac{1}{3}\right)^2 \times \left(\dfrac{1}{3}\right)^2$ 3. $\dfrac{x^{-3}}{x^{-2}} \times \dfrac{x^5}{x^4}$ 4. $\dfrac{(2a^3)^3}{(b^2)^2}$

5. $\dfrac{3a^m(5b^n)^2}{(a^{2m})^2}$ 6. $\left(\dfrac{1}{2}\right)^{-3} \times \left(\dfrac{1}{2}\right)^4$ 7. $(\sqrt{2})^2 \times (\sqrt{2})^2 \times (\sqrt{2})^2 \times (\sqrt{2})^2$

8. $\left(\dfrac{2^{-2}}{7}\right)^2$ 9. $\left[(6)^2 \times (4)^2\right]^{\frac{1}{2}}$ 10. $\dfrac{a^{-1}m^{-2}}{a^{-3}m^{-4}}$ 11. $\dfrac{4^{-3} \times a^{-5} \times b^{-4}}{4^{-5} \times a^{-8} \times b^3}$

B. Find the value of :

12. $(243)^{\frac{2}{5}}$ 13. $(512)^{\frac{-2}{9}}$ 14. $\left[(216)^{\frac{2}{3}}\right]^{\frac{1}{2}}$

15. $(18)^{\frac{1}{3}} \times (768)^{\frac{1}{3}}$ 16. $10 \div (8)^{\frac{-1}{3}}$ 17. $\left(\dfrac{16}{81}\right)^{\frac{-3}{4}}$

18. $9^{\frac{1}{2}} \times 16^{\frac{1}{2}}$ 19. $(11^{\frac{1}{2}})^2$ 20. $(16)^{\frac{3}{4}}$

C. Simplify :

21. $64^{\frac{5}{3}} \div 64^{\frac{2}{3}}$ 22. $(6^2 + 8^2)^{\frac{1}{2}}$ 23. $x^{\frac{1}{3}} \div x^{\frac{7}{3}}$

24. $(125)^{\frac{-2}{3}} \times (27)^{\frac{-2}{3}}$ 25. $(\cdot000729)^{\frac{5}{6}}$ 26. $64^{\frac{-2}{3}} \times 27^{\frac{-2}{3}}$

D. Simplify and express with positive exponents :

27. $\left[\sqrt[3]{x^4y} \times \dfrac{1}{\sqrt[3]{xy^7}}\right]^{-4}$ 28. $a^{\frac{4}{7}} \div a^{\frac{10}{7}}$ 29. $\dfrac{(5)^2 \times (3)^2 \times (125)^{\frac{1}{3}}}{(27)^{\frac{2}{3}} \times (32)^{\frac{1}{5}}}$ 30. $(\cdot03125)^{\frac{-3}{5}}$

49

6 RADICALS OR SURDS

The word—**radical**—means *fundamental, i.e. of the root.*

In mathematics, this word is used in connection with the process of finding roots of quantities—*square root, cube root, fourth root etc.*

The other word for *root* is the **surd**. It applies especially to roots of integers that result in irrational numbers. Try to understand the following terms :

1. *The number whose root is to be found is called the* **radicand**.

2. *The sign used to indicate the root is called the* **radical sign.**

3. *The result got after the process is called* **root** *or* **radical.**

4. *The small number written in the bend of the radical sign is called the* **root index**.

PURE AND MIXED RADICALS

A radical that contains no rational factor is a **pure radical** *or* **pure surd** ; as :
$\sqrt{21}$, $\sqrt[3]{16}$, $\sqrt[4]{29}$ etc.

A radical that contains a rational factor as well as an irrational factor is called *a* **mixed radical** *or* **mixed surd** ; as : $2\sqrt{3}$, $3\sqrt{5}$ etc.

CONVERTING RADICALS

A. MIXED TO PURE

Example 1. Reduce into a pure radical (a) $3\sqrt{5}$ (b) $4\sqrt[3]{2}$

Solution : (a) $3\sqrt{5} = \sqrt{3^2 \times 5}$ *(Taking 3 under the radical sign)*

$= \sqrt{9 \times 5} = \sqrt{45}$ *Ans.*

(b) $4\sqrt[3]{2} = \sqrt[3]{4^3 \times 2}$ *(Taking 4 under the radical sign)*

$= \sqrt[3]{64 \times 2} = \sqrt[3]{128}$ *Ans.*

B. PURE TO MIXED

Example 2. Reduce to mixed radicals : (a) $\sqrt[3]{432}$ (b) $\sqrt[3]{24}$

Solution :   (a) $\sqrt[3]{432} = \sqrt[3]{2 \times 2 \times 2 \times 3 \times 3 \times 3 \times 2}$

$= \sqrt[3]{2^3 \times 3^3 \times 2} = 2 \times 3 \times \sqrt[3]{2} = \mathbf{6\ \sqrt[3]{2}}$ *Ans.*

(b) $\sqrt[3]{24} = \sqrt[3]{2 \times 2 \times 2 \times 3}$

$= \sqrt[3]{2^3 \times 3} = \mathbf{2\ \sqrt[3]{3}}$ *Ans.*

LIKE AND UNLIKE RADICALS

A. LIKE RADICALS

Radicals or surds with the **same root-index** *are called like radicals ; as—*

(a) $\sqrt{3}, \sqrt{13}, \sqrt{28}, \sqrt{92}$ (b) $\sqrt[3]{19}, \sqrt[3]{29}, \sqrt[3]{90}$

B. UNLIKE RADICALS

Radicals or surds with **different root indices** *are called unlike radicals ; as—*

$\sqrt{3}, \sqrt[3]{29}, \sqrt[5]{25}$

SIMILAR AND DISSIMILAR RADICALS

A. SIMILAR RADICALS

Radicals are said to be **similar** *if their irrational part is the same ; as—*

$3\sqrt[3]{7}, 5\sqrt[3]{7}, 4\sqrt[3]{7}$

B. DISSIMILAR RADICALS

Radicals are said to be **dissimilar** *if their irrational parts are different ; as—*

$3\sqrt{7}, 4\sqrt{11}, 5\sqrt[3]{15}$

ADDITION AND SUBTRACTION OF RADICALS

Remember that before performing *addition, subtraction, multiplication* and *division* of radicals, the following steps are taken :

(a) Reduce each radical to its simplest form.

(b) Express the sum or difference of similar radical as one term.

(c) Connect dissimilar radicals with their proper signs.

Example 1. Simplify the following :

(a) $\sqrt{50} + \sqrt{32}$ (b) $\sqrt{80} - \sqrt{45}$

(c) $\sqrt{48} + \sqrt{75} - \sqrt{192}$ (d) $\sqrt[3]{1080} - \sqrt[3]{40} + \sqrt[3]{625}$

Solution : (a) $\sqrt{50} + \sqrt{32} = \sqrt{25 \times 2} + \sqrt{16 \times 2} = \sqrt{5^2 \times 2} + \sqrt{4^2 \times 2}$

$$= 5\sqrt{2} + 4\sqrt{2} = \sqrt{2}\,(5 + 4) = \mathbf{9\sqrt{2}} \text{ Ans.}$$

(b) $\sqrt{80} - \sqrt{45} = \sqrt{16 \times 5} - \sqrt{9 \times 5} = \sqrt{4^2 \times 5} - \sqrt{3^2 \times 5}$

$$= 4\sqrt{5} - 3\sqrt{5}$$

$$= \sqrt{5}\,(4 - 3) = \mathbf{\sqrt{5}} \text{ Ans.}$$

(c) $\sqrt{48} + \sqrt{75} - \sqrt{192} = \sqrt{16 \times 3} + \sqrt{25 \times 3} - \sqrt{64 \times 3}$

$$= 4\sqrt{3} + 5\sqrt{3} - 8\sqrt{3}$$

$$= \sqrt{3}\,(4 + 5 - 8) = \mathbf{\sqrt{3}} \text{ Ans}$$

(d) $\sqrt[3]{1080} - \sqrt[3]{40} + \sqrt[3]{625}$

$$= \sqrt[3]{216 \times 5} - \sqrt[3]{8 \times 5} + \sqrt[3]{125 \times 5}$$

$$= \sqrt[3]{6^3 \times 5} - \sqrt[3]{2^3 \times 5} + \sqrt[3]{5^3 \times 5}$$

$$= 6\sqrt{5} - 2\sqrt{5} + 5\sqrt{5} = \sqrt{5}\,(6 - 2 + 5) = \mathbf{9\sqrt{5}} \text{ Ans.}$$

MULTIPLICATION AND DIVISION OF RADICALS

While multiplying and dividing radicals, take care that these two operations can be done with like radicals only, *i.e.* the radicals that have the same index.

Example 2. Solve : (a) $\mathbf{\sqrt{3} \times \sqrt{6}}$ $\qquad$ (b) $\mathbf{3\sqrt{5} \times 5\sqrt{10} \times 6\sqrt{32}}$

(c) $\mathbf{(125)^{\frac{-2}{3}} \times (64)^{\frac{4}{3}}}$ $\qquad$ (d) $\mathbf{2 \times 9^{\frac{-1}{2}}(9^{\frac{1}{2}} + 9^{\frac{5}{2}})}$

Solution : (a) $\sqrt{3} \times \sqrt{6} = \sqrt{3 \times 6} = \mathbf{\sqrt{18}}$ Ans.

(b) $3\sqrt{5} \times 5\sqrt{10} \times 6\sqrt{32}$

$$= 3 \times 5 \times 6\sqrt{5 \times 10 \times 32} = 90\sqrt{1600}$$

$$= 90\sqrt{40^2} = 90 \times 40 = \mathbf{3600} \text{ Ans.}$$

(c) $(125)^{\frac{-2}{3}} \times (64)^{\frac{4}{3}} = (5^3)^{\frac{-2}{3}} \times (4^3)^{\frac{4}{3}}$

$$= (5)^{-2} \times (4)^4 = \frac{1}{(5)^2} \times 256$$

$$= \frac{1}{25} \times 256 = \frac{256}{25} = \mathbf{10\frac{6}{25}} \text{ Ans.}$$

(d) $2 \times 9^{\frac{-1}{2}}(9^{\frac{1}{2}} + 9^{\frac{5}{2}})$

$$= 2 \times (9^{\frac{-1}{2}} \times 9^{\frac{1}{2}}) + (9^{\frac{-1}{2}} \times 9^{\frac{5}{2}}) = 2 \times \left(9^{\frac{-1}{2} + \frac{1}{2}} + 9^{\frac{-1}{2} + \frac{5}{2}}\right)$$

$$= 2 \times (9^0 + 9^2) = 2 \times (1 + 81) = 2 \times 82 = \mathbf{164} \text{ Ans.}$$

Example 3. Solve : $(100)^{\frac{1}{2}} \div (100)^{\frac{3}{2}}$

Solution : $\quad (100)^{\frac{1}{2}} \div (100)^{\frac{3}{2}}$

$$= 100^{\frac{1}{2}} \div (100^1 \times 100^{\frac{1}{2}})$$

$$= \sqrt{100} \div (100 \times \sqrt{100}) = 10 \div (100 \times 10)$$

$$= 10 \div 1000 = \frac{1}{100} = \mathbf{0 \cdot 01} \ Ans.$$

Example 4. Simplify : $\dfrac{\sqrt{75} \times \sqrt{60} \times \sqrt{10}}{\sqrt{40} \times \sqrt{50}}$

Solution : $\quad$ (a) $\dfrac{\sqrt{75} \times \sqrt{60} \times \sqrt{10}}{\sqrt{40} \times \sqrt{50}} = \sqrt{\dfrac{75 \times 60 \times 10}{40 \times 50}}$

$$= \sqrt{\frac{75 \times 6}{20}} = \sqrt{\frac{90}{4}} = \sqrt{\frac{9 \times 10}{4}}$$

$$= \frac{3 \times \sqrt{10}}{2} = \frac{\mathbf{3}}{\mathbf{2}}\sqrt{\mathbf{10}} \ Ans.$$

RATIONALISATION

Rationalisation means getting the denominator of a radical free from radicals.

Example 5. Rationalise : (a) $\dfrac{5}{\sqrt{3}}$ $\qquad$ (b) $\dfrac{1}{6 - \sqrt{3}}$

Solution : (a) $\dfrac{5}{\sqrt{3}} = \dfrac{5 \times \sqrt{3}}{\sqrt{3} \times \sqrt{3}} = \dfrac{5\sqrt{3}}{3} = \dfrac{\mathbf{5}}{\mathbf{3}}\sqrt{3} \ Ans.$

$\qquad$ (b) $\dfrac{1}{6 - \sqrt{3}} = \dfrac{1 \times (6 + \sqrt{3})}{(6 - \sqrt{3})(6 + \sqrt{3})} = \dfrac{6 + \sqrt{3}}{6^2 - (\sqrt{3})^2}$

$$= \frac{6 + \sqrt{3}}{36 - 3} = \frac{\mathbf{6 + \sqrt{3}}}{\mathbf{33}} \ Ans.$$

Example 6. Solve : (a) $\dfrac{2 - \sqrt{3}}{2 + \sqrt{3}}$ $\qquad$ (b) $(\sqrt{3} - 1)^2 + (\sqrt{3} + 1)^2$

$\qquad\qquad\qquad$ (c) $(\sqrt{5} + \sqrt{3})^2 - (\sqrt{5} - \sqrt{3})^2$

Solution : $\quad$ (a) $\dfrac{2 - \sqrt{3}}{2 + \sqrt{3}} = \dfrac{(2 - \sqrt{3})(2 - \sqrt{3})}{(2 + \sqrt{3})(2 - \sqrt{3})} = \dfrac{(2 - \sqrt{3})^2}{4 - 3}$

$$= \frac{4 + 3 - 2 \times 2\sqrt{3}}{1} = \mathbf{7 - 4}\sqrt{\mathbf{3}} \ Ans.$$

$\qquad$ (b) $(\sqrt{3} - 1)^2 + (\sqrt{3} + 1)^2$

$$= [(\sqrt{3})^2 + 1 - 2 \times 1\sqrt{3})] + (\sqrt{3})^2 + 1 + 2 \times 1\sqrt{3})$$

$$= (3 + 1 - 2\sqrt{3}) + (3 + 1 + 2\sqrt{3})$$
$$= (4 - 2\sqrt{3}) + (4 + 2\sqrt{3})$$
$$= 4 - 2\sqrt{3} + 4 + 2\sqrt{3} = \textbf{8} \; Ans.$$

(c) $(\sqrt{5} + \sqrt{3})^2 - (\sqrt{5} - \sqrt{3})^2$

$= \left(\sqrt{5} + \sqrt{3} + \sqrt{5} - \sqrt{3}\right)\left(\sqrt{5} + \sqrt{3} - \sqrt{5} + \sqrt{3}\right)$ *(using $a^2 - b^2 = (a+b)(a-b)$)*

$= 2\sqrt{5} \times 2\sqrt{3} = \textbf{4}\sqrt{\textbf{15}} \; Ans.$

PRACTICE EXERCISES 10

A. Write as pure radicals :

1. $2\sqrt{3}$ **2.** $5\sqrt{2}$ **3.** $4\sqrt{5}$ **4.** $2\sqrt[3]{4}$

5. $3\sqrt{5}$ **6.** $5\sqrt{3}$ **7.** $2\sqrt{5}$ **8.** $6\sqrt{3}$

B. Write as mixed radicals :

9. $\sqrt{50}$ **10.** $\sqrt{84}$ **11.** $\sqrt[3]{72}$ **12.** $\sqrt[3]{108}$

13. $\sqrt{75}$ **14.** $\sqrt{45}$ **15.** $\sqrt{20}$ **16.** $\sqrt{12}$

C. Solve :

17. $\sqrt{27} + \sqrt{12}$ **18.** $\sqrt{320} - \sqrt{125}$ **19.** $\sqrt{20} + \sqrt{180} - \sqrt{80}$

20. $\sqrt{18} + \sqrt{50} - \sqrt{32}$ **21.** $2\sqrt{3} + 3\sqrt{27} - \sqrt{32} + \sqrt{98}$

22. $\sqrt{20} - \sqrt{125} + \sqrt{80}$ **23.** $\sqrt{75} - \sqrt{48} + \sqrt{300} - \sqrt{147}$

24. $\sqrt{40} - \sqrt{18} + \sqrt{90} + \sqrt{32} - \sqrt{160}$ **25.** $3\sqrt{2} + 2\sqrt{27} - \sqrt{32} + \sqrt{12} - \sqrt{3}$

D. Evaluate :

26. $\sqrt{3} \times \sqrt{2}$ **27.** $\sqrt{12} \div \sqrt{3}$ **28.** $\sqrt{12} \times \sqrt{24} \times \sqrt{18}$

29. $\sqrt{84} \div \sqrt{7}$ **30.** $2\sqrt{6} \times 3\sqrt{8}$ **31.** $3\sqrt{15} \times 2\sqrt{5} \div 5\sqrt{3}$

32. $3\sqrt{6} \times 2\sqrt{8}$ **33.** $2\sqrt{5} \times 7\sqrt{10} \times 3\sqrt{2}$ **34.** $8\sqrt{3} \times \sqrt{8} \times \sqrt{3} \times \sqrt{30}$

E. Simplify :

35. $\dfrac{\sqrt{50} \times \sqrt{20} \times \sqrt{54}}{\sqrt{200} \times \sqrt{135}}$ **36.** $\dfrac{\sqrt{75} \times \sqrt{63} \times \sqrt{60}}{\sqrt{40} \times \sqrt{200}}$

37. $\dfrac{\sqrt{98} \times \sqrt{48} \times \sqrt{12}}{\sqrt{49} \times \sqrt{8} \times \sqrt{24}}$ **38.** $\dfrac{\sqrt{126} \times \sqrt{105} \times \sqrt{48}}{\sqrt{98} \times \sqrt{12}}$

39. $\dfrac{\sqrt{21} \times \sqrt{49}}{\sqrt{98}}$ **40.** $\dfrac{3\sqrt{15} \times 2\sqrt{5}}{5\sqrt{3}}$

41. $\dfrac{\sqrt{45} \times \sqrt{63} \times \sqrt{126}}{\sqrt{147} \times \sqrt{243}}$

42. $\dfrac{\sqrt{108} \times \sqrt{363} \times \sqrt{48}}{\sqrt{192} \times \sqrt{72} \times \sqrt{242}}$

43. $\dfrac{(25)^{\frac{5}{2}} + (25)^{\frac{7}{2}}}{(25)^{\frac{3}{2}}}$

44. $\dfrac{2\sqrt[3]{24} \times 4\sqrt[3]{18}}{\sqrt[3]{16}}$

F. Solve by rationalisation :

45. $\dfrac{7}{\sqrt{3}}$ **46.** $\dfrac{5}{\sqrt{8}}$ **47.** $\dfrac{a}{\sqrt{b}}$ **48.** $\dfrac{1}{3 + \sqrt{5}}$

49. $\dfrac{5}{\sqrt{6} - \sqrt{3}}$ **50.** $\dfrac{5 + \sqrt{2}}{5 - \sqrt{2}}$ **51.** $\dfrac{\sqrt{3} - 1}{\sqrt{3} + 1}$ **52.** $\dfrac{2 - \sqrt{3}}{2 + \sqrt{3}}$

53. $\dfrac{\sqrt{3} + \sqrt{2}}{\sqrt{3} - \sqrt{2}}$ **54.** $\dfrac{\sqrt{5} + \sqrt{2}}{\sqrt{5} - \sqrt{2}}$ **55.** $\dfrac{\sqrt{2} - 1}{\sqrt{2} + 1}$ **56.** $\dfrac{\sqrt{5} + 1}{\sqrt{5} - 1}$

G. Simplify :

57. $(\sqrt{5} + \sqrt{3})^2 + (\sqrt{5} - \sqrt{3})^2$ **58.** $(\sqrt{3} - 1)^2 + (\sqrt{3} + 1)^2$

59. $(4 - \sqrt{10})^2 - (4 + \sqrt{10})^2$ **60.** $(\sqrt{a} + \sqrt{b})(\sqrt{a} - \sqrt{b})$

MISCELLANEOUS EXERCISES I

A. Define :

1. *sq.* of a quantity **2.** *sq. root* of a quantity **3.** a *perfect square*

4. a *Pythagorean Triplet* **5.** *real numbers* **6.** a *cube*

7. *cube root* **8.** an *exponent* **9.** a *radical*

10. a *pure radical* **11.** a *mixed radical* **12.** a radicand

B. Prove by examples that—

11. any odd natural number, half its square decreased by 1 and half its square increased by 1 make a Pythagorean Triplet.

12. twice any natural number, its square decreased by 1 and its square increased by 1 form a Pythagorean Triplet.

13. Difference between the squares of two consecutive natural numbers is equal to the sum of both the numbers.

C. How will you prove that the following are perfect squares ?

14. 576 **15.** 15625 **16.** 11025

D. 17. Find the smallest square number that is exactly divisible by 6, 9, 15 and 20.

18. Express 49 and 36 as the sum of natural odd numbers.

19. Find the smallest number by which 9408 be multiplied to make it a perfect square.

20. Find the square root :

    (a) 1234321   (b) 4401604   (c) 447·4225

    (d) ·00008281   (e) $332\frac{61}{169}$ (f) $1125\frac{711}{729}$

21. Simplify : (a) $\sqrt{\dfrac{·0441}{·000441}}$ (b) $\sqrt{156·25} - \sqrt{1·5625}$

E. Find the approximate square root up to 3 decimal places :

22. 0·019   **23.** 5   **24.** $2\frac{1}{12}$ **25.** 14·58   **26.** 2·8   **27.** 5·6

F. Solve :

28. $\dfrac{1}{\sqrt{3}} + \sqrt{2}$ **29.** $\dfrac{3}{\sqrt{5}-1}$ **30.** $\dfrac{\sqrt{3}+1}{\sqrt{3}-1}$

G. 31. Represent a point on a number-line that stands for $\sqrt{5}$.

32. Prove that $\sqrt[3]{8} \times \sqrt[3]{729} = \sqrt[3]{8 \times 729}$

33. Prove that $\dfrac{\sqrt[3]{343}}{\sqrt[3]{729}} = \sqrt[3]{\dfrac{343}{729}}$

34. Find the smallest number by which 26244 be multiplied to make it a perfect cube.

35. Find the smallest number by which 26244 be divided to make it a perfect cube.

H. Find the cube root :

36. $\sqrt{\dfrac{-64}{1331}}$ **37.** 32·768   **38.** ·001331

I. 39. A rectangular metallic piece measures 25 cm. × 15 cm. × 9 cm. It was melted to form a cube. Find the side of the cube.

40. A cubical box measures 343000 cubic centimetres. Find its side.

MEMORABLE FACTS

1. A. **square** is a quantity that results when another quantity is multiplied by itself *once*.

2. A **cube** is a quantity that results when another quantity is multiplied by itself *twice*.

3. If the sum of the squares of two quantities equals the square of a third quantity, the three quantities form a **Pythagorean Triplet**.

4. A perfect square **with 1 or 2 digits** has its square root with **only 1 digit**.

5. A perfect square with **3 or 4 digits** has its square root with only **2 digits**.

6. A perfect square with **5 or 6 digits** has its square root with only **3 digits**.

7. If a, b are two different whole numbers, then $\dfrac{\sqrt{a}}{\sqrt{b}} = \sqrt{\dfrac{a}{b}}$ and $\sqrt{ab} = \sqrt{a} \times \sqrt{b}$

8. The **cube of a rational number** is equal to the *cube of its numerator* divided by the *cube of its denominator*.

9. If the **index** of a quantity is **a fraction**, its numerator is the *exponent* of the quantity while its denominator is its *root*.

10. **Rationalisation** means getting the denominator of a rational number free form radicals.

COMMERCIAL ARITHMETIC

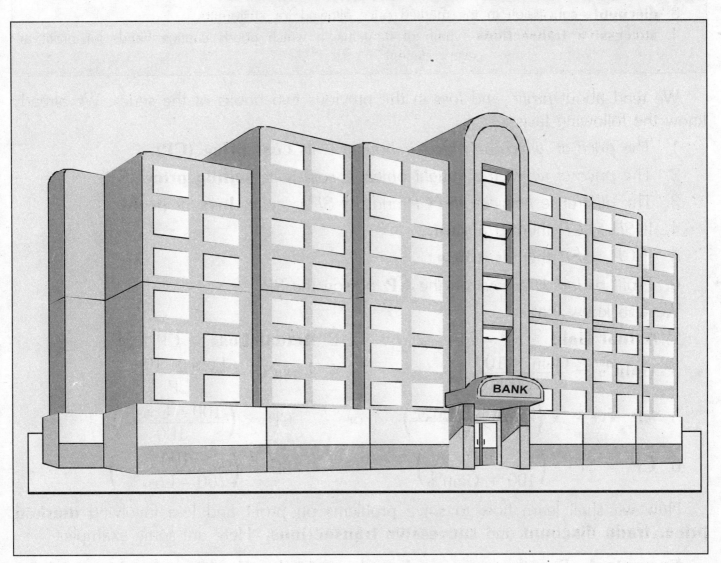

IN THIS UNIT—

7 PROFIT AND LOSS

We read about *profit* and *loss* in the previous two books of the series. We already know the following facts :

1. The *price at which an object is bought* is its **cost price (CP)**.

2. The *price at which the bought object is sold* is its **selling price (SP)**.

3. The *difference between the CP and the SP* is either **loss** or **profit**.

4. If *SP > CP*, there is a **gain**.

5. If *CP > SP*, there is a **loss**.

6. *Profit or loss is always on the* **CP**, not on the SP.

We also know that—

1. **Actual Gain** = SP – CP

2. **Actual Loss** = CP – SP

3. **Gain%** $= \dfrac{\text{Gain} \times 100}{\text{CP}}$

4. **Loss%** $= \dfrac{\text{Loss} \times 100}{\text{CP}}$

5. **SP** $= \text{CP} \times \left(\dfrac{100 + \text{Gain}\%}{100} \right)$ or $\text{CP} \times \left(\dfrac{100 - \text{Loss}\%}{100} \right)$

6. **CP** $= \text{SP} \times \left(\dfrac{100}{100 + \text{Gain}\%} \right)$ or $\text{SP} \times \left(\dfrac{100}{100 - \text{Loss}\%} \right)$

Now we shall learn how to solve problems on profit and loss involving **marked price, trade discount** and **successive transactions.** Here are some examples.

Example 1. Pencils were purchased at 11 for Rs 10 and sold at 10 for Rs 11. Find the gain or loss per cent.

Solution : Let the No. of pencils purchased = 110   *(LCM of 10 and 11)*

CP of 110 pencils at 11 for Rs 10 = $110 \times \frac{10}{11}$ = **Rs 100**

SP of 110 pencils at 10 for Rs 11 = $110 \times \frac{11}{10}$ = **Rs 121**

∴ Actual gain   = Rs (121 – 100) = **Rs 21**

This gain is on CP which is Rs 100. So, **gain % = 21%** *Ans.*

Example 2. Selling wheat at Rs 750 per quintal, a farmer gains 12½ %. What will he gain or lose on selling it at Rs 7.40 per kg ?

Solution : **First SP** of wheat = Rs 750 per quintal

Gain % = 12½ % = $\frac{25}{2}$ %

∴ CP of wheat = SP $\times \frac{100}{100 + \text{gain } \%}$ = Rs 750 $\times \frac{100}{100 + 12\frac{1}{2}\%}$

= Rs 750 $\times \frac{100}{112\frac{1}{2}}$ = Rs $\frac{750 \times 100 \times 2}{225}$ = **Rs $\frac{6000}{9}$**

Second SP of wheat = Rs (7.40 × 100) = **Rs 740** per quintal.

∴ Actual gain = Rs $(740 - \frac{6000}{9})$ = Rs $\frac{6660 - 6000}{9}$ = **Rs $\frac{660}{9}$**

∴ Gain % = $\frac{660 \times 100 \times 9}{9 \times 6000}$ = **11%** *Ans.*

SUCCESSIVE TRANSACTIONS

Successive transactions mean a chain of bargains starting from the manufacturer and ending with the customer. The item to be sold passes through several hands—*wholesaler*, *dealer* and the *retailer* to finally reach the *customer*. At every stage the process of gain or loss is repeated and the final SP is quite different from the real cost of the item. Let us solve an example to clarify the point.

Example 3. A watch costs Rs 320 to be made. Its maker sells it to a wholesaler at a gain of 25%. The wholesaler sells it to a dealer at a gain of 12½ % . The dealer sells it to a retailer at a loss of 10% in a clearance sale. The retailer sells it to the customer at a gain of 20%. What did the customer pay for the watch ?

Solution : Original cost of the watch = Rs 320

SP of the **maker** at 25% gain = Rs $(320 \times \frac{125}{100})$ = **Rs 400**

The SP of the maker (Rs 400) is the CP of the wholesaler who sells the watch at a profit of 12½ %.

∴ **Wholesaler's** SP = Rs $(400 \times \frac{112\frac{1}{2}}{100})$ = Rs $(400 \times \frac{225}{200})$ = **Rs 450**

Again SP of the wholesaler (Rs 450) is the CP of the dealer who sells the watch at a loss of 10%

∴ **Dealer's** SP = Rs $(450 \times \frac{90}{100})$ = **Rs 405**

The retailer buys the watch for Rs 405 and sells it to the customer at a gain of 20% .

∴ **Retailer's** SP = Rs $(405 \times \frac{120}{100})$ = **Rs 486**

Hence the customer will pay **Rs 486** for the watch. *Ans.*

MARKED PRICE AND DISCOUNT

It is a general practice that goods are marked at higher prices and then sold after allowing some discount just to convince the customers that they are being given a favour. But, in fact, it is just an eye-wash as the seller still makes a handsome profit.

The *price marked on the goods* is called the **marked price** while the *selling price after allowing the discount* is called the **reduced price** or **discounted price**. Let us solve some examples to understand this practice.

Example 4. **A trader diclares a discount of 10% off the marked prices of his articles. Find the marked price of the article that is sold by him for Rs 900.**

Solution :

Suppose the marked price = Rs 100

Discount given = 10% = Rs 10

∴ Reduced SP of the article = Rs (100 – 10) = Rs 90

Actual reduced SP = Rs 900 *(Given)*

∴ *By Unitary Method—*

If the SP is Rs 90, MP = Rs 100

If the SP is Re 1, MP = Rs 100 ÷ 90

If the SP Rs 900, MP = Rs $\frac{100}{90}$ × 900 = **Rs 1000** *Ans.*

Example 5. **A trader marks his goods 12% above his cost price. Then he allows a discount of Rs 7.50 for a bill of Rs 280. Find his profit per cent.**

Solution :

Suppose the CP of the goods = Rs 100

∴ Its marked price (MP) = Rs (100 + 12) = Rs 112

Discount on Rs 280 = Rs 7.50 = Rs $\frac{15}{2}$

∴ Discount on Re 1 = Rs $\frac{15}{2} \times \frac{1}{280}$

∴ Discount on Rs 112 = Rs $\frac{15}{2} \times \frac{1}{280} \times 112$ = Rs 3

Clearly, discounted price of goods = Rs (112 – 3) = Rs 109

∴ Trader's gain = Rs (109 – 100) = Rs 9, *i.e.* **9%** *Ans.*

Example 6. **A bicycle dealer allows a discount of 25% on his marked prices. Even then he is able to make a profit of 20 per cent on his cost. Find the marked price of the bicycle on which he gains Rs 30.**

Solution :   Suppose the MP of the bicycle = Rs 100

Discount allowed = 25% = Rs 25

$\therefore$ Discounted price of the bicycle = Rs (100 – 25) = Rs 75

Even this discounted price brings in a gain of 20%

$\therefore$ CP of the bicycle = Rs ($\frac{100}{120} \times 75$) = Rs $\frac{125}{2}$

$\therefore$ Gain = Rs ($75 - \frac{125}{2}$) = Rs $\frac{25}{2}$

By Unitary Method—

If the gain is Rs $\frac{25}{2}$, MP = Rs 100

If the gain is Re 1, MP = Rs 100 $\times \frac{2}{25}$

If the gain is Rs 30, MP = Rs (100 $\times \frac{2}{25} \times 30$)

= **Rs 240** *Ans.*

PRACTICE EXERCISES 11

A. 1. By selling a toy for Rs 3.12 there is a profit of 4%. At what price must it be sold to gain 8% ?

2. What per cent gain or loss will be there by selling a ribbon at Rs 5.25 per metre if 5% is gained by selling it at Rs 6.30 per metre ?

3. A baker bought a crate of 200 eggs out of which 20 eggs were found to be broken. He sold the remaining eggs at 5 for 90 paise and thus gained 8%. At what price per dozen did the baker buy the eggs ?

4. A fruiterer sold oranges at 12 for Rs $12\frac{3}{5}$ and lost 10% on his outlay. What would he have gained, had he sold them at Rs 1.25 per orange ?

5. A man sold a small cottage at a loss of 5%. Had he sold it at a gain of 7%, he would have got Rs 480 more. Find the cost price of the cottage.

6. 20% more would be gained by selling a T-shirt for Rs 45.50 instead of Rs 39.00. Find the cost price of the T-shirt.

7. A soft-drink seller was selling his drink so as to gain 20%. He increased the price of the drink by Rs 5 per dozen bottles and his profit increased to be 32½ %. At what price was he selling the soft drink earlier ?

B. 8. A sells an article to B at a profit of 10% while B sells it for Rs 121 and thus reaps a profit of 10%. What did A pay for the article ?

9. It costs A Rs 600 to manufacture an item which he sells to B at a gain of 10%. B further sells it to C at a gain of 5%. How much will C have to pay for it ?

10. A manufacturer sells an article to a dealer at a gain of 10%. The dealer sells it to a retailer at a certain gain per cent. The retailer obtains it at a price which is 21% above the original cost of the article. Find the gain per cent of the dealer.

11. A certain article passes through three hands before reaching a customer who buys it at a price 57.5 % above its original cost. If the first two hands make profits of 20% and 25% respectively, what profit does the third hand make ?

12. The cost of making a toy-jeep is Rs 160. The maker sells it at a gain of 25% to a dealer who further sells it to a customer for Rs 250. find the dealer's gain per cent.

13. The original cost of an article is Rs 40. Its maker sells it to a dealer making a profit of 20%. The dealer, in turn, sells it to a retailer at a profit of 25%. But the retailer has to sell it at a loss of 4%. What is the selling price of the retailer ?

14. A makes an almirah which costs him Rs 360. He sells it to B at a profit of 25%. B sells the almirah to C making a certain gain per cent. C sells it for Rs 550 thus making a profit of 10% on his outlay. Find the gain per cent made by B.

15. A manufacturer sells an article at a profit of 20% to a dealer who further sells it to a shopkeeper at a gain of 10%. The shopkeeper sells it to a customer making a profit of 12½ %. If the manufacturer's cost is Rs 75, calculate—

(a) *retail price* of the article   (b) *selling price* of the dealer

C.16. A trader marks his goods 12% above his cost price but then allows a discount of 5% for cash payment. Find the cost price of a vase which he sells for Rs 266.

17. At what price must an article we marked above its cost so as to gain 5% after allowing a discount of 5% on the marked price if the cost of the article is Rs 38 ?

18. A shopkeeper sends his customer a bill for his shopping. The bill amounted to Rs 190. But he is ready to accept Rs 180.50 as full and final payment if it is made in ready cash. Calculate the rate of discount ?

8 COMPOUND INTEREST

> *KNOW THESE TERMS :*
> 1. **simple interest**—interest that is always calculated on the original principal
> 2. **compound interest**—interest in which the amount at simple interest for a year becomes the principal for the next year
> 3. **half-year and quarter-year**—A year has *two half-years* and *four quarter-years*

WHAT IS COMPOUND INTEREST ?

We read about *simple interest* in the previous two books of the series. In this chapter, we shall read about **compound interest**.

The word—**compound**—means *combination of two different substances*. Clearly, *compound interest* is a combination of *two types of sums of money* :

(a) **interest** on the *principal* that is borrowed.

(b) **interest** on the **interest** on the *principal*.

To be more clear, **let us suppose that a farmer borrows Rs. 2000 from a bank for 2 years at a rate of 10% per annum at compound interest.**

The farmer is to pay interest to the bank.

Now, if he is to pay **simple interest,** he will pay

Rs. $\dfrac{P \times R \times T}{100}$ = Rs. $\dfrac{2000 \times 10 \times 2}{100}$ = **Rs. 400** for two years.

But if he is to pay **compound interest**, he will have to pay more. For it, at first the simple interest for the first year will be calculated as below :

S.I. for 1 year = Rs. $\dfrac{2000 \times 1 \times 10}{100}$ = Rs. 200

This Rs. 200 will be added to the principal, *i.e.*

The principal for the **second year** will become Rs. (2000 + 200) = Rs. 2200

So, the interest for the second year will be Rs. $\dfrac{2200 \times 1 \times 10}{100}$ = Rs. 220

∴ Total compound interest will be Rs. (200 + 220) = **420** for two years.

Clearly, the compound interest (C.I.) is **Rs. 20 more** than the S.I.

In short, we can say that in compound interest—

(a) **Amount at S.I. after the 1st year is the principal for the 2nd year.**

(b) **Amount at C.I. after two years is the principal for the 3rd year.**

(c) **(The final amount) — (Initial principal) = Compound Interest.**

CALCULATION OF COMPOUND INTEREST (C.I.)

It is quite evident that if we calculate the interest for each year and then add all the interests, the process will be very lengthy. So, a handy formula has been evolved for finding C.I.

Suppose Re 1 is borrowed at C.I. for 3 years at an annual rate of 5%. Then—

Int. on Rs. 1 for the first year. Rs. $\dfrac{1 \times 1 \times 5}{100}$ = Rs. $\dfrac{5}{100}$

Amount of Rs. 1 after the **first year** = Rs. $\left(1 + \dfrac{5}{100}\right)$ *(This is the P for the 2nd year)*

Amount of Rs. $\left(1 + \dfrac{5}{100}\right)$ after **2nd year** = Rs. $1 \times \left(1 + \dfrac{5}{100}\right)\left(1 + \dfrac{5}{100}\right)$

Similarly amount of Rs. $\left(1 + \dfrac{5}{100}\right)\left(1 + \dfrac{5}{100}\right)$ is the principal for the 3rd year

Amount after the **3rd year** = Rs. $1 \times \left(1 + \dfrac{5}{100}\right)\left(1 + \dfrac{5}{100}\right)\left(1 + \dfrac{5}{100}\right)$

$$= \text{Rs. } 1 \times \left(1 + \dfrac{5}{100}\right)^3$$

$$\boxed{\text{So, C.I.} = P \times \left(1 + \dfrac{r}{100}\right)^{\text{No. of time units}} - P}$$

Example 1. Find the C.I. on Rs. 2500 for two years at 12% per annum.

Solution :   Principal = Rs. 2500 ; Time units = 2 ; Rate = 12%

$\therefore$ Amount at C.I. = $P\left(1 + \dfrac{R}{100}\right)^2$ = Rs. $2500\left(1 + \dfrac{12}{100}\right)^2$

$$= \text{Rs. } 2500 \times \dfrac{112}{100} \times \dfrac{112}{100} = \text{Rs. } 112 \times 28$$
$$= \text{Rs. } 3136$$

$\therefore$ C.I. = Amount – Principal = Rs. (3136 – 2500) = **Rs. 636** *Ans.*

Example 2. Find the C.I. on Rs. 8000 for 3 years at 15% per annum.

Solution :   P = Rs. 8000 ; Time units = 3 ; R = 15%

$\therefore$ Amount at C.I. = $P\left(1 + \dfrac{R}{100}\right)^3$ = Rs. $8000\left(1 + \dfrac{15}{100}\right)^3$

$$= \text{Rs. } 8000 \times \dfrac{115}{100} \times \dfrac{115}{100} \times \dfrac{115}{100}$$

$$= \text{Rs. } 8000 \times \dfrac{23}{20} \times \dfrac{23}{20} \times \dfrac{23}{20}$$

$$= \text{Rs. } 23 \times 23 \times 23 = \text{Rs. } 12167$$

$\therefore$ C.I. = (A – P) = Rs. (12167 – 8000) = **Rs. 4167** *Ans.*

WHEN THE INTEREST COMPOUNDS HALF-YEARLY

Example 3. Manoj deposits Rs. 32500 in a bank for two years. The bank gives a half-yearly compound interest at 20% per annum. Find the compound interest.

Solution : P = Rs. 32500 ;   Time units = 2 years = 4 half-years

Rate = 20% yearly = 10% half-yearly

$\therefore$ A at C.I. $= P \left(1 + \dfrac{R}{100}\right)^{\text{time units}} = $ Rs. $32500 \left(1 + \dfrac{10}{100}\right)^4$

$= $ Rs. $32500 \times \dfrac{110}{100} \times \dfrac{110}{100} \times \dfrac{110}{100} \times \dfrac{110}{100}$

$= $ Rs. $32500 \times \dfrac{11}{10} \times \dfrac{11}{10} \times \dfrac{11}{10} \times \dfrac{11}{10}$

$= $ Rs. $\dfrac{13 \times 11 \times 11 \times 11 \times 11}{4} = $ Rs. $\dfrac{190333}{4}$

$\therefore$ C.I. $= $ Rs. $\left(\dfrac{190333}{4} - 32500\right) = $ Rs. $\dfrac{190333 - 130000}{4}$

$= $ Rs. $\dfrac{60333}{4} = $ **Rs. 15083·25** *Ans.*

WHEN THE INTEREST COMPOUNDS QUARTERLY

Example 4. Find the compound interest on Rs. 15625 for 9 months at 16% per annum when the interest is compounded quarterly.

Solution : P = Rs. 15625 ; Time = 9 months = 3 quarter-years

R = Rs. 16% per annum = 4% quarterly

$\therefore$ A at C.I. $= $ Rs. $P \left(1 + \dfrac{R}{100}\right)^{\text{time units}} = $ Rs. $15625 \left(1 + \dfrac{4}{100}\right)^3$

$= $ Rs. $15625 \times \dfrac{104}{100} \times \dfrac{104}{100} \times \dfrac{104}{100}$

$= $ Rs. $15625 \times \dfrac{26}{25} \times \dfrac{26}{25} \times \dfrac{26}{25}$

$= $ Rs. $26 \times 26 \times 26 = $ Rs. 17576

$\therefore$ C.I. $= $ Rs. $(17576 - 15625) = $ **Rs. 1951** *Ans.*

Example 5. Puran borrowed Rs. 20,000 from a money-lender at S.I. for two years at 18% per annum. At once he lent the amount to Javed at the same rate and for the same period but at compound interest. Find his gain.

Graded Maths-Part-8

Solution :   P = Rs. 20000 ; T = 2 years ; Rate = 18%

$$\therefore \text{ S.I.} = \text{Rs. } \frac{20000 \times 2 \times 18}{100} = \textbf{Rs. 7200}$$

$$\text{Amount at C.I.} = \text{Rs. } 20000 \left(1 + \frac{18}{100}\right)^2$$

$$= \text{Rs. } 20000 \times \frac{118}{100} \times \frac{118}{100} = \text{Rs. } 2 \times 118 \times 118$$

$$= \text{Rs. } 27848$$

$\therefore$ C.I.   = Rs. (27848 – 20000) = **Rs. 7848**

$\therefore$ Puran's gain   = Rs. (7848 – 7200) = **Rs. 648** *Ans.*

The table given below shows how to deal with the time-units and the **rate per cent** in case of **yearly, half-yearly** and **quarterly** compounding of interest.

Compounding	Principal	Rate	Time units
Annual	same	as is per annum	**as many as** years
Half-yearly	same	**half** the per-annum rate	**double** the yearly units
Quarterly	same	**one-fourth** of the per-annum rate	**four times** the yearly units

PRACTICE EXERCISES 12

A. Calculate the amount at C.I., if the interest is compounded yearly :

1. Principal = Rs. 2000   Rate = 5%   Time = 1 year
2. Principal = Rs. 5000   Rate = 10%   Time = 2 years
3. Principal = Rs. 1200   Rate = 4%   Time = 3 years
4. Principal = Rs. 1000   Rate = 5%   Time = 3 years
5. Principal = Rs. 2000   Rate = 10%   Time = 2 years
6. Principal = Rs. 5000   Rate = 8%   Time = 2 years
7. Principal = Rs. 10000   Rate = 10%   Time = 3 years
8. Principal = Rs. 2000   Rate = 15%   Time = 2 years
9. Principal = Rs. 25000   Rate = 12·5%   Time = 3 years
10. Principal = Rs. 6400   Rate = 17·5%   Time = 2 years

B. Find the amount and C.I., if the interest is compounded half-yearly :

11. Principal = Rs. 4000   Rate = 10%   Time = $1\frac{1}{2}$ years
12. Principal = Rs. 2560   Rate = $12\frac{1}{2}$%   Time = 1 year
13. Principal = Rs. 20000   Rate = 8%   Time = 1 year

14. Principal = Rs. 1600   Rate = 5%   Time = 1 year
15. Principal = Rs. 10000   Rate = 20%   Time = 2 years
16. Principal = Rs. 4096   Rate = 10%   Time = 18 months

C. Find the amount and C.I. if the interest is compounded quarterly :

17. Principal = Rs. 15625   Rate = 16%   Time = 9 months
18. Principal = Rs. 4096   Rate = $12\frac{1}{2}$%   Time = $\frac{1}{2}$ year
19. Principal = Rs. 8000   Rate = 16%   Time = 9 months
20. Principal = Rs. 20000   Rate = 16%   Time = 6 months

D. 21. Raman deposited Rs. 32000 in a bank that gives compound interest at 12·5% per annum. How much money will Raman get back after 3 years. Find the compound interest also.

22. Karam Chand deposits Rs. 20,000 with a company that pays compound interest at 8% per annum. How much money will he get back after 2 years ?

23. Manish deposits Rs. 1000 at 5% per annum of compound interest for 3 years with State Bank of India. What will he get back at the expiry of this period.

24. Find the interest paid by a borrower after a period of three years on a loan of Rs. 2000 at 10% per annum interest being compounded annually.

25. Find the amount and compound interest on Rs. 16000 at 15% per annum for $2\frac{1}{3}$ years.

   (**Hint** : Amount = $P\left(1 + \dfrac{r}{100}\right)^2 \times \left(1 + \dfrac{\frac{1}{3}r}{100}\right)$

26. Find the amount of Rs. 12500 for two years if the interest is compounded annually and the rate of interest is 15% for the first year and 16% for the second year.

INVERSE CASES OF C.I.

In inverse cases of compound interest, we find **principal**, **rate** or **time** while the *amount* or *C.I.* is given. Let us solve some examples :

Example 6. **A sum of money lent at compound interest for 2 years at 10% per annum amounts to Rs. 756·25. Find the sum.**

Solution :   Suppose the sum = Rs. 100

                  Rate = 10% ;   Time = 2 years.

$$\therefore \text{ Amount at C.I.} = \text{Rs. } 100 \left(1 + \frac{r}{100}\right)^2 = \text{Rs. } 100 \left(1 + \frac{10}{100}\right)^2$$

$$= \text{Rs. } 100 \times \frac{110}{100} \times \frac{110}{100} = \textbf{Rs. 121}$$

Actual amount = Rs. 756·25 = Rs. $756\frac{1}{4}$ = **Rs. $\dfrac{3025}{4}$**

Using Unitary Method—

If the amount is Rs. 121, sum = Rs. 100

If the amount is Rs. 1, sum = Rs. $\dfrac{100}{121}$

If the amount is Rs. $\dfrac{3025}{4}$, sum = Rs. $\dfrac{100}{121} \times \dfrac{3025}{4}$ = **Rs. 625** *Ans.*

Example 7. **The difference between the compound interest and the simple interest on a certain sum of money at 10% per annum for 3 years is Rs. 93. Find the sum.**

Solution : Suppose the sum = Rs. 100

Rate = 10% ; Time = 3 years

$$\therefore \text{ S.I.} = \text{Rs. } \frac{100 \times 10 \times 3}{100} = \textbf{Rs. 30}$$

$$\therefore \text{ Amount at C.I.} = \text{Rs. } 100 \left(1 + \frac{10}{100}\right)^3$$

$$= \text{Rs. } 100 \times \frac{11}{10} \times \frac{11}{10} \times \frac{11}{10} = \text{Rs. } \frac{1331}{10}$$

$$\therefore \text{ C.I.} = \text{Rs. } \frac{1331}{10} - 100 = \text{Rs. } \frac{1331 - 1000}{10} = \textbf{Rs. } \frac{\textbf{331}}{\textbf{10}}$$

$$\therefore \text{ Difference between S.I. and C.I.} = \text{Rs. } \frac{331}{10} - 30$$

$$= \text{Rs. } \frac{331 - 300}{10} = \textbf{Rs. } \frac{\textbf{31}}{\textbf{10}}$$

Actual difference = Rs 93

Using Unitary Method—

If the difference is Rs. $\dfrac{31}{10}$, sum = Rs. 100

If the difference is Rs. 1, sum = Rs. $100 \times \dfrac{10}{31}$

If the difference is Rs. 93, sum = Rs. $100 \times \dfrac{10}{31} \times 93$

$$= \textbf{Rs. 3000} \textit{ Ans.}$$

Example 8. **At what rate per cent of compound interest will Rs. 625 become Rs 784 in 2 years ?**

Solution :   Suppose Rate = r % ;   Time = 2 years

$\therefore$ Amount a C.I. on Rs. 625 = Rs. $625 \times \left(1 \times \dfrac{r}{100}\right)^2$

It means $625 \left(1 + \dfrac{r}{100}\right)^2 = 784$

$\therefore$ $\left(1 + \dfrac{r}{100}\right)^2 = \dfrac{784}{625} = \left(\dfrac{28}{25}\right)^2$ or $1 + \dfrac{r}{100} = \dfrac{28}{25}$

or $\dfrac{r}{100} = \dfrac{28}{25} - 1 = \dfrac{3}{25}$ or $r = \dfrac{3}{25} \times 100 = 12$

Hence rate = **12% Ans.**

Example 9. **In what time will Rs. 500 amount to Rs. 605 at 10% per annum at compound interest ?**

Solution :   Suppose the time = t years ; R = 10% ; P = Rs. 500

$\therefore$ Amount of Rs. 500 at C.I. = Rs $500 \left(1 + \dfrac{r}{100}\right)^t$

$= $ Rs. $500 \left(1 + \dfrac{10}{100}\right)^t$

Actual amount = Rs. 605

$\therefore$ $500 \left(1 + \dfrac{10}{100}\right)^t = 605$ or $500 \times \left(\dfrac{11}{10}\right)^t = 605$

or $\left(\dfrac{11}{10}\right)^t = \dfrac{605}{500} = \dfrac{121}{100} = \left(\dfrac{11}{10}\right)^2$

$\because$ Base $\dfrac{11}{10}$ is the same on both sides

$\therefore$ Index = Index *i.e.* $t = 2$

Hence the Reqd. Time = **2 years** *Ans.*

Example 10. **A certain sum of money lent at compound interest becomes Rs. 7396 in 2 years and Rs. 7950·70 in 3 years. Find the rate of interest.**

Solution :   We know that in compound interest, the amount at the end of 1 year is the principle for the *second year*. Similarly the amount at the end of 2 years is the principal for the *third year*.

$\therefore$ Rs. 7396 is the *principal* for the **3rd** year and Rs 7950.70 is its *amount* at simple interest.

Clearly, Rs. (7950·70 – 7396) is the S.I. on Rs. 7396 for 1 year

or Rs. 554·70 is the S.I. on Rs. 7396 for 1 year.

Now $R = \dfrac{S.I. \times 100}{P \times T} = \dfrac{(554·70) \times 100}{7396 \times 1}$

or $R = \dfrac{55470 \times 100}{100 \times 7396 \times 1} = \dfrac{15}{2}$

Hence Rate $= \dfrac{15}{2}\% = \mathbf{7\frac{1}{2}\%}$ *Ans.*

Example 11. **The S.I. on a certain sum of money for 2 years at 14% per annum is 2100. Find the compound interest on the sum.**

Solution :   S.I. = Rs. 2100 ; T = 2 years ; R = 14%

$\therefore P = \dfrac{S.I. \times 100}{T \times R} = Rs. \dfrac{2100 \times 100}{14 \times 2} = \mathbf{Rs.\ 7500}$

Now A at C.I. on Rs. 7500 $= 7500\left(1 + \dfrac{14}{100}\right)^2$

$= Rs. 7500 \times \dfrac{114}{100} \times \dfrac{114}{100}$

$= Rs. 9747$

$\therefore$ C.I. = Rs. (9747 – 7500) = **Rs. 2247** *Ans.*

PRACTICE EXERCISES 13

A. Find the *principal,* **if—**

1. Amount at C.I. = Rs. 3041·75   Time = 3 years   Rate = 15%

2. Amount at C.I. = Rs. 35123·20   Time = 3 years   Rate = 12%

3. Amount at C.I. = Rs. 8836   Time = 2 years   Rate = $17\frac{1}{2}\%$

4. Amount at C.I. = Rs. 22218   Time = $2\frac{1}{3}$ years   Rate = 15%

5. Compound Interest C.I. = Rs. 108·50   Time = 3 years   Rate = $12\frac{1}{2}\%$

6. Compound Interest C.I. = Rs. 24964   Time = $2\frac{1}{4}$ years   Rate = 16%

B. Find the *principal,* **if the C.I. is compounded half-yearly and :**

7. C.I. = Rs. 129856   Time = $1\frac{1}{2}$ years   Rate = 16%

8. C.I. = Rs. 4641   Time = 2 years   Rate = 20%

9. C.I. = Rs. 817   Time = $1\frac{1}{2}$ years   Rate = $12\frac{1}{2}\%$

10. C.I. = Rs. 1632   Time = 1 year   Rate = 8%

11. C.I. = Rs. 196·84   Time = $1\frac{1}{2}$ year   Rate = 5%

12. C.I. = Rs. 330   Time = 1 year   Rate = 12·5%

C. Find the *principal*, if the C.I. is compounded quarterly and :

13. C.I. = Rs. 1951   Time = 9 months   Rate = 16%

14. C.I. = Rs. 1724·05   Time = 1 year   Rate = 20%

15. C.I. = Rs. 936·48   Time = 9 months   Rate = 16%

16. C.I. = Rs. 1224   Time = 6 months   Rate = 16%

D. 17. At what rate of compound interest will Rs. 25,000 become Rs. 36000 in two years ?

18. In what time will Rs. 1600 amount to Rs. 2025 at C.I. at $12\frac{1}{2}$% per annum ?

19. In what time will Rs. 800 amount to Rs, 882 at 5% per annum compounded annually.

20. At what rate per cent per annum will Rs. 2000 amount to Rs. 2315·25 in 1½ years if the interest is compounded half-yearly ?

21. At what rate per cent will Rs, 2000 amount to Rs, 3041·75 in three years if the interest is compounded annually ?

22. Find the time if Rs. 5000 lent at C.I. at 16% amount to Rs. 5832, the interest being compound half yearly ?

23. Find the time if Rs. 8000 amount to Rs. 8820 at 20%, the interest being compounded quarterly.

24. Rs. 10,000 yield Rs. 4641 as compound interest in 2 years. Find the rate per cent if the interest is compounded half yearly.

25. A sum of money lent at C.I. amounts to Rs. 2970·25 in 2 years at 9% per annum. What will be the S.I. on it for the same period ?

26. The difference between the S.I. and C.I. on a certain sum of money at 15% per annum is Rs. 283·50 in 3 years. Find the sum.

27. At what rate will Rs. 640 amount to Rs. 774·40 in 2 years if the interest compounds annually ? Find the corresponding amount at S.I. also.

28. In what time will Rs. 1000 amount to Rs. 1331 at 10% per annum compound interest. Find the corresponding amount at S.I. also.

29. What sum will produce a compound interest of Rs. 164 in two years at 5% ? find the corresponding S.I. also.

30. In a certain period, Rs. 800 amount to Rs. 882 at 5% per annum at compound interest annually. Find the period and the corresponding amount at S.I. also.

31. Raghu borrowed a certain sum of money for two years from a company at 10% simple interest. He lent this money to a farmer at the same rate and for the same period of time at C.I. Thus he earned a profit of Rs. 10 in interest. Find the sum.

32. Find the C.I. on Rs. 12500 for $2\frac{3}{4}$ years at 12% per annum.

33. Find the amount at C.I. of Rs. 16000 for 2 years if the rate of interest is 15% for the first year and 16% for the second year and the interest is compounded annually.

34. A sum of Rs. 20,000 was lent out for 2 years at 20% per annum, the interest being compounded annually. What would have been the gain in interest if the interest had been compounded half yearly.

35. The difference between the S.I. and C.I. on a certain sum of money for 2 years at 5% per annum is Rs. 2·50. Find the sum.

36. Ramesh borrowed from Rakesh a certain sum of money at compound interest at 5% per annum. The interest was to be compounded annually. After 2 years Ramesh paid back Rs. 5512·50 to clear the loan once for all. What sum did Ramesh borrow ?

37. In how much time will Rs. 5400 yield a compound interest of Rs. 1373·76 at 12% per annum ?

38. Sudha borrowed a certain sum out of her fixed deposit from Andhra Bank at 8% per annum the interest was to be compounded every 6 months. Sudha paid back Rs. 21,632 to clear off the account after a year. How much money did she borrow ?

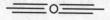

9 APPLICATION OF C.I. FORMULA

The formula for finding compound interest (C.I.) can be used to solve other problems as well. We know that some entities keep *increasing* or *decreasing* with the passage of time. The *relative increase* of an item is called it **growth** or **appreciation** while the *relative decrease* of an item is called its **decrease** or **depreciation**.

Growth or depreciation for *every unit of time* is called its **rate of growth** or **rate of depreciation**.

A. POPULATION

Suppose the population of a city keeps increasing at the growth rate of $R\%$ per annum. What will it be after T years if at present it is P.

Population of the city at present = P

And the rate of its growth $\quad = R\,\%$

While the units of time $\quad\quad = T$

Clearly, we can calculate the required population using a formula which is similar to that for finding amount at compound interest, *i.e.*

Population after 1 year $= P\left(1 + \dfrac{R}{100}\right)^1$

Population after 2 years $= P\left(1 + \dfrac{R}{100}\right)^2$

Population after 3 years $= P\left(1 + \dfrac{R}{100}\right)^3$.......... and so on

We can generalise this formula as—

Increasing population after T years $= P\left(1 + \dfrac{R}{100}\right)^T$

Inversely,

Decreasing population after T years $= P\left(1 - \dfrac{R}{100}\right)^T$

Le us now solve some examples :

Example 1. **The population of a city is 12500 at present. What will it be after 2 years if it increases at the rate of 8% per annum ?**

Solution :   Population at present = 12500

Rate of growth = 8%   Time = 2 years

Using the Increase formula—

∴   Population after 2 years $= P \left(1 + \dfrac{R}{100}\right)^T$

$$= 12500 \times \left(1 + \dfrac{8}{100}\right)^2$$

$$= 12500 \times \dfrac{108}{100} \times \dfrac{108}{100}$$

$$= 5 \times 27 \times 108 = \mathbf{14580} \; Ans.$$

Example 2. **Due to migration to factory areas, the population of a town decreases at the rate of 4% per annum. what will it be after 2 years if at present it is 6250 ?**

Solution :   Present population of the town = 6250

Annual decrease = 4%   Time = 2 years

Using the Decrease Formula—

∴   Population after 2 years $= P \left(1 - \dfrac{R}{100}\right)^T$

$$= 6250 \left(1 - \dfrac{4}{100}\right)^2$$

$$= 6250 \times \dfrac{96}{100} \times \dfrac{96}{100}$$

$$= 6250 \times \dfrac{24}{25} \times \dfrac{24}{25}$$

$$= 10 \times 24 \times 24 = \mathbf{5760} \; Ans.$$

Example 3. **Three years ago, the population of a town was 50000. During the past three years, it decreased at 4%, 5% and 6% respectively due to migration to industrial areas. What is the present population of the town ?**

Solution :   Population 3 years ago = 50000

Decrease rates for 3 years = 4% , 5%, 6%

Using the Decrease Formula—

$\therefore$ Present Population $= 50000 \left(1 - \dfrac{4}{100}\right) \times \left(1 - \dfrac{5}{100}\right) \times \left(1 - \dfrac{6}{100}\right)$

$$= 50000 \times \frac{96}{100} \times \frac{95}{100} \times \frac{94}{100}$$

$$= 24 \times 19 \times 94 = \textbf{42864} \ Ans.$$

Example 4. **The present population of a town is 64000. The yearly birth-rate in the town is 10·7% while the yearly death-rate is 3·2%. What will the population of the town be after 3 years ?**

Solution : Present population of the town = 64000

Annual birth-rate = 10·7%

Annual death-rate = 3·2%

$\because$ birth-rate is higher than the death-rate

$\therefore$ The population **will increase** every year

And net growth rate will be (10·7 – 3·2)% = 7·5%

Now using the Increase Formula—

Population after 3 years $= P \left(1 + \dfrac{7 \cdot 5}{100}\right)^{T}$

$$= 64000 \times \left(\frac{215}{200}\right)^{3}$$

$$= 64000 \times \frac{43}{40} \times \frac{43}{40} \times \frac{43}{40}$$

$$= 43 \times 43 \times 43 = \textbf{79507} \ Ans.$$

Example 5. **There was a continuous increase in the population of a small village at 5% per year for 3 successive years before the present year. Its present population is 37044. What was it 3 years ago ?**

Solution : Suppose the population 3 years ago = P

$\therefore$ Population at present $= P \left(1 + \dfrac{5}{100}\right)^{3} = P \times \left(\dfrac{105}{100}\right)^{3}$

$$= P \times \frac{105}{100} \times \frac{105}{100} \times \frac{105}{100}$$

$$= P \times \frac{21}{20} \times \frac{21}{20} \times \frac{21}{20}$$

or $P \times \frac{21}{20} \times \frac{21}{20} \times \frac{21}{20} = 37044$

$\therefore \quad P \qquad = 37044 \times \frac{20 \times 20 \times 20}{21 \times 21 \times 21}$

$= 4 \times 20 \times 20 \times 20 = \mathbf{32000}$ *Ans.*

PRACTICE EXERCISES 14

A. Complete the following formulae by putting the correct sign :

1. Increasing Population $= P \left(1 \; \text{......} \; \frac{R}{100}\right)^T$

2. Decreasing Population $= P \left(1 \; \text{....} \; \frac{R}{100}\right)^T$

B. 3. The present population of a town is 28000. What will it be after 2 years, if it increases at the growth rate of 5% per annum ?

4. The population of a small town is 24000. What will it be after 3 years, if it increases at 5% per years ?

5. The population of a town is 80000 at present. What will it be after 2 years, if it increases at the rate of 75 per thousand ?

6. The population of a big town was 160000 two years ago. It increased at the rate of 3%, 2·5% respectively during the last two successive years. What is its population now ?

7. The annual rate of growth in the population of a town is 4%. What will its population be after 3 years, if at present it is 31250 ?

8. The population of a town was 25000. Three years ago. It grew at the rates of 4%, 5% and 8% respectively during the three successive years since then. What is its present population ?

9. The population of a town has been continuously increasing at the rate 5% per year. If its present population is 9261, what was it two years ago ?

10. The population of a country was $7·95 \times 10^7$ in 1991. After 3 years it became $8·65 \times 10^7$. What was the annual growth, if $(8·65 \div 7·95)^{\frac{1}{3}} = 1·02853$?

11. In 1981, the population of India was $6·7 \times 10^8$. In 2½ years, the population increased to become $7·128 \times 10^8$. Find its half-yearly rate of growth, if $(7·128 \div 6·7)^{\frac{1}{5}} = 1·01246$

12. The export of books from India was 60 lakhs in a certain year. But it rose to become 25 crore in 20 years. Find the annual rate of its growth. If $(125 \div 3)^{\frac{1}{20}} = 1·205$.

B. PROPERTY

Example 6. The value of a machine depreciates at the rate of 10% every year. Its present value is Rs. 100000. What will its value be after 2 years ? Find the total depreciation also.

Solution : Present value of the machine = Rs. 100000

Rate of yearly depreciation = 10%

Using the Depreciation Formula—

Value of the machine after 2 years $= P\left(1 - \dfrac{R}{100}\right)^{T}$

$$= \text{Rs. } 100000 \left(1 - \dfrac{10}{100}\right)^{2}$$

$$= \text{Rs. } 100000 \times \dfrac{90}{100} \times \dfrac{90}{100}$$

$$= \text{Rs. } 90 \times 90 \times 10$$

$$= \textbf{Rs. 81000}$$

$\therefore$ Total depreciation = Rs. 100000 – 81000 = **Rs. 19000** $\Big]$ *Ans.*

Example 7. The value of a printing machine depreciates at the rate of 10% per annum. It was purchased new 3 years back. Its present depreciated value is Rs. 43740. For how much was the new machine purchased ?

Solution : Suppose the value of the new machine = x

Rate of depreciation = 10%

Using the Depreciation Formula—

Present value $= x\left(1 - \dfrac{R}{100}\right)^{T}$

$$= x\left(1 - \dfrac{10}{100}\right)^{3} = x \times \left(\dfrac{90}{100}\right)^{3}$$

The given present value = Rs. 43740

$\therefore$ $x \times \left(\dfrac{90}{100}\right)^{3}$ = Rs. 43740

$\therefore$ x = Rs. $43740 \times \left(\dfrac{100}{90}\right)^{3}$

$$= \text{Rs. } 43740 \times \dfrac{100}{90} \times \dfrac{100}{90} \times \dfrac{100}{90}$$

$$= \text{Rs. } 60000$$

Hence the machine was bought for **Rs. 60000** *Ans.*

Example 8. The wholesale price index on 1st September 1999 was 400. After 10 months, this index stood at 435 on 30th June 2000. What was rate of monthly appreciation ?

$$\left(\text{Given that } \sqrt[10]{\frac{435}{400}} = 1{\cdot}00842\right)$$

Solution :   Index on 1st September 1999 = 400

Index after 10 months = 435

In other words, $400 \left(1 + \dfrac{R}{100}\right)^{10} = 435$

or $\left(1 + \dfrac{R}{100}\right)^{10} = \dfrac{435}{400}$ or $1 + \dfrac{R}{100} = \sqrt[10]{\dfrac{435}{400}}$

or $1 + \dfrac{R}{100} = 1{\cdot}00842$, i.e. $\dfrac{R}{100} = 1{\cdot}00842 - 1 = {\cdot}00842$

$\therefore$ $R = {\cdot}00842 \times 100 = {\cdot}842$

Hence monthly rate of appreciation = **·842%** *Ans.*

PRACTICE EXERCISES 15

A. Answer :

1. What is meant by *growth* ?

....

2. What is meant by *depreciation* ?

....

3. What is meant by *growth rate* ?

....

4. What is meant by *depreciation rate* ?

....

B. 5. Ramesh bought Indira Vikas Patras for Rs. 20000 in 1995. Their value came to be Rs. 40000 in five years at a certain rate of interest which was compounded half-yearly. Find the rate of interest.

(given that $\sqrt[10]{2} = 1{\cdot}072$)

6. Chandra bought National Savings Certificates for Rs. 5000. At the end of the 6th year their value became 10075. Find the rate of interest which is compounded half-yearly. (given that $\sqrt[12]{2{\cdot}015} = 1{\cdot}06012$)

7. A car's value depreciates at 10% yearly. What will be the value of the car after 3 years, if its present value is Rs. 65000 ?

8. The cost of a TV-set was Rs. 7500. Its price went up by 5% by the end of the first year but came down by 4% by the end of the second year. But during the third year, it again went up by 5%. Find its price at the end of the third year.

9. A money invested in a scheme doubles itself in 5 years. Find the rate of interest if it is compounded annually and also if it is compounded half yearly.

(given that $\sqrt[5]{2} = 1\cdot1487$ and $\sqrt[10]{2} = 1\cdot07177$)

10. The content of carbon in wood decreases at a rate such that it comes to be half (50%) in 5568 years. After how many years will it be reduced to 12½% of the original ?

Hint : $100(1-r)^{5568} = 50$ or $(1-r)^{5568} = \dfrac{50}{100} = \dfrac{1}{2}$

and $100(1-r)^{t} = \dfrac{1}{2}$ or $(1-r)^{t} = \dfrac{25}{2} \times \dfrac{1}{100} = \dfrac{1}{8} = \left(\dfrac{1}{2}\right)^{3}$

∴ Reqd. Time $= \left[(1-r)^{5568}\right]^{3}$

11. The population of the world stood at 450 crore in a certain year. It doubles itself in 38 years. What will it be in 380 years ?

Hint : $450\left(1 + \dfrac{R}{100}\right)^{38} = 900$ crore

∴ $450\left(1 + \dfrac{R}{100}\right)^{380} = 450\left[\left(1 + \dfrac{R}{100}\right)^{38}\right]^{10} = (900)^{10}$ crore

12. The population of a state was $5\cdot4 \times 10^{7}$ crore in a certain year. It grows at a uniform rate of $2\cdot4\%$ per annum. What will it be after 20 years ?

(given that $\left(\dfrac{102\cdot4}{1000}\right)^{20} = 1\cdot60694$

13. The production of food grains was 1520 lakh tons in a country in a certain year. It goes up at $2\cdot8\%$ per annum. What will the production be at the end of the 16th year ? $(1\cdot028)^{16} = 1\cdot55557$.

14. National textile corporation of India imported 2000 looms from a foreign country on a ten-year credit. Its value was Rs. $5\cdot21$ crore and the rate of interest settled was 4% per annum which was to be compounded annually. How much total interest will the corporation pay ? $(1\cdot04)^{10} = 1\cdot48024$.

15. A scooter-producing plant was able to produce 80000 scooters a year 2 years back. Better supply of power increased the production by 15% during the first year and 20% during the second year. How many scooters does the factory produce now ?

MISCELLANEOUS EXERCISE II

A. Complete each formula :

1. Amount at C.I. $= P\left(1 + \dfrac{......}{100}\right)^{......}$

2. C.I. $= P\left(1 + \dfrac{r}{100}\right)^{......} - ......$

3. Increase Formula $=$ Original Value $\left(1 + \dfrac{\text{Growth Rate}}{100}\right)^{......}$

4. Decrease Formula $=$ Original Value $\left(1 ...... \dfrac{\text{Decrease Rate}}{100}\right)^{\text{time units}}$

B. 5. After how much time will Rs. 5400 yield Rs. 1373·76 as compound interest at 12% per annum.

6. The difference between the C.I. and the S.I. for 2 years at 5% per annum on a certain sum is Rs. 2·50. Find the sum.

7. Ramu deposited Rs. 32000 in a bank for 3 years. The yearly rate of compound interest was 12·5%. How much money will he get at the expiry of the period ?

8. Mrs Chopra borrowed Rs. 1600 for 1 year and the interest was to be compounded half yearly. At the end of the year, she returned Rs. 1831·84 to clear off the debt. What was the rate of interest ?

9. Jatin borrowed Rs. 8000 from a bank that charged 16% per annum and the interest was compounded quarterly. What will he return after 9 months ?

10. Kavita lends Rs. 40960 to Asha at 12·5% per annum. If the interest is compounded half-yearly, what will Asha pay as interest after 1·5 years ?

11. What sum will amount to Rs. 4913 in 1½ years if the rate of interest is 12½% per annum and the interest is compounded half-yearly ?

12. In what period will the compound interest on Rs. 2000 at 4% become Rs. 163·20, if the interest is compounded annually ?

13. The value of a car depreciates by 10% every year. It is at present worth Rs. 65000. What will its value be after 3 years ?

14. The present population of a town is 84500. Two years back it was 72000. What is the rate of growth ?

15. Sonu set up a business with Rs. 50000. During the first year, it gave a profit of 10% but in the second year there was a loss of 5%. If the business brings a profit of 12½% in the third year, what was Sonu's net profit after 3 years ?

D. Write *True* **or** *False* **against each statement :**

16. If the compound interest compounds *quarterly,* the time .... units become *4 times* the number of years.

17. In compound interest, the *amount at the end of the* .... *first year* is the *principal for the second year.*

E. 18. The population of a town increases at the rate of 12% every 10 years. It was 37632 in 2001. What was it in 1991 and 1981 ?

19. The difference between the simple and compound interests on a certain sum of money becomes Rs 5.60 in 2 years if the rate of interest is 4%. Find the sum.

20. A man buys 50 bicycles for Rs 50000 but 20 of them turn out to be a bit defective. So, he decides to sell each defective piece at 75% the price of the new bicycle. If he makes a profit of 35% on the entire outlay, find the SP of a defective bicycle.

21. The populations of the two part of a town, each on the opposite bank of a river that flows through the town were equal. In a year the population of one part decreases by 20% but that of the other part increases by 15%. The present population of both the parts together is 39,390. What was the population of the either part before a year ?

22. At what price must an article be marked so that it may bring a profit of 5% after allowing a discount of 5% to the customer on the marked price, if its real cost be Rs 76.

23. The marked price of a watch is Rs. 115. The seller will make a profit of 9¼ % allowing a discount of 5% on the marked price. Find the CP of the watch.

24. A manufacturer earns a profit of 20% on an article from the dealer who makes a profit of 25% selling it to a retailer. The retailer sells the article to a customer at a profit of 40% for Rs 1260. Find the cost of the manufacturer.

81

25. Which is the more profitable investment : 4½% debentures selling at Rs 162 or 2½% debentures selling at Rs 85 ? If Rs 36 and Rs 34 is invested in either case respectively, what will be the difference in the annual incomes ?

26. A trader allows a discount of 5% to his customers. What price should he mark on an article that costs him Rs 712½ so as to make a net profit of 33½% on his actual outlay ?

27. A sum of money was lent at 8% for two years at compound interest. It was not mentioned in the document whether the interest was to be compounded yearly or half yearly. So, a dispute of Rs 54.04 arose. Find the sum that was lent.

MEMORABLE FACTS

1. *Interest* is of two types—**simple** and **compound.**

2. *Simple interest* on a sum is the **same for each year**.

3. *Compound interest* on a sum is **different for each year.**

4. **S.I.** $= \dfrac{P \times T \times R}{100}$ but **C.I.** $= P\left(1+ \dfrac{R}{100}\right)^t - P$

5. The *C.I. formula* can be used for calculating **growth** and **depreciation** also.

6. Result of Growth = Original Value $\left(1 + \dfrac{\text{Growth Rate}}{100}\right)^{\text{time units}}$

7. Result of Depreciation = Original Value $\left(1 - \dfrac{\text{Decrease Rate}}{100}\right)^{\text{time units}}$

8. *Shares* are an **asset** as they *bring in income*.

9. *Debentures* are a **loan** that has a *short life*.

10. The *income* from shares is called **dividend**.

11. The *dividend* is calculated on the **face value of a share**.

12. The *brokerage* is paid by both the **buyer** and the **seller**.

13. The *brokerage* is calculated on the **market value of a share**.

14. A *Payee's Account Cheque* is the **safest cheque**.

15. A *pay-in-slip* has two parts—**foil** and **counter-foil**.

ALGEBRA

$$a^3 + b^3 = (a + b)(a^2 - ab + b^2)$$

$$a^3 - b^3 = (a - b)(a^2 + ab + b^2)$$

$$(a + b)^3 = a^3 + b^3 + 3ab(a + b)$$

$$(a - b)^3 = a^3 - b^3 - 3ab(a - b)$$

IN THIS UNIT—

10 POLYNOMIALS OR MULTINOMIALS

WHAT IS A POLYNOMIAL/MULTINOMIAL ?

We know that—

1. an algebraic expression with only *one term* is a **monomial.**

2. an algebraic expression with *two terms* is a **binomial.**

3. an algebraic expression with *more than two terms* is called a **polynomial.**

A polynomial may be a **trinomial** *(expression with 3 terms)*, a **quadrinomial** *(expression with four terms)* or with even more terms.

A *polynomial* **is an expression that has more than two terms with different powers of one variable or of more variables** ; as—

1. $x^4 + 5x^3 + 2x^2 + 7x + 6$

2. $x^4y^3 + 3x^2y^2 + 4x^3y + 6xy^3 + 5x - 8y + 7$

DEGREE OF A POLYNOMIAL

(a) In the case of a **polynomial in one variable,** the **highest index** of the variable marks the *degree of the polynomial* ; as—

1. $x^6 - 2x^5 + 3x^4 - 4x^3 + 2x - 7$ is a polynomial of the **6th degree** of x.

2. $7x^4 - 5x^2 + 3$ is a multinomial of the **4th degree** of x.

(b) But in the case of a **polynomial with two or more variables, the highest sum of the exponents of the variables** marks the *degree of the multinomial* ; as—

1. $5x^3 + 4x^3y^2 + 7x^2y^2 + 8xy^3 + 6xy + 8$ has the highest sum of exponents in its second term $(4x^3y^2)$. It **3 + 2 = 5** (exponents of x and y). So, this expression is a multinomial of the **5th degree** of x, y.

2. $3x^4y + 2x^3y^3 + 5xy^6 - 15x$ is a multinomial of the **7th degree** of x, y (see the third term).

So, Remember the following terms in regard to polynomials.

A. IN RESPECT OF NUMBER OF TERMS :
1. a polynomial with *three terms* is called a **trinomial**.
2. a polynomial with *four term* is called a **quadrinomial**.
3. a polynomial with *more than four terms* is called a **multinomial**.

B. IN RESPECT OF DEGREE :
1. a polynomial consisting of a *constant term* only is called a **constant polynomial**. (Its degree is 0)
2. a polynomial of the *first degree* is called a **linear polynomial**.
3. a polynomial of the *second degree* is called a **quadratic polynomial**.
4. a polynomial of the *third degree* is called a **cubic polynomial**.
5. a polynomial of the *fourth degree* is called a **biquadratic polynomial**.

ASCENDING AND DESCENDING ORDERS

Polynomials can be written in two ways in respect of the order of their terms :
1. *If the degrees of the terms of a polynomial fall in an order* **from the lowest to the highest,** *it is in* **ascending order** ; as—
   (a) $5 - 4x + 7x^2 + 8x^3 + 5x^4$ (b) $2x^4y + 3x^3y^3 - 5xy^6 + 8x^8$
2. *If the degrees of the terms of a polynomial fall in an order* **from the highest to the lowest,** *it is in* **descending order** ; as—
   (a) $5x^4 + 8x^3 + 7x^2 - 4x + 5$ (b) $8x^8 - 5xy^6 + 3x^3y^3 + 2x^4y$

OPERATIONS IN POLYNOMIALS

We have already studied how to add and subtract algebraic expressions. Let us review the process through a few examples :

Example 1. Add up :

$$3x - 5 + 6x^2 + x^3 - x^4 \text{ and } 6 - 5x + 2x^3 + 3x^2 + 3x^4.$$

Solution : Writing the terms in columns and then adding them one by one

$$
\begin{array}{r}
- x^4 + x^3 + 6x^2 + 3x - 5 \\
3x^4 + 2x^3 + 3x^2 - 5x + 6 \\
\hline
\mathbf{2x^4 + 3x^3 + 9x^2 - 2x + 1} \quad Ans.
\end{array}
$$

> *Remember that while adding—*
> 1. We arrange the like terms in separate columns.
> 2. We add each column carefully considering the signs of the terms in each column.
> 3. We **add up the co-efficients** of the terms in each column and write the **sum** as a term of the answer.

Example 2. Subtract :

$$3x^4 - 7x^3 + 4x^2 - 6x + 8 \text{ from } x^4 - 6x^3 + x^2 - 3x + 1$$

Solution :   Writing the *minuend* above and the *subtrahend* below it :

$$x^4 - 6x^3 + x^2 - 3x + 1 \qquad \textit{(Minuend)}$$
$$3x^4 - 7x^3 + 4x^2 - 6x + 8 \qquad \textit{(Subtrahend)}$$
$$\underline{\;-\quad +\quad -\quad +\quad - \quad\qquad \textit{(Changing the signs)}}$$
$$-2x^4 + x^3 - 3x^2 + 3x - 7 \qquad \textit{(Adding up)}$$

> *Remember that while subtracting—*
> 1. We write the *minuend* above.
> 2. We write the *subtrahend* below the minuend.
> ☞ 3. **We change the sign of each term of the subtrahend.**
> 4. Then we add up column-wise to get the **remainder**.

PRACTICE EXERCISES 16

A. Define—

1. a *polynomial*   **2.** a *trinomial*   **3.** a *quadrinomial*

4. a *constant polynomial*   **5.** a *linear polynomial*   **6.** a *quadratic polynomial*

7. a *cubic polynomial*   **8.** a *biquadratic polynomial*

9. *degree* of a polynomial with *one variable*

10. *degree* of a polynomial *with two* or *more variables*

B. Write in ascending order :

11. $5x^2 + 7x - 3$ **12.** $-3x^2y + 4xy - 8x + 5x^4$

13. $y^3 - x^4 + 2xy - 3x^3y^2 - 5x$ **14.** $15x^8 + 5xy^6 + 3x^4y + 2x^3y^3$

15. $3x^4y - 15x^2 + 5xy^2 - 2x^3y$ **16.** $3 + x^5 + 5x^2 - 3x^4 - 7x$

17. $5x^3 + 7x^4 - 8x + 3x^2 + 1$ **18.** $4x^3 + 3x^2y - \dfrac{1}{2}xy^2 + 5y^3$

C. Write in the descending order :

19. $5x^4 - 4x^3 + 2x^2 - 3 + x$ **20.** $-5xy^6 - 4x^3y^3 + 5x^4y + 16x^8$

21. $5x^2y - 6xy^3 + 4xy - 3x^3y^2$ **22.** $-x^2 + y^6 + 4x^2y^3 - 6x^2y^2 - 4x^2y + 8x$

23. $7x + 3 + 5x^2 + 8x^3 + 9x^4$ **24.** $6x^2y + 5xy - 7x + 4x^4 - 11$

D. Add up :

25. $5x^2 - 7xy + 4y^2 - 3x + 6$ and $x^2 + 5xy + 2y^2 - 3x + 5$

26. $4x^2 + 2xy - 3y^2 + x + 9$ and $15x^2 + xy - 6y^2 + 4x - 7$

27. $\frac{2}{3}y^3 - \frac{3}{4}y^2 + \frac{1}{3}y + 7$ and $\frac{7}{3}y^3 + \frac{3}{2}y^2 - \frac{2}{3}y + 11$

28. $4x^3 + 3x^2y - \frac{1}{2}xy^2 + 5y^3$ and $5y^2 - \frac{2}{3}y^3 + \frac{4}{3}x^2y + 5x^3$

29. $\frac{3}{2}x - \sqrt{3}x^2 + \frac{1}{\sqrt{3}}x^3$ and $\frac{1}{2}x + \sqrt{3}x^2 + \frac{2}{\sqrt{3}}x^3$

E. Subtract :

30. $5x^3 + \frac{4}{5}x^2y + 5y^3 + 3xy^2$ from $4x^3 + x^2y + 2xy^2 + 8y^3$

31. $y^3 - x^3 + 2xy^2 - 3x^2y$ from $x^3 - y^3 + 5x^2y - xy^2$

32. $x^3 - 7x^2 + 13x - 19$ from $20 + 4x^3 + 4x^2 - 3x$

33. $\frac{1}{3}x^3 + x^2 + \frac{1}{6}y^3 + \frac{5}{7}xy$ from $\frac{2}{3}x^3 + 4x^2 + \frac{5}{6}y^3 - \frac{6}{7}xy$

34. $\frac{3}{2}x - \sqrt{3}x^3 + \frac{1}{\sqrt{3}}x^2$ from $\frac{1}{2}x + \sqrt{2} + 3x^3 - \frac{2}{\sqrt{3}}x^2$

F. 35. What must be added to $3x^3 - 5x^2 + 1$ to get $x^3 - x^2 + 5$ as sum ?

36. What must be subracted from the expression $3x^5 - 4x^4 + 6x^3 - 8x^2 + 4$ to get $2x^5 - 4x^3 + 5x^2 - 7$ as remainder ?

G. Simplify :

37. $\left(\frac{4}{3}x^2y + 5x^3 - \frac{2}{3}y^3 + 5xy^2\right) + \left(3x^2y + 4x^3 + 5y^3 - \frac{1}{2}xy^2\right)$

38. $\left(\frac{1}{4}x^2 + \frac{1}{3}x + \frac{5}{6}\right) + \left(\frac{3}{4}x^2 + \frac{2}{3}x + \frac{1}{7}\right) - \left(\frac{1}{2}x^2 + \frac{5}{6}x + \frac{4}{7}\right)$

39. $\left(\frac{1}{\sqrt{2}}x^2 + \frac{1}{2}x + 1\right) - \left(\frac{1}{\sqrt{2}}x^2 - \frac{1}{2}x + 5\right) + \left(\sqrt{2}x^2 - \frac{3}{4}x + 4\right)$

40. $\left(\sqrt{3}x^2 - 10x + 7\sqrt{3}\right) + \left(3\sqrt{3}x^2 + 2x - 2\sqrt{3}\right) - \left(2\sqrt{3}x^2 - 9x + 9\sqrt{3}\right)$

11 OPERATIONS IN POLYNOMIALS

A. MULTIPLICATION OF POLYNOMIALS

Multiplication **is a shorter way of the process of addition.**

1. In order to multiply two polynomials, each term of one of the polynomials is multiplied by each term of the other polynomial.

2. While multiplying two terms, their co-efficients are multiplied at first. This product becomes the co-efficient of the entire term in the product.

3. Then the variable parts of the two terms are multiplied as per *laws of indices*.

4. The products of terms are linked together by appropriate signs.

MULTIPLYING A POLYNOMIAL BY A MONOMIAL

Example 1. **Multiply :** (a) $4x^2$ **by** $-5x^3$ (b) $(2x)^3 \times (-5x^2) \times (-3x^4)$

(c) $(-x^4 + 2x^3 + 3x^2 + 5)$ **by** $8x^2$

Solution : (a) $4x^2 \times (-5x^3) = 4 \times (-5) \times x^2 \times x^3$

$$= -20 \times x^{2+3} = -20x^5 \text{ Ans.}$$

(b) $2x^3 \times (-5x^2) \times (-3x^4) = 2 \times (-5) \times (-3) \times x^3 \times x^2 \times x^4$

$$= 30 \times x^{3+2+4} = 30x^9 \text{ Ans.}$$

(c) Product of $(-x^4 + 2x^3 + 3x^2 + 5)$ and $8x^2$

$$= 8x^2 (-x^4 + 2x^3 + 3x^2 + 5)$$

$$= 8x^2 (-x^4) + (8x^2 \times 2x^3) + (8x^2 \times 3x^2) + (8x^2 \times 5)$$

$$= -8x^6 + 16x^5 + 24x^4 + 40x^2 \text{ Ans.}$$

Example 2. **Multiply :** $6x^3 - x^2 + 2x + 3$ **by** $-2x$

Solution : Product of $-2x$ and $(6x^3 - x^2 + 2x + 3)$

$$= -2x (6x^3 - x^2 + 2x + 3)$$

$$= (-2x \times 6x^3) - (-2x \times x^2) + (-2x \times 2x) - (-2x \times 3)$$

$$= -12x^4 + 2x^3 - 4x^2 + 6x \text{ Ans.}$$

MULTIPLICATION OF POLYNOMIALS

In order to multiply two polynomials, we multiply each term of the multiplicand by each term of the multiplier in turn and add up their products.

Example 3. **Multiply : $6x^3 - x^2 + 2x - 3$ by $2x + 7$**

Solution : Writing the *multiplicand* above and the *multiplier* below it—

$6x^3 - x^2 + 2x - 3$ *(multiplicand)*

$2x + 7$ *(multiplier)*

$12x^4 - 2x^3 + 4x^2 - 6x$ *(multiplying by 2x)*

$\qquad 42x^3 - 7x^2 + 14x - 21$ *(multiplying by + 7)*

$12x^2 + 40x^3 - 3x^2 + 8x - 21$ *(adding up)*

∴ **Product $= 12x^2 + 40x^3 - 3x^2 + 8x - 21$** Ans.

Example 4. **Multiply : $6x^3 - 5x^2 + 4x + 1$ by $x^2 + 7x - 1$**

Solution : Writing the *multiplicand* above and the *multiplier* below it—

$6x^3 - 5x^2 + 4x + 1$ *(multiplicand)*

$x^2 + 7x - 1$ *(multiplier)*

$6x^5 - 5x^4 + 4x^3 + x^2$ *(multiplying by x^2)*

$\qquad 42x^4 - 35x^3 + 28x^2 + 7x$ *(multiplying by + 7x)*

$\qquad\qquad - 6x^3 + 5x^2 - 4x - 1$ *(multiplying by – 1)*

$6x^5 + 37x^4 - 37x^3 + 34x^2 + 3x - 1$ *(adding up)*

∴ **Product $= 6x^5 + 37x^4 - 37x^3 + 34x^2 + 3x - 1$** Ans.

Example 5. **Multiply : $\dfrac{1}{3}x^2 - \dfrac{1}{2}xy + \dfrac{1}{5}y^2$ by $x - 3y$.**

Solution : Writing the *multiplicand* above and the *multiplier* below it—

$\dfrac{1}{3}x^2 - \dfrac{1}{2}xy + \dfrac{1}{5}y^2$ *(multiplicand)*

$x - 3y$ *(multiplier)*

$\dfrac{1}{3}x^3 - \dfrac{1}{2}x^2y + \dfrac{1}{5}xy^2$ *(multiplying by x)*

$\qquad\qquad x^2y + \dfrac{3}{2}xy^2 - \dfrac{3}{5}y^3$ *(multiplying by – 3y)*

$\dfrac{1}{3}x^3 + \dfrac{1}{2}x^2y + \dfrac{17}{10}xy^2 - \dfrac{3}{5}y^3$ *(adding up)*

∴ **Product $= \dfrac{1}{3}x^3 + \dfrac{1}{2}x^2y + \dfrac{17}{10}xy^2 - \dfrac{3}{5}y^3$** Ans.

A. Define :

    1. a *multiplicand* ?   **2.** a *multiplier* ?   **3.** a *product* ?

B. Find the product of :

    4. $7x^2$ and $-6x^3$ **5.** $-8xy^2$ and $\dfrac{3}{4}x^2y$ **6.** $x \times \dfrac{1}{x}$

    7. $3a^3$ and $4b^4$ **8.** $-16c^2d$ and $\dfrac{5}{8}cd^2$ **9.** $a^3 \times \dfrac{1}{a}$

    10. $-3xy$, $-4x^2z$ and $-7x^2y^3z^2$ **11.** $\dfrac{2}{3}xy^2$ and $\dfrac{3}{4}xyz^2$ **12.** $\dfrac{5}{6}x^2z$ and $\dfrac{12}{25}xy^2$

C. Multiply :

    13. $2x^3 - 4x^2 + 7x - 5$ by $3x^2$ **14.** $5x^4 - 3x^2 - 1$ by $2x^3$

    15. $4x^4 - x^2y^2 - 9y^4$ by $-2x^2y$ **16.** $\dfrac{2}{3}x^2y^3z^4 \times \left(-\dfrac{9}{32}x^2y\right)$

    17. $3x^3 - 2x^2 + 4x - 1$ by $2x - 5$ **18.** $7x - 4x^2 + 2x^3 - 5$ by $3x - 2$

    19. $5x^2 - 7xy + 4y^2 - 3x$ by $x + 3y$ **20.** $5xy - 2y^2 + 3x - y$ by $3x + 4$

D. Find the product of :

    21. $x^3 - x^2 + 2x + 5$ and $x^2 + 1$ **22.** $5x^2 - 7xy + 6y^2$ and $5x^2 + 7xy - 6y^2$

    23. $3x^5 - 7x^3 + 2x^2 - x + 4$ and $x^3 - 2x^2 + 3x - 1$

    24. $\dfrac{1}{2}x^2 + \dfrac{1}{3}x - 1$ and $\dfrac{3}{4}x^2 - \dfrac{2}{3}x + \dfrac{1}{9}$

    25. $2x^2 + 7x - 1$ and $5x^2 - 9x + 3$

    26. $x^5 - 3x^4 - 5x^3 + 14x^2 + 39x - 11$ and $x^2 + 4x - 2$

    27. $x^2 + 4x - 2$ and $x^3 - x^2 + x + 8$

    28. $8x^4 - 3x^2 + 9x - 8$ and $2x^2 - 5x + 3$

    29. $6x^3 - 5x^2 + 4x + 1$ and $x^2 + 7x - 1$

    30. $1 + x - x^2 - x^3$ by $2x^3 + x + 5$

B. DIVISION OF POLYNOMIALS

The *operation* of **division** is just the converse of the *process* of **multiplication**. It is a shorter way of the process of *subtraction* also. It is carried out as under :

1. The expression to be divided *(dividend)* is written under a line.

2. From the left end of the line draw a perpendicular line downwards.

3. On the left of the dividend is written the expression with which the dividend is to be divided. It is called *divisor*.

4. Above the first line is written the result of the division which is called *quotient*.

5. Remember that **Dividend = Divisor × Quotient + Remainder**

Example 6. **Divide :** *(a)* $- 8x^3$ **by** $- 2x$ *(b)* $- 63x^2y^3$ **by** $7xy^2$

               (c) $8x^4 - 32x^3 + 16x^2$ **by** $- 4x^2$

Solution :   *(a)* $- 8x^3 \div - 2x = \dfrac{- 8 \times x \times x \times x}{- 2 \times x}$

$$= \frac{-8}{-2} \times x \times x = \mathbf{4x^2} \; Ans.$$

     (b) $- 63x^2y^3 \div 7xy^2 = \dfrac{- 63 \times x \times x \times y \times y \times y}{7 \times x \times y \times y}$

$$= \frac{-63}{7} \times x \times y = -\mathbf{9xy} \; Ans.$$

     (c) $\dfrac{8x^4 - 32x^3 + 16x^2}{- 4x^2} = \dfrac{8x^4}{-4x^2} - \dfrac{32x^3}{-4x^2} + \dfrac{16x^2}{-4x^2}$

$$= \left(\frac{8}{-4} \times \frac{x^4}{x^2}\right) - \left(\frac{32}{-4} \times \frac{x^3}{x^2}\right) + \left(\frac{16}{-4} \times \frac{x^2}{x^2}\right)$$

$$= -\mathbf{2x^2 + 8x - 4} \; Ans.$$

Example 7. **Divide** $\dfrac{3}{4}abc^3 - \dfrac{2}{3}ab^3c + \dfrac{2}{5}a^3bc$ **by** $- \dfrac{1}{6}abc$

Solution : $\dfrac{3}{4}abc^3 - \dfrac{2}{3}ab^3c + \dfrac{2}{5}a^3bc - \dfrac{1}{6}abc$

$$= \left(\frac{3}{4}abc^3 \times \frac{-6}{abc}\right) - \left(\frac{2}{3}ab^3c \times \frac{-6}{abc}\right) + \left(\frac{2}{5}a^3bc \times \frac{-6}{abc}\right)$$

$$= \frac{-18}{4}c^2 - \frac{-12}{3}b^2 + \frac{-12}{5}a^2$$

$$= -\frac{9}{2}c^2 + 4b^2 - \frac{12}{5}a^2 = \mathbf{4b^2 - \frac{9}{2}c^2 - \frac{12}{5}a^2} \; Ans.$$

Example 8. **Divide** $\mathbf{2x^3 + 11x^2 + 17x + 5}$

             by $\mathbf{2x + 5}$

Solution :   Dividend $= 2x^3 + 11x^2 + 17x + 5$

              Divisor $= 2x + 5$

              Performing the division, we get

              $\mathbf{x^2 + 3x + 1}$ as quotient

$$
\begin{array}{r}
x^2 + 3x + 1 \\
2x+5 \overline{\smash{\big)}\, 2x^3 + 11x^2 + 17x + 5} \\
\underline{2x^3 + 5x^2} \\
6x^2 + 17x + 5 \\
\underline{6x^2 + 15x} \\
2x + 5 \\
\underline{2x + 5} \\
0
\end{array}
$$

> **Note :** Long division in Algebra is performed just as in Arithmetic. There may be a **remainder** also.

91

Example 9. **Divide :**

$$2x^4 - x^3 + 10x^2 + 8x - 5$$

by $x^2 - x + 6$

Solution : Dividend $= 2x^4 - x^3 + 10x^2 + 8x - 5$

Divisor $= x^2 - x + 6$

Quotient $= 2x^2 + x - 1$

Remainder $= x + 1$ *Ans.*

$$
\begin{array}{r}
2x^2+x-1 \\
x^2-x+6 \overline{\smash{)}\ 2x^4- x^3+10x^2+8x-5} \\
\underline{2x^4-2x^3+12x^2} \\
x^3 - 2x^2+8x-5 \\
\underline{x^3 - x^2+6x} \\
-x^2+2x-5 \\
\underline{-x^2+ x-6} \\
x+1
\end{array}
$$

Example 10. **Find the values of a and b so that $x^4 + x^3 + 8x^2 + ax + b$ may be exactly divisible by $x^2 + 1$.**

Solution : For finding the values of a and b, we shall divide the expression by $x^2 + 1$

now to get 0 as the remainder—

$a - 1 =$ must be 0 or $a = 1$

$b - 7$ must be 0 or $b = 7$

$\therefore$ **$a = 1$ and $b = 7$** *Ans.*

$$
\begin{array}{r}
x^2+x+7 \\
x^2+1 \overline{\smash{)}\ x^4+x^3+8x^2+ax+b} \\
\underline{x^4 \quad + x^2} \\
x^3+7x^2+ax+b \\
\underline{x^3 \quad + x} \\
7x^2+(a-1)x+b \\
\underline{7x^2 \quad +7} \\
(a-1)x+(b-7)
\end{array}
$$

Example 11. **How will you show that $x^4 + 4x^3 - 2x^2 + 10x - 25$ has $x + 5$ as its factor ?**

Solution :   Let us see through division that whether $x + 5$ is a factor of the given expression or not.

On dividing $x^4+4x^3-2x^2+10x-25$

by $x+5$, we find that it divides the expression exactly.

The quotient is x^3-x^2+3x-5 and no remainder is left behind.

In other words, the expression is divisible by $x + 5$ exactly.

$\therefore$ **It is a factor of the expression**

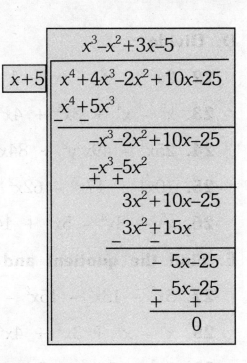

$$\begin{array}{r} x^3-x^2+3x-5 \\ \hline x+5\,\big|\,x^4+4x^3-2x^2+10x-25 \\ \underline{\overset{-}{x^4}+\overset{-}{5x^3}} \\ -x^3-2x^2+10x-25 \\ \underline{\overset{+}{-x^3}\overset{+}{-5x^2}} \\ 3x^2+10x-25 \\ \underline{\overset{-}{3x^2}+\overset{-}{15x}} \\ -5x-25 \\ \underline{\overset{+}{-5x}\overset{+}{-25}} \\ 0 \end{array}$$

PRACTICE EXERCISES 18

A. Define :

1. a *dividend*   **2.** a *divisor*   **3.** a *quotient*   **4.** a *remainder*

B. Divide :

5. $8x^2y^3$ by $-2xy$

6. $-15x^3yz^3$ by $-5xyz$

7. $15abc$ by $5bc$

8. $36a^3b^5c^6$ by $-12a^2bc$

9. $-156x^3y^5z^8$ by $-13x^2y^2z^3$

10. $-4x^3-6x^2+8x$ by $2x$

11. $3x^4y-4x^3y^2+5x^2y^3$ by $-6x^2y$ **12.** $8x^4yz-5xy^3z+24x^2yz^4$ by $3xyz$

13. $\dfrac{1}{6}x^4-\dfrac{13}{36}x^3+3x^2-\dfrac{13}{28}x+5$ by $\dfrac{x^3}{2}$

14. $-a^8b^5+\sqrt{3}a^7b^6-\dfrac{1}{6}a^6b^7$ by $-2a^8b^6$

15. $\dfrac{1}{3}x^3y-\dfrac{3}{2}x^2y+\dfrac{17}{10}xy^2-\dfrac{3}{5}xy^3$ by $\dfrac{1}{30}xy$

C. Find the quotient after dividing :

16. x^2+5x+6 by $x+3$

17. $6x^2-29x+28$ by $3x-4$

18. $4x^3-37x^2+52x-15$ by $4x-5$

19. x^3-1 by $x-1$

20. $x^4+4x^3-2x^2+10x-25$ by $x+5$

21. $6x^2-31x+47$ by $2x-5$

D. Divide :

22. $2x^3 + x^2 - 3x + 1$ by $x^2 + x - 1$

23. $x^5 - x^4 + 3x^3 + 4x^2 + 2x + 5$ by $x^3 - x^2 + 2x + 5$

24. $25x^4 - 49x^2y^2 + 84xy^3 - 36y^4$ by $5x^2 - 7xy + 6y^2$

25. $10x^4 + 17x^3 - 62x^2 + 30x - 3$ by $2x^2 + 7x - 1$

26. $x^5 + 3x^4 - 5x^3 + 14x^2 + 30x - 16$ by $x^3 - x^2 + x + 8$

E. Find the quotient and the remainder after dividing :

27. $5x^5 - 13x^4 - 15x^2 - 20$ by $x - 3$

28. $x^5 - x^4 + 3x^3 + 4x^2 + 4x + 6$ by $x^2 + 1$

29. $8x^4 + 14x^3 + 7x - 8$ by $4x^2 + 3x - 2$

30. $2x^4 + x^3 - 27x^2 + 36x - 15$ by $2x - 5$

F. How will you show through division that—

31. $x^2 + 1$ is a factor of $x^4 + x^3 + 8x^2 + x + 7$?

32. $2x^2 - x + 3$ is a factor of $6x^5 - x^4 + 4x^3 - 5x^2 - x - 15$?

G. 33. What must be subtracted from $6x^4 - 16x^3 + 29x^2 - 32x + 13$ so that the remainder may be exactly divisible by $3x - 2$?

34. What must be added to $x^5 - x^4 + 3x^3 + 4x^2 - 3x - 3$ so that the sum may be exactly divisible by $x^2 + 1$?

H. Complete the following statements :

35. Divisor × .... + ... = Dividend.

36. If division is exact, the quotient is a .... of the dividend.

37. The quotient is never an expression of a .... degree than the dividend.

38. The process of .... is the converse of the process of multiplication.

39. Multiplication is a shorter way of the process of ....

40. Division is a shorter way of the process of ....

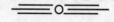

94

12 RATIONAL EXPRESSION

KNOW THESE TERMS :
1. **rational numbers**—a number that is expressed in the form $\frac{a}{b}$ (a, b being integers)
2. **rational expression**—an expression that is expressed in the form $\frac{a}{b}$ (a, b, being polynomials)

WHAT IS A RATIONAL EXPRESSION ?

We read about **rational numbers** in the previous book of the series, we know that a *rational number* **is a number that can be expressed in the form** $\frac{a}{b}$ **where** a, b **are integers and** b **is not other than 0.**

For example, $\frac{3}{4}$, $\frac{2}{3}$, $\frac{-1}{3}$ etc. are examples of rational numbers.

Similarly, a *rational expression* **is an expression which is expressed in the form** $\frac{a}{b}$ **in terms of polynomials.**

Clearly, $\frac{a+1}{2a-4}$, $\frac{2x-3}{3x+2}$, $\frac{4y^2-2y+1}{5y-1}$ are all rational expressions. Note that—

1. $\frac{a+1}{2a-4}$ is a rational expression in the variable a.

2. $\frac{2x-3}{3x+2}$ is a rational expression in the variable x.

3. $\frac{4y^2-2y+1}{5y-1}$ is a rational expression in the variable y.

4. We generally get a rational expression when we place two polynomials in the form $\frac{a}{b}$.

OPERATIONS IN RATIONAL EXPRESSIONS

Two or more rational expressions can be added just as rational numbers are added.

Example 1. **Add up** $\frac{2x+1}{2x-1}$ **and** $\frac{x-1}{x+1}$

Solution : $\quad \frac{2x+1}{2x-1} + \frac{x-1}{x+1}$

$$= \frac{(2x+1)(x+1) + (x-1)(2x-1)}{(2x-1)(x+1)} \quad ..(L.C.M. \ of \ denominators)$$

$$= \frac{(2x^2+2x+x+1) + (2x^2-x-2x+1)}{(2x-1)(x+1)}$$

$$= \frac{2x^2 + 3x + 1 + 2x^2 - 3x + 1}{(2x - 1)(x + 1)}$$

$$= \frac{4x^2 + 2}{(2x - 1)(x + 1)} = \frac{2(2x^2 + 1)}{(2x - 1)(x + 1)} \quad Ans.$$

Example 2. **Subtract :** $\dfrac{2x + 1}{2x - 1}$ **from** $\dfrac{x - 1}{x + 1}$

Solution : $\qquad \dfrac{x - 1}{x + 1} - \dfrac{2x + 1}{2x - 1}$

$$= \frac{(x - 1)(2x - 1) - (2x + 1)(x + 1)}{(x + 1)(2x - 1)} \quad ...(L.C.M.\ of\ denominators)$$

$$= \frac{(2x^2 - x - 2x + 1) - (2x^2 + 2x + x + 1)}{(x + 1)(2x - 1)}$$

$$= \frac{(2x^2 - 3x + 1) - (2x^2 + 3x + 1)}{(x + 1)(2x - 1)}$$

$$= \frac{2x^2 - 3x + 1 - 2x^2 - 3x - 1}{(x + 1)(2x - 1)} = \frac{-6x}{(x + 1)(2x - 1)} \quad Ans.$$

Example 3. **Simplify :** $\dfrac{x - 1}{x + 1} + \dfrac{x - 2}{x + 2} - \dfrac{2x^2 + 3x - 1}{(x + 1)(x + 2)}$

Solution : $\qquad \dfrac{x - 1}{x + 1} + \dfrac{x - 2}{x + 2} - \dfrac{2x^2 + 3x - 1}{(x + 1)(x + 2)}$

$$= \frac{(x - 1)(x + 2) + (x - 2)(x + 1) - (2x^2 + 3x - 1)}{(x + 1)(x + 2)}$$

$$= \frac{(x^2 + 2x - x - 2) + (x^2 + x - 2x - 2) - (2x^2 + 3x - 1)}{(x + 1)(x + 2)}$$

$$= \frac{(x^2 + x - 2) + (x^2 - x - 2) - (2x^2 + 3x - 1)}{(x + 1)(x + 2)}$$

$$= \frac{x^2 + x - 2 + x^2 - x - 2 - 2x^2 - 3x + 1)}{(x + 1)(x + 2)}$$

$$= \frac{-3x - 3}{(x + 1)(x + 2)} = \frac{-3(x + 1)}{(x + 1)(x + 2)} = \frac{-3}{x + 2} \quad Ans.$$

> Remember :
> 1. Addition and subtraction of rational expressions are performed after taking the L.C.M. of their denominators.
> 2. Simplification sums generally involve four basic operations.

PRACTICE EXERCISES 19

A. 1. What is a *rational expression* ? Give three examples.

B. Which of the following are *rational polynomials* and which are *rational expressions* :

2. $\dfrac{2x + 1}{x + 2}$

3. $\sqrt{3}x^2 - x + 4$

4. $\dfrac{y^2 - y + 2}{2 + y}$

5. $y^2 + y - 2$

6. $\dfrac{x^2 - 3xy + y^2}{x - y}$

7. $2a^2 - a + 1$

8. $\dfrac{x - 1}{x + 1}$

9. $x + \dfrac{1}{x} + 3$

10. $\dfrac{2}{3}a^2 - \dfrac{3}{4}a + 7$

C. Add up the following rational expressions :

11. $\dfrac{x + 1}{2x - 5} + \dfrac{2x - 1}{3x + 2}$

12. $\dfrac{2x + 1}{2x - 5} + \dfrac{x - 1}{x + 2}$

13. $\dfrac{x^2 - x + 5}{(x + 1)} + \dfrac{x^2 + x - 5}{(x - 1)}$

14. $\dfrac{2y^2 - 3y + 1}{y + 1} - \dfrac{y + 1}{y - 1}$

15. $\dfrac{y^2 - y + 2}{y - 3} + \dfrac{4y - y^2 + 1}{2 + y}$

16. $\dfrac{y^2 + y - 2}{y + 3} + \dfrac{4y + y^2 - 1}{2 - y}$

17. $\dfrac{4x + 9}{2x - 1} + \dfrac{6x + 5}{3x - 2}$

18. $\dfrac{3x - 5}{2x + 3} + \dfrac{2x - 3}{3x + 2}$

19. $\dfrac{x^2 + 4x + 4}{x + 2} + \dfrac{x^2 + 7x + 12}{x + 3} + \dfrac{x^2 + 6x + 7}{(x + 2)\,(x + 3)}$

D. Perform the following subtractions :

20. $\dfrac{2x - 1}{3x + 2} - \dfrac{x + 1}{2x - 5}$

21. $\dfrac{2x + 1}{2x - 5} - \dfrac{x - 1}{x + 2}$

22. $\dfrac{y^2 - y + 5}{y + 1} - \dfrac{y^2 + y - 5}{y - 1}$

23. $\dfrac{2x^2 - 3x + 1}{x + 1} - \dfrac{x + 1}{x - 1}$

24. $\dfrac{2x + 5}{(x + 1)} - \dfrac{1 + 4x}{2x + 1}$

25. $\dfrac{2x + 3}{3x + 1} - \dfrac{2x + 1}{2x + 3}$

97

26. $\dfrac{x^2 - x + 2}{x - 3} - \dfrac{4x - x^2 + 1}{2 + x}$

27. $\dfrac{x^2 + x - 2}{x + 3} - \dfrac{4x + x^2 - 1}{2 - x}$

28. $\dfrac{x^2 - 3xy + y^2}{x - y} - \dfrac{x^2 + 3xy - y^2}{x + 1}$

29. $\dfrac{x - 1}{x + 1} - \dfrac{3x - 5}{2x + 3} - \dfrac{5x + 6}{(2x + 3)(x + 1)}$

E. Simplify :

30. $\dfrac{x^2 + 3x - 2}{x + 5} + \dfrac{x^2 - 2x - 8}{x + 4} - \dfrac{2x^2 + 3x + 2}{(x + 5)(x + 4)}$

31. $\dfrac{x^2 + 4x - 5}{x + 5} + \dfrac{x^2 - 9x + 20}{x - 3} - \dfrac{x^2 - 8x - 20}{(x - 3)(x + 5)}$

32. $\dfrac{a^2 - 3a - 10}{a + 2} - \dfrac{a^2 - 4}{a - 4} + \dfrac{3a^2 + 5a - 6}{(a + 2)(a - 4)}$

33. $\dfrac{y^2 + 10y - 24}{y + 3} + \dfrac{y^2 + 4y - 32}{y - 2} - \dfrac{y^2 - y - 72}{(y - 2)(y + 3)}$

34. $(a^2 + 3a + 1) - \dfrac{2a}{a + 2} + \dfrac{a + 2}{a - 1}$

35. $\dfrac{4x + 1}{3x - 1} + \dfrac{3x + 1}{2x + 1} - \dfrac{2x - 1}{3x + 1} + \dfrac{x - 2}{2x + 1}$

MULTIPLICATION OF RATIONAL EXPRESSIONS

Multiplication and *division* of rational expression are also carried out just like those of rational numbers. We also make use of formulas while simplifying these expressions.

Example 4. **Multiply :** $\dfrac{2a^2b}{3b^2c}$ **and** $\dfrac{-9a^3c^2}{8a^4c}$

Solution : $\dfrac{2a^2b}{3b^2c} \times \dfrac{-9a^3c^2}{8a^4c} = \dfrac{2 \times a^2 \times b}{3 \times b^2 \times c} \times \dfrac{-9 \times a^3 \times c^2}{8 \times a^4 \times c}$

$= \dfrac{2 \times (-9)}{3 \times 8} \times \dfrac{a^2 \times a^3 \times b \times c^2}{a^4 \times b^2 \times c^2} = \dfrac{-18}{24} \times \dfrac{a^5 \times b \times c^2}{a^4 \times b^2 \times c^2}$

$= \dfrac{-3}{4} \times \dfrac{a^5 \times b}{a^4 \times b^2} = -\dfrac{3a}{4b}$ *Ans.*

Example 5. Multiply : $\dfrac{x^2 - 4y^2}{xy\,(x + 2y)}$ and $\dfrac{x^3y^3}{2x - 4y}$

Solution : $\dfrac{x^2 - 4y^2}{xy\,(x + 2y)} \times \dfrac{x^3y^3}{2x - 4y}$

$= \dfrac{(x)^2 - (2y)^2}{xy\,(x + 2y)} \times \dfrac{x^3y^3}{2\,(x - 2y)} = \dfrac{(x + 2y)\,(x - 2y)}{xy\,(x + 2y)} \times \dfrac{x^3y^3}{2\,(x - 2y)}$

$= \dfrac{1}{xy} \times \dfrac{x^3y^3}{2} = 1 \times \dfrac{x^2y^2}{2} = \dfrac{1}{2}x^2y^2$ Ans.

Example 6. Simplify : $\left(\dfrac{1}{x} + \dfrac{1}{y}\right) \times \dfrac{xy}{x^2 + 2xy + y^2} \times \dfrac{x^2 - y^2}{x - y}$

Solution : $\left(\dfrac{1}{x} + \dfrac{1}{y}\right) \times \dfrac{xy}{x^2 + 2xy + y^2} \times \dfrac{x^2 - y^2}{x - y}$

$= \dfrac{y + x}{xy} \times \dfrac{xy}{(x + y)^2} \times \dfrac{(x + y)\,(x - y)}{(x - y)}$

$= \dfrac{(x + y)}{xy} \times \dfrac{xy}{(x + y)\,(x + y)} \times \dfrac{(x + y)\,(x - y)}{x - y} = 1$ Ans.

Example 7. Divide $\dfrac{2a^3b^2}{3x^2y^3}$ by $\dfrac{4a^4b}{9x^3y^4}$

Solution : $\dfrac{2a^3b^2}{3x^2y^3} \div \dfrac{4a^4b}{9x^3y^4} = \dfrac{2a^3b^2}{3x^2y^3} \times \dfrac{9x^3y^4}{4a^4b}$

$= \dfrac{2 \times a^3 \times b^2 \times 9 \times x^3 \times y^4}{3 \times x^2 \times y^3 \times 4 \times a^4 \times b}$

$= \dfrac{18 \times a^3 \times b^2 \times x^3 \times y^4}{12 \times a^4 \times b \times x^2 \times y^3} = \dfrac{3 \times b \times x \times y}{2 \times a}$

$= \dfrac{3b \times x \times y}{2 \times a} = \dfrac{3bxy}{2a}$ Ans.

Example 8. Divide : $\dfrac{x^2 + 2x + 1}{x + 1}$ by $\dfrac{x^2 - 1}{x + 3}$

Solution :

$$\frac{x^2 + 2x + 1}{x + 1} \div \frac{x^2 - 1}{x + 3}$$

$$= \frac{x^2 + 2x + 1}{x + 1} \times \frac{x + 3}{x^2 - 1}$$

$$= \frac{(x + 1)^2}{(x + 1)} \times \frac{x + 3}{(x + 1)(x - 1)}$$

$$= \frac{(x + 1)(x + 1)}{x + 1} \times \frac{x + 3}{(x + 1)(x - 1)} = \frac{x + 3}{x - 1} \text{ Ans.}$$

Example 9. **Divide :** $\dfrac{5x + 3}{5x - 1}$ **by** $\dfrac{x + 1}{2x - 1}$

Solution :

$$\frac{5x + 3}{5x - 1} \div \frac{x + 1}{2x - 1} = \frac{5x + 3}{5x - 1} \times \frac{2x - 1}{x + 1}$$

$$= \frac{(5x + 3)(2x - 1)}{(5x - 1)(x + 1)} = \frac{10x^2 - 5x + 6x - 3}{5x^2 + 5x - x - 1}$$

$$= \frac{10x^2 + x - 3}{5x^2 + 4x - 1} \text{ Ans.}$$

Example 10. **Simplify :** $\left(\dfrac{x + 2y}{x - 2y} + \dfrac{x - 2y}{x + 2y}\right) \div \dfrac{x^2 + 4y^2}{x^2 - 4y^2}$

Solution :

$$\left(\frac{x + 2y}{x - 2y} + \frac{x - 2y}{x + 2y}\right) \div \frac{x^2 + 4y^2}{x^2 - 4y^2}$$

$$= \frac{(x + 2y)(x + 2y) + (x - 2y)(x - 2y)}{(x - 2y)(x + 2y)} \div \frac{x^2 + 4y^2}{x^2 - 4y^2}$$

$$= \frac{(x + 2y)^2 + (x - 2y)^2}{x^2 - 4y^2} \div \frac{x^2 + 4y^2}{x^2 - 4y^2}$$

$$= \frac{x^2 + 4y^2 + 4xy + x^2 + 4y^2 - 4xy}{x^2 - 4y^2} \div \frac{x^2 + 4y^2}{x^2 - 4y^2}$$

$$= \frac{2x^2 + 8y^2}{x^2 - 4y^2} \times \frac{x^2 - 4y^2}{x^2 + 4y^2}$$

$$= \frac{2(x^2 + 4y^2)}{x^2 - 4y^2} \times \frac{x^2 - 4y^2}{(x^2 + 4y^2)} = \textbf{2} \text{ Ans.}$$

A. Multiply :

1. $\dfrac{5x^2}{y^2}$ and $\dfrac{-4x^4y^3}{25xy^4}$

2. $\dfrac{14x^2}{(x-1)(x+1)}$ by $\dfrac{x^2-1}{21x^5}$

3. $\dfrac{-8p^2q^2r}{9p^4q^3r^2}$ and $\dfrac{27p^5q^2r^4}{16p^3q^7r^6}$

4. $\dfrac{x+2}{x-1}$ and $\dfrac{x-5}{x+2}$

B. Find the product of :

5. $\dfrac{14x^2}{x^2-y^2} \times \dfrac{x+y}{7x}$

6. $\dfrac{(a+b)^2}{(a+b)^3} \times \dfrac{a^2-b^2}{a-b}$

7. $\dfrac{2x+1}{x-1} \times \dfrac{3x-2}{x+2} \times \dfrac{x-1}{3x-2}$

8. $\dfrac{x+6}{x+7} \times \dfrac{x+7}{2x-5} \times \dfrac{2x-5}{x-6}$

9. $\dfrac{x^2-4x+4}{x-3} \times \dfrac{x^2-9}{x-2}$

10. $\dfrac{3x+x^2}{8x-1} \times \dfrac{5}{4x+1}$

C. Divide :

11. $\dfrac{4a^2b^3c^2}{3a^3b^2c}$ by $\dfrac{8a^3b^4}{6ab^2}$

12. $\dfrac{38x^2y^3}{80x^3y^2}$ by $\dfrac{57xy^4}{40x^2y^2}$

13. $\dfrac{2x-8}{x^2-4}$ by $\dfrac{4-x}{2x^2+10x+16}$

14. $\dfrac{x^2+x+1}{x+1}$ by $\dfrac{x^2-1}{x+3}$

D. Simplify :

15. $\dfrac{x^2-4x+4}{x-3} \times \dfrac{x^2-9}{x-2} \div \dfrac{x-2}{x+3}$

16. $\left(\dfrac{2x^2+1}{x+1} \times \dfrac{x+1}{x-1}\right) \times \dfrac{x^2-1}{2x}$

17. $\left(\dfrac{1}{a}+\dfrac{1}{b}\right)\left(\dfrac{ab}{a^2+2ab+b^2}\right)\left(\dfrac{a^2-b^2}{a-b}\right) \div \dfrac{a+b}{a-b}$

18. $\dfrac{3-m}{m-3} \times \dfrac{4-m}{m-4} \div \dfrac{1}{m^2-16}$

19. $\dfrac{x^2-9}{x^2-4} \times \dfrac{x^2-2x}{x^2+2x+4} \div \dfrac{x+3}{x+2}$

20. If $A = \dfrac{a}{a+1}$, $B = \dfrac{a}{a-1}$, find—

     (a) A + B   (b) A – B   (c) A ÷ B   (d) AB

13 IDENTITIES

> **KNOW THESE TERMS :**
>   1. **identity**—equation that is true for any value of the variable
>   2. **common term**—term that is a factor of two or more expressions is their common term
>   3. **whole square**—square of an expression consisting of two or more terms

We studied **three identities** in the previous class. They are—

1. $(a + b)^2 = a^2 + b^2 + 2ab$ **2.** $(a - b)^2 = a^2 + b^2 - 2ab$

3. $a^2 - b^2 = (a + b)(a - b)$

We learnt to apply these binomial identities in mathematical operations—*multiplying, simplifying, evaluating* and *factorising* of given expressions.

In this chapter, we shall study some more identities and their application in mathematical operations.

$\boxed{\text{IDENTITY 4}}$ $(x + a)(x + b) = x^2 + x(a + b) + ab$

$$(x + a)(x + b) = x^2 + bx + ax + ab$$
$$= x^2 + ax + bx + ab$$
$$= x^2 + x(a + b) + ab$$

The terms a, b may be **positive** or **negative** ; as—

1. $(x + a)(x - b) = x^2 + x(a - b) - ab$
2. $(x - a)(x + b) = x^2 + (b - a) - ab$
3. $(x - a)(x - b) = x^2 + x(-a - b) + ab = x^2 - (a + b) + ab$

This identity states :

Product of two binomials with one *Common Term (CT)* =
(CT)^2 + CT (sum of the other terms) + product of the other terms

Let us now solve some example involving the application of the above identity.

Example 1. Find the product of :

(a) $(x + c)(x + d)$ (b) $(a + 5)(a + 7)$

(c) $(y + 4)(y + 9)$ (d) $(x + 3)(x - 5)$

(e) $(a - 8)(a + 9)$ (f) $(y - 9)(y - 4)$

Solution :

(a) $(x + c)(x + d)$ has x as its Common Term (CT)

$\therefore \quad (x + c)(x + d)$

$= (CT)^2 + CT$ (sum of c and d) + Product of c and d

$= x^2 + x(c + d) + c \times d$

$= \mathbf{x^2 + x(c + d) + cd}$ *Ans.*

(b) $(a + 5)(a + 7)$ has a as its Common Term

$(a + 5)(a + 7) = CT^2 + CT(5 + 7) + (5 \times 7)$

$\qquad\qquad\qquad = a^2 + a(5 + 7) + (5 \times 7)$

$\qquad\qquad\qquad = \mathbf{a^2 + 12a + 35}$ *Ans.*

(c) $(y + 4)(y + 9)$ has y as its Common Term

$(y + 4)(y + 9) = CT^2 + CT(4 + 9) + (4 \times 9)$

$\qquad\qquad\qquad = y^2 + y(4 + 9) + (4 \times 9)$

$\qquad\qquad\qquad = \mathbf{y^2 + 13y + 36}$ *Ans.*

(d) $(x + 3)(x - 5)$ has x as its Common Term

$(x + 3)(x - 5) = CT^2 + CT(+ 3 - 5) + (+3)(-5)$

$\qquad\qquad\qquad = x^2 + x \times (-2) + (- 15)$

$\qquad\qquad\qquad = \mathbf{x^2 - 2x - 15}$ *Ans.*

(e) $(a - 8)(a + 9)$ has a as its Common Term

$(a - 8)(a + 9) = CT^2 + CT(- 8 + 9) + (- 8)(+9)$

$\qquad\qquad\qquad = a^2 + a(1) + (-72)$

$\qquad\qquad\qquad = \mathbf{a^2 + a - 72}$ *Ans.*

(f) $(y - 9)(y - 4)$ has y as its Common Term

$(y - 9)(y - 4) = CT^2 + CT(- 9 - 4) + (-9)(-4)$

$\qquad\qquad\qquad = y^2 + y(-13) + (36)$

$\qquad\qquad\qquad = \mathbf{y^2 - 13y + 36}$ *Ans.*

Example 2. Find the value of :

    (a) **102 × 106**   (b) **95 − 97**

Solution :   (a) $102 \times 106 = (100 + 2)(100 + 6)$

                Clearly 100 is the Common Term (CT)

$$(100 + 2)(100 + 6) = (100)^2 + 100(2 + 6) + 2 \times 6$$
$$= 10000 + (100 \times 8) + 12$$
$$= 10000 + 800 + 12 = \textbf{10812} \text{ Ans.}$$

(b) $95 \times 97 = (100 - 5)(100 - 3)$

Clearly 100 is the Common Term

$$(100 - 5)(100 - 3) = (100)^2 + 100(-5 - 3) + (-5)(-3)$$
$$= 10000 + 100(-8) + 15$$
$$= 10000 - 800 + 15 = \textbf{9215} \text{ Ans.}$$

IDENTITY 5 $(a + b + c)^2 = a^2 + b^2 + c^2 + 2ab + 2bc + 2ca$

This identity is an extension of the identity $(a + b)^2$ which is the *whole square of a binomial*. This identity is the **whole square of a trinomial**.

$$(a + b + c)^2 = [a + (b + c)]^2$$
$$= (a)^2 + (b + c)^2 + 2 \times a \times (b + c)$$
$$= a^2 + b^2 + c^2 + 2bc + 2a(b + c)$$
$$= a^2 + b^2 + c^2 + 2bc + 2ab + 2ca$$
$$= \textbf{\textit{a}}^2 + \textbf{\textit{b}}^2 + \textbf{\textit{c}}^2 + \textbf{2\textit{ab}} + \textbf{2\textit{bc}} + \textbf{2\textit{ca}}$$

This identity states :

The whole square of a trinomial = squares of the terms of trinomial + twice their products taken two by two.

The terms of the trinomial may be positive or negative ; as—

1. $(a - b + c)^2$ 2. $(a + b - c)^2$
3. $(a - b - c)^2$ 4. $(b + c - a)^2$

Let us now solve some examples involving the use of the above identity.

Example 3.   **Find the value of :**

     (a) $(x + y + z)^2$ (b) $(a + b - c)^2$

     (c) $(l - m - n)^2$ (d) $(y + z - x)^2$

Solution : (a) $(x + y + z)^2 = x^2 + y^2 + z^2 + (2 \times x \times y) + (2 \times y \times z)$
$$+ (2 \times z \times x)$$
$$= \textbf{\textit{x}}^2 + \textbf{\textit{y}}^2 + \textbf{\textit{z}}^2 + \textbf{2\textit{xy}} + \textbf{2\textit{yz}} + \textbf{2\textit{zx}} \text{ Ans.}$$

(b) $(a + b - c)^2 = a^2 + b^2 + c^2 + (2 \times a \times b) + 2 \times b$
$\times (-c) + 2 \times (-c) \times a$

$$= a^2 + b^2 + c^2 + 2ab - 2bc - 2ca \text{ Ans.}$$

(c) $(l - m - n)^2 = l^2 + m^2 + n^2 + 2 \times l \times (-m) + 2 \times$
$(-m)(-n) + 2 \times (-n) \times l$

$$= l^2 + m^2 + n^2 - 2lm + 2mn - 2ln \text{ Ans.}$$

(d) $(y + z - x) = y^2 + z^2 + x^2 + (2 \times y \times z) + 2 \times z (-x)$
$+ 2 (-x) \times y$

$$= y^2 + z^2 + x^2 + 2yz - 2zx - 2xy$$

$$= x^2 + y^2 + z^2 - 2xy + 2yz - 2zx \text{ Ans.}$$

Example 4. **Find the value of :**

(a) $(x + 2y + 3z)^2$ (b) $9x - 2y - 3z)^2$ (c) $(134)^2$

Solution :   (a) $(x + 2y + 3z)^2$

$$= x^2 + (2y)^2 + (3z)^2 + (2 \times x \times 2y) + (2 \times 2y \times 3z)$$
$$+ (2 \times 3z \times x)$$

$$= x^2 + 4y^2 + 9z^2 + 4xy + 12yz + 6zx \text{ Ans.}$$

(b) $(9x - 2y - 3z)^2$

$$= (9x)^2 + (2y)^2 + (3z)^2 + 2 \times 9x \times (-2y)$$
$$+ 2 \times (- 2y) \times (-3z) + 2 \times (-3z) \times 9x$$

$$= 81x^2 + 4y^2 + 9z^2 - 36xy + 12yz - 54zx \text{ Ans.}$$

(c) $(134)^2 = (100 + 30 + 4)^2$

$$= (100)^2 + (30)^2 + (4)^2 + (2 \times 100 \times 30)$$
$$+ (2 \times 30 \times 4) + (2 \times 4 \times 100)$$

$$= 10000 + 900 + 16 + 6000 + 240 + 800 = 17956 \text{ Ans.}$$

PRACTICE EXERCISES 21

A. Find the value of :

1. $(x + 7) (x + 5)$
2. $(x - 8) (x + 2)$
3. $(x - 5) (x - 6)$
4. $(x + 9) (x - 7)$
5. $(3x - 7) 3x + 4)$
6. $(2x + 3) (2x - 4)$
7. $\left(x - \dfrac{1}{2}\right)\left(x + \dfrac{1}{3}\right)$
8. $\left(x + \dfrac{3}{4}\right)\left(x + \dfrac{5}{6}\right)$
9. $\left(a + \dfrac{1}{3}\right)\left(a - \dfrac{2}{3}\right)$

B. Find the value of :

10. 136×107 **11.** 102×103 **12.** 52×47

13. 105×108 **14.** 98×97 **15.** 55×58

C. Fill up each blank with the correct term :

16. $(x + 2)\ x + 3) = x^2 + x\ (\text{..........} + \text{...........}) + \text{...........} \times \text{............}$

17. $\left(x + \dfrac{3}{4}\right)\left(x - \dfrac{1}{4}\right) \text{.........} + x\ (\text{.......} - \text{........} + \text{........} \times \text{.........})$

18. $(p + 2)\ (p - 7) = \text{.........} + \text{...........}\ (2 - 7) + \text{...........} \times \text{......}\ 7$

D. Find the value of :

19. $(2x + 3y + 4z)^2$ **20.** $(3x - y - 2z)^2$ **21.** $(9x + 2y + z)^2$

22. $\left(3p + \dfrac{1}{2}q - 2r\right)^2$ **23.** $(2x - 3y + 5z)^2$ **24.** $(x - y - 2)^2$

25. $\left(x + \dfrac{1}{x} - \dfrac{x}{2}\right)^2$ **26.** $\left(5x - \dfrac{1}{5x} + \dfrac{x}{5}\right)^2$ **27.** $(\sqrt{3} + \sqrt{2} + \sqrt{4})^2$

E. Find the value using the whole square of a trinomial :

28. $(123)^2$ **29.** $(111)^2$ **30.** $(364)^2$ **31.** $(254)^2$

F. 32. Find the values of $x^2 + \dfrac{1}{x^2}$ and $x^4 + \dfrac{1}{x^4}$ if $x - \dfrac{1}{x} = 5$

33. If $x^2 + \dfrac{1}{x^2} = 23$, find the value of $x + \dfrac{1}{x}$

34. If $x^2 + \dfrac{1}{x^2} = 66$, find the value of $x - \dfrac{1}{x}$

35. Find the value of $x + \dfrac{1}{x}$, if $x^2 + \dfrac{1}{x^2} = 62$

36. If $x + \dfrac{1}{x} = \sqrt{3}$, find $x^2 + \dfrac{1}{x^2}$ and $x^4 + \dfrac{1}{x^4}$

G. Using the whole square of a binomial, find the value of—

37. $(143)^2$ **38.** $(199)^2$ **39.** $(7·5)^2$ **40.** $(401)^2$

$\boxed{\text{IDENTITY 6}}$ $\ (a + b)^3 = a^3 + 3ab\ (a + b) + b^3$

$$(a + b)^3 = (a + b)\ (a + b)\ (a + b)$$
$$= (a + b)\ (a + b)^2$$

$$= (a + b) (a^2 + b^2 + 2ab)$$
$$= a \times (a^2 + b^2 + 2ab) + b(a^2 + b^2 + 2ab)$$
$$= (a^3 + ab^2 + 2a^2b) + (a^2b + b^3 + 2ab^2)$$
$$= a^3 + ab^2 + 2a^2b + a^2b + b^3 + 2ab^2$$
$$= a^3 + \boxed{ab^2 + 2ab^2} + \boxed{2a^2b + a^2b} + b^3$$
$$= a^3 + 3ab^2 + 3a^2b + b^3$$
$$= a^3 + 3a^2b + 3ab^2 + b^3$$
$$= \mathbf{a^3 + b^3 + 3ab\ (a + b)}$$

IDENTITY 7. $\mathbf{(a - b)^3 = a^3 - 3ab\ (a - b) - b^3}$

$$(a - b)^3 = (a - b)\ (a - b)\ (a - b)$$
$$= (a - b)\ (a - b)^2$$
$$= (a - b)\ (a^2 + b^2 - 2ab)$$
$$= a\ (a^2 + b^2 - 2ab) - b\ (a^2 + b^2 - 2ab)$$
$$= a^3 + ab^2 - 2a^2b - a^2b - b^3 + 2ab^2$$
$$= a^3 - \boxed{2a^2b - a^2b} + \boxed{2ab^2 + ab^2} - b^3$$
$$= a^3 - 3a^2b + 3ab^2 - b^3$$
$$= \mathbf{a^3 - 3ab\ (a - b) - b^3}$$

It can also be proved as under :

$$(a - b)^3 = [a + (-b)]^3$$
$$= a^3 + (-b)^3 + 3a\ (-b)\ [a + (-b)]$$
$$= a^3 - b^3 - 3ab\ (a - b)$$
$$= \mathbf{a^3 - 3ab\ (a - b) - b^3}$$

Let us now solve some examples involving the use of identities 6 and 7

Example 5. **Write in the expanded form :**

(a) $\mathbf{(x + 3y)^3}$ (b) $\mathbf{(2a + b)^3}$ (c) $\mathbf{(6l + 7m)^3}$

Solution :   (a) $(x + 3y)^3 = (x)^3 + 3 \times x \times 3y\ (x + 3y) + (3y)^3$
$$= x^3 + 3x \times 3y\ (x + 3y) + 27y^3$$
$$= x^3 + 9xy\ (x + 3y) + 27y^3$$
$$= \mathbf{x^3 + 9x^2y + 27xy^2 + 27y^3}\ Ans.$$

(b) $(2a + b)^3 = (2a)^3 + 3 \times 2a \times b\,(2a + b) + (b)^3$

$\qquad\qquad = 8a^3 + 6ab\,(2a + b) + b^3$

$\qquad\qquad = \mathbf{8a^3 + 12a^2b + 6ab^2 + b^3}$ *Ans.*

(c) $(6l + 7m) = (6l)^3 + 3 \times 6l \times 7m\,(6l + 7m) + (7m)^3$

$\qquad\qquad = 216l^3 + 126lm\,(6l + 7m) + 343m^3$

$\qquad\qquad = \mathbf{216l^3 + 756l^2m + 882lm^2 + 343m^3}$ *Ans.*

Example 6. **Find the value of $(105)^3$**

Solution : $\quad (105)^3 = (100 + 5)^3$

$\qquad\qquad = (100)^3 + 3 \times 100 \times 5\,(100 + 5) + (5)^3$

$\qquad\qquad = 1000000 + 1500\,(100 + 5) + 125$

$\qquad\qquad = 1000000 + (1500 \times 105) + 125$

$\qquad\qquad = 1000000 + 157500 + 125 = \mathbf{1157625}$ *Ans.*

Example 7. **Write in expanded form :** *(a)* $\mathbf{(3x - 2y)^3}$ *(b)* $\left(\dfrac{2}{3}x - \dfrac{1}{3}y\right)^3$

Solution : $\quad$ *(a)* $(3x - 2y)^3 = (3x)^3 - 3 \times 3x \times 2y\,(3x - 2y) - (2y)^3$

$\qquad\qquad = 27x^3 - 9x \times 2y\,(3x - 2y) - 8y^3$

$\qquad\qquad = 27x^3 - 18xy\,(3x - 2y) - 8y^3$

$\qquad\qquad = \mathbf{27x^3 - 54x^2y + 36xy^2 - 8y^3}$ *Ans.*

(b) $\left(\dfrac{2}{3}x - \dfrac{1}{3}y\right)^3 = \left(\dfrac{2}{3}x\right)^3 - 3 \times \dfrac{2}{3}x \times \dfrac{1}{3}y\left(\dfrac{2}{3}x - \dfrac{1}{3}y\right) - \left(\dfrac{1}{3}y\right)^3$

$\qquad\qquad = \dfrac{8}{27}x^3 - \dfrac{2}{3}xy\left(\dfrac{2}{3}x - \dfrac{1}{3}y\right) - \dfrac{1}{27}y^3$

$\qquad\qquad = \mathbf{\dfrac{8}{27}x^3 - \dfrac{4}{9}x^2y + \dfrac{2}{9}xy^2 - \dfrac{1}{27}y^3}$ *Ans.*

Example 8. **Find the value of $(99)^3$**

Solution : $\quad (99)^3 = (100 - 1)^3$

$\qquad\qquad = (100)^3 - 3 \times 100 \times 1\,(100 - 1) - (1)^3$

$\qquad\qquad = 1000000 - 300\,(99) - 1$

$\qquad\qquad = 1000000 - 29700 - 1 = \mathbf{970299}$ *Ans.*

PRACTICE EXERCISES 22

A. Expand the following cubes :

1. $(2x + 3y)^3$
2. $\left(\dfrac{x}{3} + \dfrac{y}{4}\right)^3$
3. $(5x + 9y)^3$

4. $(3p + 2q)^3$
5. $\left(x + \dfrac{1}{x}\right)^3$
6. $\left(a + \dfrac{1}{a}\right)^3$

7. $(3x + 3y)^3$
8. $(3x + 4y)^3$
9. $\left(3x + \dfrac{1}{2}y\right)^3$

B. Expand the following cubes :

10. $(4x - 5y)^3$
11. $(3x - 4y)^3$
12. $(x - y)^3$

13. $(4 - 3x)^3$
14. $(3x + 5y)^3$
15. $(2x + 3)^3$

16. $\left(2x - \dfrac{1}{2x}\right)^3$
17. $\left(\dfrac{a}{3} + \dfrac{2b}{3}\right)^3$
18. $\left(x - \dfrac{1}{x}\right)^3$

C. Find the cubes using $(a + b)^3$ or $(a - b)^3$

19. $(295)^3$
20. $(999)^3$
21. $(9 \cdot 9)^3$

D. Find the value of :

22. $x^3 + y^3$, if $x + y = 5$ and $xy = 4$

23. $x^3 - y^3$, if $x - y = 2$ and $xy = 3$

24. $a^3 + 8b^3$, if $a + 2b = 10$ and $ab = 15$

25. $27x^3 + 64y^3$, if $3x + 4y = 11$ and $xy = 2$

26. $343x^3 - 125y^3$, if $7x - 5y = 6$ and $xy = 9$

E. Evaluate :

27. $x^3 - \dfrac{1}{x^3}$ when $x - \dfrac{1}{x} = 5$
28. $x^3 - \dfrac{1}{x^3}$, if $x - \dfrac{1}{x} = 3$

29. $x^3 + \dfrac{1}{x^3}$ when $x + \dfrac{1}{x} = 10$
30. $x^3 + \dfrac{1}{x^3}$, if $x + \dfrac{1}{x} = 4$

31. $x^3 + \dfrac{1}{x^3}$ when $x^2 + \dfrac{1}{x^2} = 14$
32. $x^3 - \dfrac{1}{x^3}$, if $x^2 + \dfrac{1}{x^2} = 51$

33. $x^3 + \dfrac{1}{x^3}$ when $x^4 + \dfrac{1}{x^4} = 47$
34. $x^3 + \dfrac{1}{x^3}$, if $x^4 + \dfrac{1}{x^4} = 527$

F. Simplify :

35. $(3x - 4)^3 - (3x + 4)^3$
36. $(2x + 3y)^3 - (2x - 3y)^3$

37. $\left(\dfrac{p}{3} + \dfrac{q}{2}\right)^3 - \left(\dfrac{p}{3} - \dfrac{q}{2}\right)^3$ **38.** $(a + 7)^3 - (a - 7)^3$

39. $\left(\dfrac{x}{3} + \dfrac{y}{4}\right)^3 - \left(\dfrac{x}{3} - \dfrac{y}{4}\right)^3$ **40.** $(2x + 5)^3 - (2x - 5)^3$

$\boxed{\text{IDENTITY 8}}$ $a^3 + b^3 = (a + b)^3 - 3ab\,(a + b)$

This identity follows from **Identity 6** as under :

$$(a + b)^3 = a^3 + 3ab\,(a + b) + b^3$$

or $a^3 + b^3 + 3ab\,(a + b) = (a + b)^3$

$a^3 + b^3 = (a + b)^3 - 3ab\,(a + b)$ *(By Transposition)*

$\boxed{\text{IDENTITY 9}}$

Just like **identity 8**, this identity follows from **Identity 7** as under :

$$(a - b)^3 = a^3 - 3ab\,(a - b) - b^3$$

or $a^3 - 3ab\,(a - b) - b^3 = (a - b)^3$

$a^3 - b^3 = (a - b)^3 - 3ab\,(a - b)$ *(By Transposition)*

$\boxed{\text{IDENTITY 10}}$ $(a + b)\,(a^2 - ab + b^2) = a^3 + b^3$

$$(a^3 + b^3)\,(a^2 - ab + b^2) = a\,(a^2 - ab + b^2) + b\,(a^2 - ab + b^2)$$
$$= a^3 - a^2b + ab^2 + a^2b - ab^2 + b^3$$
$$= a^3 + b^3$$

$\boxed{\text{IDENTITY 11}}$ $(a - b)\,(a^2 + ab + b^2) = a^3 - b^3$

$$(a - b)\,(a^2 + ab + b^2) = a\,(a^2 + ab + b^2) - b\,(a^2 + ab + b^2)$$
$$= a^3 + a^2b + ab^2 - a^2b - ab^2 - b^3$$
$$= a^3 - b^3$$

Let us now solve some examples involving the use of the above two identities.

Example 10.   Find the products :

(a) $(x + 2)\,(x^2 - 2x + 4)$

(b) $\left(\dfrac{2x}{5} - \dfrac{3y}{7}\right)\left(\dfrac{4x^2}{25} + \dfrac{6xy}{35} + \dfrac{9y^2}{49}\right)$

Solution : $(x + 2)\,(x^2 - 2x + 4)$

$$= (x + 2)\,[(x)^2 - x \times 2 + (2)^2]$$
$$= x^3 + 2^3 = x^3 + 8 \text{ } Ans.$$

(b) $\left(\dfrac{2x}{5} - \dfrac{3y}{7}\right)\left(\dfrac{4x^2}{25} + \dfrac{6xy}{35} + \dfrac{9y}{49}\right)$

$= \left(\dfrac{2x}{5} - \dfrac{3y}{7}\right)\left[\left(\dfrac{2x}{5}\right)^2 + \left(\dfrac{2x}{5} \times \dfrac{3y}{7}\right) + \left(\dfrac{3y}{7}\right)^2\right]$

$= \left(\dfrac{2x}{5}\right)^3 - \left(\dfrac{3y}{7}\right)^3 = \dfrac{\mathbf{8}x^3}{\mathbf{125}} - \dfrac{\mathbf{27}y^3}{\mathbf{343}}$ *Ans.*

IDENTITY 12 $(a + b + c)(a^2 + b^2 + c^2 - ab - bc - ca)$
$= a^3 + b^3 + c^3 - 3abc$

$(a + b + c)(a^2 + b^2 + c^2 - ab - bc - ca)$

$= a(a^2 + b^2 + c^2 - ab - bc - ca) + b(a^2 + b^2 + c^2 - ab - bc - ca) + c(a^2 + b^2 + c^2 - ab - bc - ca)$

$= a^3 + ab^2 + ac^2 - a^2b - abc - ca^2 + a^2b + b^3 + bc^2 - ab^2 - b^2c - abc + ca^2 + b^2c + c^3 - abc - bc^2 - c^2a$

$= a^3 + b^3 + c^3 - abc - abc - abc$ *(all other terms cancel out)*

$= a^3 + b^3 + c^3 - 3abc$

AN IMPORTANT COROLLARY

If $a + b + c = 0$, then $a^3 + b^3 + c^3 = 3abc$

We have just proved that—

$a^3 + b^3 + c^3 - 3abc = (a + b + c)(a^2 + b^2 + c^2 - ab - bc - ca)$

$\qquad\qquad\qquad\quad = 0 \times (a^2 + b^2 + c^2 - ab - bc - ca) = 0$

$\qquad\qquad\qquad\quad = a^3 + b^3 + c^3 - 3abc = 0$ *(By Transposition)*

or $= \boldsymbol{a^3 + b^3 + c^3 = 3abc}$

Example 13. **Prove that :**

$\qquad\qquad (p - q)^3 + (q - r)^3 + (r - p)^3 = 3(p - q)(q - r)(r - p)$

Solution : Suppose $p - q = a$; $q - r = b$; $r - p = c$

Then the equation to be proved becomes

$a^3 + b^3 + c^3 = 3abc$

We know that if $a + b + c = 0$, then

$a^3 + b^3 + c^3 = 3abc$

111

Now $a + b + c = (p - q) + (q - r) + (r - p)$

$= p - q + q - r + r - p = 0$

Clearly, $(p - q)^3 + (q - r)^3 + (r - p)^3 = 3 (p - q) (q - r) (r - p)$

Example 14. **If $x + y + z = 6$; $xy + yz + zx = 11$ find the value of $x^3 + y^3 + z^3 - 3xyz$**

Solution : $x + y + z = 6$

$(x + y + z)^2 = 6^2 = 36$

or $x^2 + y^2 + z^2 + 2 (xy + yz + zx) = 36$

or $x^2 + y^2 + z^2 + (2 \times 11) = 36$ ($\because xy + yz + zx = 11$)

or $x^2 + y^2 + z^2 + 22 = 36$

or $x^2 + y^2 + z^2 = 36 - 22 = $ **14**

Now, we know that—

$x^3 + y^3 + z^3 - 3xyz = (x + y + z) (x^2 + y^2 + z^2 - xy - yz - zx)$

$= (x + y + z) [(x^2 + y^2 + z^2) - (xy + yz + zx)]$

$= 6 (14 - 11) = 6 \times 3 = $ **18** *Ans.*

Example 15. **Find the value of $(55)^3 - (75)^3 + (20)^3$**

Solution :   Let $55 = a$, $- 75 = b$, $20 = c$

$\therefore a + b + c = 55 - 75 + 20 = 0$

$\therefore a^3 + b^3 + c^3 = 3abc$

or $(55)^3 + (-75)^3 + (20)^3 = 3 \times 55 \times (-75) \times 20$

$= 165 \times 20 \times (-75)$

$= 3300 \times (-75) = $ **– 247500**

Example 16. **Find the value of $(7 \cdot 8)^3 - (10 \cdot 3)^3 + (2 \cdot 5)^3$**

Solution :   Let $7 \cdot 8 = a$; $- 10 \cdot 3 = b$ and $2 \cdot 5 = c$

$\therefore a + b + c = 7 \cdot 8 - 10 \cdot 3 + 2 \cdot 5 = 0$

$\therefore a^3 + b^3 + c^3 = 3abc$

or $(7 \cdot 8)^3 - (10 \cdot 3)^3 + (2 \cdot 5)^3 = 3 \times (7 \cdot 8) \times (-10 \cdot 3) \times (2 \cdot 5)$

$= 3 \times \dfrac{78}{10} \times \dfrac{-103}{10} \times \dfrac{25}{10}$

$= - \dfrac{602550}{1000} = $ **– 602·55** *Ans.*

PRACTICE EXERCISES 23

A. Find the product :

1. $(x + y)(x^2 - xy + y^2)$

2. $(4x + 3y)(16x^2 - 12xy + 9y^2)$

3. $(x + 2)(x^2 - 2x + 4)$

4. $(x + 3y)(x^2 - 3xy + 9y^2)$

5. $(2x + 3y)(4x^2 - 6xy + 9y^2)$

6. $(3x + y)(9x^2 - 3xy + y^2)$

B. Find the product :

7. $(x - y)(x^2 + xy + y^2)$

8. $(5x - 2y)(25x^2 + 10xy + 4y^2)$

9. $(5a - 3b)(25a^2 + 15ab + 9b^2)$

10. $(p - 2q)(p^2 + 2pq + 4q^2)$

11. $(x - 3)(x^2 + 3x + 9)$

12. $(5 - 2x)(25 + 10x + 4x^2)$

C. Find the product :

13. $\left(3x - \dfrac{y}{2}\right)\left(9x^2 + \dfrac{3}{2}xy + \dfrac{1}{4}y^2\right)$

14. $\left(\dfrac{2x}{5} - \dfrac{3y}{7}\right)\left(\dfrac{9y^2}{49} + \dfrac{6xy}{35} + \dfrac{4x^2}{25}\right)$

15. $\left(3x + \dfrac{y}{2}\right)\left(9x^2 - \dfrac{3xy}{2} + \dfrac{y^2}{4}\right)$

16. $\left(\dfrac{3p}{2} - \dfrac{q}{3}\right)\left(\dfrac{9p^2}{4} + \dfrac{pq}{2} + \dfrac{q^2}{9}\right)$

17. $\left(\dfrac{1}{2}p - \dfrac{1}{3}q\right)\left(\dfrac{1}{4}p^2 + \dfrac{1}{6}pq + \dfrac{1}{9}q^2\right)$

18. $\left(\dfrac{2x}{5} - \dfrac{3y}{4}\right)\left(\dfrac{4x^2}{25} + \dfrac{3xy}{10} + \dfrac{9y^2}{16}\right)$

D. Write the correct term in each blank :

19. $(2a + b)(\text{........} - 2ab + \text{.........}) = 8a^3 + b^3$

20. $\left(\dfrac{y}{7} - 3x\right)(\text{.......} + \text{........} + 9x^2) = \text{........} - 27x^3$

21. $(\text{......} - \text{......})\left(4x^2 + \dfrac{xy}{3} + \dfrac{y^2}{36}\right) = \text{.........} + \dfrac{y^3}{216}$

22. $(\sqrt{5} + \sqrt{3})(\text{.......} - \sqrt{15} + \text{.......}) = 5\sqrt{5} + \text{.........}$

E. Simplify :

23. $(2a + b)(4a^2 - 2ab + b^2) - (5a - 3b)(25a^2 + 15ab + 9b^2)$

24. $(x + 2)(x^2 - 2x + 4) + (x - 3)(x^2 + 3x + 9)$

25. $\left(3x - \dfrac{y}{2}\right)\left(9x^2 + \dfrac{3xy}{2} + \dfrac{y^2}{4}\right) - \left(3x + \dfrac{y}{2}\right)\left(9x^2 - \dfrac{3xy}{2} + \dfrac{y^2}{4}\right)$

F. Prove that—

26. $(x - y)^3 + (y - z)^3 + (z - x)^3 = 3(x - y)(y - z)(z - x)$

27. $(2x + 2y)^3 + (3y - 5x)^3 + (4x - 5y)^3 = 3(2x + 2y)(3y - 5x)(3x - 5y)$

113

G. Expand the following :

28. $(9x + 2y + z)^2$ **29.** $(3x - 2y - z)^2$

30. $(5x + y - 2z)^2$ **31.** $(3q + 2 - 2p)^2$

H. Find the product :

32. $(a + b + c)(a^2 + b^2 + c^2 - ab - bc - ca)$

33. $(2x - 3y + 5z)(4x^2 + 9y^2 + 25z^2 + 6xy + 15yz - 10zx)$

34. $(l - m - 2)(l^2 + m^2 + 4 + lm - 2m + 2l)$

I. Find the value of :

35. $x^3 + y^3 + z^3 - 3xyz$, if $x + y + z = 9$, $xy + yz + zx = 26$

36. $a^3 + b^3 + c^3 - 3abc$, if $a + b + c = 10$, $ab + bc + ca = 31$

37. $l^3 + m^3 + n^3 - 3lmn$, if $l + m + n = 15$, $l^2 + m^2 + n^2 = 83$

38. $p^3 + q^3 + r^3 - 3pqr$, if $p + q + r = 9$, $p^2 + q^2 + r^2 = 35$

J. Do as directed :

39. If $p + q + r = 0$, prove that $p^3 + q^3 + r^3 = 3pqr$

40. Find the value of $(28)^3 - (78)^3 + (50)^3$

41. Find the value of $(38)^3 - (20)^3 - (18)^3$

42. Find the value of $(6·5)^3 - (9·7)^3 + (3·2)^3$

43. Find the value of $(a - b)^3 + (b - c)^3 + (c - a)^3$

44. Solve : $(2x - 3)(4x^2 - 3x + 5) + x^2 - 3x + 1$

45. Find $x^2 + y^2$, if $x - y = 5$, $xy = 12$

46. Find xy, if $x + y = 5$ and $x - y = 3$

47. Find $xy + yz + zx$, if $x + y + z = 13$, $x^2 + y^2 + z^2 = 69$

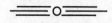

Graded Maths-Part-8

14 PRODUCTS AND FACTORS

> **KNOW THESE TERMS :**
> 1. **product**—result of multiplying two or more expressions
> 2. **factor**—expressions multiplied to get a product are factors of the product
> 3. **factorisation**—process of resolving an expression into its factors
> 4. **common factor**—a factor common among two or more terms

We have studied several identities which are *special products* and are always true. In this chapter, we shall study how to resolve a given product into its **factors**. Remember that if two expressions are multiplied, they are **factors** of their **product**.

FACTORIZATION

Factorization **is the process of expressing a product into its divisors** (*factors*).

Let us review all the identities that we studied in the previous chapter as they are to be used while factorizing algebraic expressions :

1. $(a + b)^2 = a^2 + b^2 + 2ab$ **2.** $(a - b)^2 = a^2 + b^2 - 2ab$

3. $a^2 - b^2 = (a + b)(a - b)$

4. $(a + b + c)^2 = a^2 + b^2 + c^2 + 2ab + 2bc + 2ca$

5. $(a + b)^3 = a^3 + b^3 + 3ab(a + b)$ **6.** $(a - b)^3 = a^3 - b^3 - 3ab(a - b)$

7. $a^3 + b^3 = (a + b)(a^2 - ab + b^2)$ **8.** $a^3 - b^3 = (a - b)(a^2 + ab + b^2)$

9. $a^3 + b^3 + c^3 - 3abc = (a + b + c)(a^2 + b^2 + c^2 - ab - bc - ca)$

10. If $a + b + c = 0$, then $a^3 + b^3 + c^3 = 3abc$

Let us now solve examples on various types of factorization

TYPE I   A COMMON FACTOR

Example 1. Factorize : (a) $a^2 - a^3b - a^2b^2$

              (b) $21x - 14xy + 28x^2$

Solution :   (a) $a^2 - a^3b - a^2b^2$

              Clearly, a^2 is common in all the three terms.

            ∴ $a^2 - a^3b - a^2b^2 = $ **$a^2 (1 - ab - b^2)$** *Ans.*

              (b) $21x - 14xy + .28x^2 = 28x + 21x - 14xy$

              Clearly, $7x$ is common in all the terms

            ∴ $28x^2 + 21x - 14xy = $ **$7x (4x + 3 - 2y)$** *Ans.*

Example 2. Factorize : $4 (3x + 7y) - 6 (3x + 7y)$

Solution : $2 (3x + 7y)$ is common in both the terms

$$\therefore \quad 4 (3x + 7y) - 6 (3x + 7y)$$
$$= 2 (3x + 7y) (2 - 3) = 2 (3x + 7y) \times (-1)$$
$$= \mathbf{- 2 (3x + 7y)} \text{ Ans.}$$

Example 3. Factorize :

$$8 - 4x - 2x^3 + x^4 \quad = \quad x^4 - 2x^3 - 4x + 8$$

Clearly, x^3 is common in the first two terms and 4 is common in the last two terms.

$$\therefore \quad x^4 - 2x^3 - 4x + 8 \quad = \quad x^3 (x - 2) - 4 (x - 2)$$

Again $(x - 2)$ is common in both the terms

$$\therefore \quad x^3 (x - 2) - 4 (x - 2) = \mathbf{(x - 2) (x^3 - 4)} \text{ Ans.}$$

PROCESS :

1. Observe the terms carefully and look for a common factor.
2. Write the common factor and divide the terms by it.
3. Write the quotients in a bracket with their proper signs.
4. Put no signs between the common factor and the brackets.
5. There may be a binomial common in pairs of terms.
6. So, terms are suitably paired off to have a common factor.

PRACTICE EXERCISES 24

Factorize :

A. **1.** $8a^2 - 6ab + 2a$ **2.** $3x^2y + 9xy^2 - 15xy$

     3. $4x^3 + 8xy - 20zx$ **4.** $2x^2y^2 - 4xyz^2 + 6xy^2z$

     5. $x^4 - x^2y^2 - x^3y$ **6.** $1 + 14x^2 + 49x^4$

B. **7.** $14 (x - y) - 21 (x - y)$ **8.** $(a + 5)^2 + 2 (a + 5)$

     9. $4 (2x - 3y)^2 + 8 (2x - 3y)$ **10.** $2a (x + y) - 3b (x + y)$

     11. $6 (3x - 4y) - 8 (3x - 4y)^2$ **12.** $4 (3x + 5y)^2 - 6 (3x - 5y)$

C. **13.** $x^3 + x^2 + x + 1$ **14.** $a^3 + a - 3a^2 - 3$

     15. $a^2 - b + ab - a$ **16.** $x^2 + y - xy - x$

     17. $xy - ab + bx - ay$ **18.** $6ab - b^2 + 12ac - 2bc$

     19. $3ax + 4bx - 6ay - 8by$ **20.** $a^2 + 2ab + b^2 - 1$

| TYPE II | DIFFERENCE OF TWO PERFECT SQUARES : |

Example 4. Factorize (a) $a^2 - 121$ (b) $5x^2 - 320$

Solution : (a) $a^2 - 121 = (a)^2 - (11)^2$ is a *difference of two perfect squares*

Using $a^2 - b^2 = (a + b)(a - b)$, we have—

$(a)^2 - (11)^2 = \boldsymbol{(a + 11)(a - 11)}$ *Ans.*

(b) $5x^2 - 320$, has 5 as a common term

$\therefore 5x^2 - 320 = 5(x^2 - 64) = 5[(x^2) - (8)^2]$

$= \boldsymbol{5(x + 8)(x - 8)}$ *Ans.*

Example 5. Factorize : (a) $x^2 + 2xy + y^2 - 81$ (b) $(a + 1)^2 - (b - 1)^2$

Solution : (a) $x^2 + 2xy + y^2 - 81 = (x^2 + 2xy + y^2) - 81$

$= (x + y)^2 - (9)^2 = \boldsymbol{(x + y + 9)(x + y - 9)}$ *Ans.*

(b) $(a + 1)^2 - (b - 1)^2 = (a + 1 + b - 1)(a + 1 - b + 1)$

$= \boldsymbol{(a + b)(a - b + 2)}$ *Ans.*

| TYPE III | PREFECT SQUARES |

Example 6. Factorize :

(a) $x^2 + 4y^2 + 4xy$ (b) $4x^2 - 12xy + 9y^2$

(c) $x^2 + 4y^2 + 9z^2 + 4xy + 12yz + 6zx$

(d) $4x^2 + 9y^2 + z^2 - 12xy - 6yz + 4zx$

Solution : (a) $x^2 + 4y^2 + 4xy = (x)^2 + (2y)^2 + 2x \times 2y$

$= (x + 2y)^2 = \boldsymbol{(x + 2y)(x + 2y)}$ *Ans*

(b) $4x^2 - 12xy + 9y^2 = (2x)^2 - (2 \times 2x \times 3y) + (3y)^2$

$= (2x - 3y)^2 = \boldsymbol{(2x - 3y)(2x - 3y)}$ *Ans.*

(c) $x^2 + 4y^2 + 9z^2 + 4xy + 12yz + 6zx$

$= (x)^2 + (2y)^2 + (3z)^2 + (2 \times x \times 2y) + (2 \times 2y \times 3z)$

$+ (2 \times 3z \times x)$

$= (x + 2y + 3z)^2 = \boldsymbol{(x + 2y + 3z)(x + 2y + 3z)}$ *Ans.*

(d) $4x^2 + 9y^2 + z^2 - 12xy - 6yz + 4zx$

$= (2x)^2 + (3y)^2 + (z)^2 + \{2 \times 2x \times (-3y)\} + \{2 \times (-3y) \times z\}$

$+ (2 \times z \times 2x)$

$= (2x - 3y + z)^2 = \boldsymbol{(2x - 3y + z)(2x - 3y + z)}$ *Ans.*

Example 7. Factorize (a) $x^2 + 12x + 27$ (b) $5x^2 - 22x + 21$

Solution :   (a) $x^2 + 12x + 27$

We shall split $+12x$ into two parts so that the expression may have four terms and each pair of terms may have a common factor. For it, do as explained below :

1. Find the product of the coefficient of x^2 i.e. 1 and the constant term, i.e. 27. It is $27 \times 1 = 27$

2. Find the two factors of 27 such that their sum is $+12$ (coefficient of the middle term)

3. Clearly, these factors are $+9$ and $+3$

$$x^2 + 12x + 27 = x^2 + 3x + 9x + 27$$
$$= (x^2 + 3x) + (9x + 27)$$
$$= x (x + 3) + 9 (x + 3)$$

Dividing by the common factor $(x + 3)$

$$= \mathbf{(x + 3)\ (x + 9)}\ Ans.$$

(b) $5x^2 - 22x + 21$

$5 \times 21 = 105$ and its factors -15 and -7 add up to -22

$\therefore\ 5x^2 - 22x + 21 = 5x^2 - 15x - 7x + 21$
$$= 5x (x - 3) - 7 (x - 3)$$
$$= \mathbf{(x - 3)\ (5x - 7)}\ Ans.$$

PRACTICE EXERCISES 25

A. Resolve into factors :

1. $x^2 + 6x + 5$ **2.** $x^2 - 7x + 12$ **3.** $x^2 + 2x - 15$

4. $x^2 - x - 12$ **5.** $x^2 + 25x + 144$ **6.** $x^2 - 9x + 18$

7. $x^2 - 3xy + 2y^2$ **8.** $x^2 + 6x - 72$ **9.** $x^2 + 25x - 84$

10. $x^2 - 8x - 33$ **11.** $x^2 + 8x - 33$ **12.** $p^2 - 26p - 120$

13. $x^2 + x - 6$ **14.** $x^2 - x - 12$ **15.** $x^2 - 6x + 8$

16. $x^2 + 2x - 15$ **17.** $x^2 + 22x + 120$ **18.** $a^2 - 3a + 2$

19. $x^2 + 9x + 8$ **20.** $x^2 + 3ax + 2a^2$ **21.** $y^2 - 20y + 51$

22. $a^2 - 4ab - 5b^2$ **23.** $p^2 - 12p + 35$ **24.** $x^2 + 14x + 48$

B. Factorize :

25. $7x^2 - 15x + 8$ **26.** $4p^2 - 2p - 72$ **27.** $8a^2 + 4a - 4$

28. $3x^2 + 10x - 8$ **29.** $5x^2 - 23xy - 10y^2$ **30.** $4x^2 - 16x + 7$

31. $10p^2 + 59pq - 6q^2$ **32.** $3x^2 + 17x - 20$ **33.** $5x^2 - 14xy - 24y^2$

34. $5m^2 - 2m - 3$ **35.** $6z^2 + z - 2$ **36.** $2x^2 - 6x + 4$

37. $12p^2 + 5pq - 3q^2$ **38.** $9a^2 + 11ab + 2b^2$ **39.** $3x^2 + 2px - p^2$

40. $6x^2 + 7x - 3$ **41.** $3a^2 - 4a - 4$ **42.** $5x^2 - 26x + 24$

43. $2a^2 + 9a + 10$ **44.** $4a^2 - 7a + 3$ **45.** $5y^2 - 8y - 13$

46. $21x^2 + 25x - 4$ **47.** $9x^2 + 23x - 12$ **48.** $6a^2 - 21a + 15$

TYPE V PERFECT CUBES

Example 8. **Factorize : $27x^3 + 8y^3 + 54x^2y + 36xy^2$**

Solution : $27x^3 + 8y^3 + 54x^2y + 36xy^2$

$= 27x^3 + 8y^3 + 18xy\ (3x + 2y)$

$= (3x)^3 + (2y)^3 + 3 \times 3x \times 2y\ (3x + 2y)$

$= (3x + 2y)^3 =$ **$(3x + 2y)\ (3x + 2y)\ (3x + 2y)$** *Ans.*

Example 9. **Factorize : $27x^3 - 108x^2 + 144x - 64$**

Solution : $27x^3 - 108x^2 + 144x - 64$

$= 27x^3 - 36x\ (3x - 4) - 64$

$= (3x)^3 - 3 \times 3x \times 4\ (3x - 4) - (4)^3$

$= (3x - 4)^3 =$ **$(3x - 4)\ (3x - 4)\ (3x - 4)$** *Ans.*

PRACTICE EXERCISES 26

A. Resolve into factors :

1. $8x^3 + 60x^2 + 150x + 125$ **2.** $125x^3 + 8y^3 + 60x^2y + 150xy^2$

3. $x^3 + 125y^3 + 75xy^2 + 15x^2y$ **4.** $216a^3 + 343b^3 + 756a^2b + 882ab^2$

5. $\dfrac{8}{27}a^3 + \dfrac{1}{b^3} + \dfrac{4a^2}{3b} + \dfrac{2a}{b^2}$ **6.** $\dfrac{125}{x^3} + \dfrac{8}{y^3} + \dfrac{150}{x^2y} + \dfrac{60}{xy^2}$

B. 7. $a^3 - 18a^2 + 108a - 216$ **8.** $x^3 - 27y^3 - 9x^2y + 27xy^2$

9. $\dfrac{x^3}{27} + \dfrac{y^3}{8} + \dfrac{xy}{2}\left(\dfrac{x}{3} + \dfrac{y}{2}\right)$ **10.** $8x^3 - y^3 - 12x^2y + 6xy^2$

11. $\dfrac{1}{64}a^3 - \dfrac{1}{125}b^3 - \dfrac{3}{80}a^2b + \dfrac{3}{100}ab^2$ **12.** $64x^3 - y^3 - 48x^2y + 12xy^2$

Example 10. **Factorize :** (a) $p^3 + 27$ (b) $64x^3 - y^3$

Solution :   (a) $p^3 + 27 = (p)^3 + (3)^3$

$\qquad\qquad = (p + 3)\ [p^2 - (p \times 3) + (3)^2]$

$\qquad\qquad = \mathbf{(p + 3)\ (p^2 - 3p + 9)}$ *Ans.*

$\qquad$ (b) $64x^3 - y^3$

$\qquad\qquad = (4x)^3 - y^3 = (4x - y)\ [(4x)^2 - (4x) \times (-y) + (y)^2]$

$\qquad\qquad = \mathbf{(4x - y)\ (16x^2 + 4xy + y^2)}$ *Ans.*

Example 11. **Factorize :** $x^6 - y^6$

Solution : $x^6 - y^6 = (x^3)^2 - (y^3)^2$

$\qquad\qquad = (x^3 + y^3)\ (x^3 - y^3)$ .... *(Difference of 2 squares)*

$\qquad\qquad = (x + y)\ (x^2 - xy + y^2)\ (x - y)\ (x^2 + xy + y^2)$

$\qquad\qquad = \mathbf{(x + y)\ (x - y)\ (x^2 - xy + y^2)\ (x^2 + xy + y^2)}$ *Ans.*

Example 12. **Factorize :** $x^3 + 8y^3 + 64z^3 - 24xyz$

Solution : $x^3 + 8y^3 + 64z^3 - 24xyz = (x)^3 + (2y)^3 + (4z)^3 - (3 \times x \times 2y \times 4z)$

$\qquad = (x + 2y + 4z)\ (x^2 + 4y^2 + 16z^2) - (x \times 2y) - (2y \times 4z) - (4z \times x)$

$\qquad = \mathbf{(x + 2y + 4z)\ (x^2 + 4y^2 + 16z^2 - 2xy - 8yz - 4zx)}$ *Ans.*

Example 13. **Factorize :** $(3x - 5y)^3 + (5y - 9z)^3 + (9z - 3x)^3$

Solution :   Let $3x - 5y = a$; $5y - 9z = b$; $9z - 3x = c$

$\qquad \because\ 3x - 5y + 5y - 9z + 9z - 3x = 0$ or $a + b + c = 0$

$\qquad \therefore\ a^3 + b^3 + c^3 = 3\ (a - b)\ (b - c)\ (c - a)$

$\qquad$ or $(3x - 5y)^3 + (5y - 9z)^3 + (9z - 3x)^3$

$\qquad\qquad = \mathbf{3\ (3x - 5y)\ (5y - 9z)\ (9z - 3x)}$

$\qquad\qquad = 3 \times 3\ (3x - 5y)\ (5y - 9z)\ (3z - x)$ *(Take out 3 as common)*

$\qquad\qquad = \mathbf{9\ (3x - 5y)\ (5y - 9z)\ (3z - x)}$ *Ans.*

Example 14. **Solve :** $55^3 - 25^3 - 30^3$

Solution : $55^3 - 25^3 - 30^3 = 55^3 + (-25)^3 + (-30)^3$

$\qquad 55 + (-25) + (-30) = 55 - 25 - 30 = 0$

$\qquad \therefore\ 55^3 - 25^3 - 30^3 = 3 \times 55 \times (-25)(-30)$

$\qquad\qquad = 3 \times 55 \times 750 = \mathbf{123750}$ *Ans.*

Example 15. Simplify : $\dfrac{0{\cdot}87\times0{\cdot}87\times0{\cdot}87 + 0{\cdot}13\times0{\cdot}13\times0{\cdot}13}{0{\cdot}87\times0{\cdot}87 - 0{\cdot}87\times0{\cdot}13 + 0{\cdot}13\times0{\cdot}13}$

Solution : $= \dfrac{0{\cdot}87\times0{\cdot}87\times0{\cdot}87\times0{\cdot}13\times0{\cdot}13\times0{\cdot}13}{0{\cdot}87\times0{\cdot}87 - 0{\cdot}87\times0{\cdot}13 + 0{\cdot}13\times0{\cdot}13}$

$= \dfrac{(0{\cdot}87)^3 + (0{\cdot}13)^3}{(0{\cdot}87)^2 - (0{\cdot}87 \times 0{\cdot}13) + (0{\cdot}13)^2}$

$= \dfrac{(0{\cdot}87+0{\cdot}13)\ \{(0{\cdot}87)^2-(0{\cdot}87\times0{\cdot}13)+0{\cdot}13^2\}}{(0{\cdot}87)^2-(0{\cdot}87\times0{\cdot}13)+(0{\cdot}13)^2} = (0{\cdot}87 + 0{\cdot}13) = \mathbf{1}\ Ans.$

PRACTICE EXERCISES 27

Resolve into factors :

A. **1.** $8x^3 + 125$ **2.** $8x^3 + 343$ **3.** $1 + 8p^3$

4. $128x^3 + 54y^3$ **5.** $8a^3 + b^3$ **6.** $\dfrac{x^3}{27} + \dfrac{y^3}{64}$

7. $27x^3 + 64y^3$ **8.** $216x^3 + 1$ **9.** $\dfrac{1}{216}x^3 + \dfrac{1}{125}y^3$

B. **10.** $x^3 - 8$ **11.** $125x^3 - 64y^3$ **12.** $\dfrac{x^3}{27} - \dfrac{y^3}{64}$

13. $\dfrac{1}{64}a^3 - \dfrac{1}{125}b^3$ **14.** $32p^3 - 108q^3$ **15.** $\cdot001a^3 - \cdot008b^3$

16. $64 - 343a^3$ **17.** $125x^3 - y^3$ **18.** $27a^3b^3 - c^3$

19. $a^6 - b^6$ **20.** $x^4y - xy^4$ **21.** $(3x + 4)^3 - (2x + 1)^3$

C. **22.** $(x - y)^3 + (y - z)^3 + (z - x)^3$ **23.** $8x^3 + 27y^3 - z^3 - 18xyz$

24. $p^3(q - r)^3 + q^3(r - p)^3 + r^3(p - q)^3$ **25.** $(2{\cdot}7)^3 - (1{\cdot}6)^3 - (1{\cdot}1)^3$

26. $-27x^3 + y^3 - z^3 - 9xyz$

D. Solve :

27. $\dfrac{(\cdot87)^3 + (\cdot13)^3}{(\cdot87)^2 - (\cdot87 \times \cdot13) + (\cdot13)^2}$ **28.** $\dfrac{(\cdot54)^3 + (\cdot46)^3}{(\cdot54)^2 - (\cdot54 \times \cdot46) + (\cdot46)^2}$

29. $\dfrac{343x^3 + 729}{49x^2 - 63x + 81}$ **30.** $45^3 - 65^3 + 20^3$ **31.** $\left(\dfrac{1}{2}\right)^3 - \left(\dfrac{1}{8}\right)^3 + \left(\dfrac{1}{4}\right)^3$

32. $56^3 - 32^3 - 24^3$ **33.** $38^3 - 80^3 + 42^3$ **34.** $55^3 - 25^3 - 30^3$

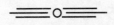

15 EQUATIONS IN ONE VARIABLE

In the earlier books of the series, we learnt how to solve linear equations in one variable. We know the following rules about equations :

1. *An **equation** is a statement of equality of two expressions involving one or more unknown quantities.*
2. *If the same quantity is **added** to either side of an equation, it remains true.*
3. *If the same quantity is **subtracted** from either side of an equation, it remains true.*
4. *If either side of an equation is **multiplied** by the same quantity, the equation remains true.*
5. *If either side of an equation is **divided** by the same quantity the equation remains true.*

B. **Transposition** : According to this process—

Any term can be *transposed (transferred)* from one side of an equation to the other side after changing its sign as under :

1. From + to –   2. From – to +   3. From × to ÷   4. From ÷ to ×

C. **Cross Multiplication** is used in the case of equations with or rational expressions :

$\dfrac{x-3}{4} = \dfrac{2x+5}{2}$ can be written as $2(x-3) = 4(2x+5)$

Now we shall solve some examples that involve rational expressions that can be reduced to simple linear equations :

Example 1. **Solve the equation :**

(a) $5x - 7 = 2x + 8$ (b) $3(x - 1) = 8$ (c) $\dfrac{7a}{5} = a - 4$

Solution :   (a) $5x - 7 = 2x + 8$ or $5x - 2x - 7 = 8$ *(Transposing 2x)*

or $5x - 2x = 8 + 7$ *(Transposing – 7)*

or $3x = 15$ or $x = 15 \div 3$ *(Transposing 3)*

Hence $x = $ **5** *Ans.*

(b) $4(x - 1) = 8$ or $4x - 4 = 8$

or $4x = 8 + 4 = 12$ ⟶ (Transposing – 4)

or $x = 12 \div 4$ ⟶ (Transposing 4)

Hence $x = \textbf{3}$ Ans.

(c) $\dfrac{7a}{5} = a + 4$ or $7a = 5(a + 4)$ ⟶ (Transposing $\tfrac{1}{5}$)

or $7a = 5a + 20$ or $7a - 5a = 20$ ⟶ (Transposing 5a)

or $2a = 20$, i.e. $a = \textbf{10}$ Ans.

Example 2. Solve $\dfrac{2x + 1}{3x - 2} = \dfrac{5}{9}$

Solution :   (a) $\dfrac{2x + 1}{3x - 2} = \dfrac{5}{9}$

or $9(2x + 1) = 5(3x - 2)$ ⟶ (Multiplying Crosswise)

or $18x + 9 = 15x - 10$ ⟶ (Removing brackets)

or $18x - 15x = -10 - 9$ ⟶ (Transposing 15x, + 9)

or $3x = -19$

or $x = \dfrac{-19}{3} = -\textbf{6}\dfrac{\textbf{1}}{\textbf{3}}$ Ans.

Example 3. Solve : $\dfrac{9x - 7}{3x + 5} = \dfrac{3x - 4}{x + 6}$

Solution : $\dfrac{9x - 7}{3x + 5} = \dfrac{3x - 4}{x + 6}$

or $(9x - 7)(x + 6) = (3x - 4)(3x + 5)$ (Multiplying Crosswise)

or $9x^2 + 54x - 7x - 42 = 9x^2 + 15x - 12x - 20$

or $9x^2 + 47x - 42 = 9x^2 + 3x - 20$

or $9x^2 + 47x - 9x^2 - 3x = -20 + 42$ (By Transposition)

or $44x = 22$ or $x = 22 \div 44 = \textbf{0·5}$ Ans.

Example 4. Solve : $\dfrac{0·7x + 0·3}{x} = \textbf{0·85}$

Solution : $\dfrac{0·7x + 0·3}{x} = 0·85$

or $\dfrac{\dfrac{7x}{10} + \dfrac{3}{10}}{x} = \dfrac{85}{100}$ or $\dfrac{\dfrac{7x + 3}{10}}{x} = \dfrac{85}{100}$

or $\dfrac{7x + 3}{10} = \dfrac{85}{100} \times x$ $\qquad$ *(Transposing $\dfrac{1}{x}$)*

or $\dfrac{7x + 3}{10} = \dfrac{85x}{100} = \dfrac{17x}{20}$ $\qquad$ or $\dfrac{14x + 6 = 17x}{20}$

or $14x + 6 = 17x$ or $14x - 17x = -6$ $\qquad$ *(By Transposition)*

or $-3x = -6$ or $x = \mathbf{2}$ *Ans.*

PRACTICE EXERCISES 28

Solve the following equations :

A. **1.** $8x = 3x + 20$ $\qquad$ **2.** $4x - 3 = 2x + 5$

3. $5 - 3(1 + x) = 2x - (1 - 2x)$ $\qquad$ **4.** $0\cdot4(8 - a) = 0\cdot3(6 + a)$

5. $x(x + 1) - (x - 2)(x - 3) = 6$ $\qquad$ **6.** $5x - (3x - 1) = x - 4$

B. **7.** $\dfrac{2}{3}x = \dfrac{7}{3}$ $\qquad$ **8.** $\dfrac{x}{4} + \dfrac{x}{6} = x - 7$ $\qquad$ **9.** $\dfrac{2x + 5}{3x + 4} = 1$

10. $\dfrac{2a - 7}{a + 4} = \dfrac{2}{5}$ $\qquad$ **11.** $\dfrac{x + 5}{3x} = 6$ $\qquad$ **12.** $\dfrac{2x - 3}{3x + 2} = \dfrac{3}{2}$

13. $\dfrac{x}{x + 4} = \dfrac{1}{5}$ $\qquad$ **14.** $\dfrac{3x + 2}{m} = 9$ $\qquad$ **15.** $\dfrac{8}{3x} = \dfrac{9}{2x - 1}$

16. $\dfrac{8x - 3}{2x + 5} = \dfrac{5}{7}$ $\qquad$ **17.** $\dfrac{0\cdot5 - x}{1\cdot5x + 9} = \dfrac{-7}{9}$ $\qquad$ **18.** $\dfrac{5x - 7}{3x} = 2$

C. **19.** $\dfrac{3x + 5}{2x - 1} = \dfrac{2}{5}$ $\qquad$ **20.** $\dfrac{8x - 3}{2x + 5} = \dfrac{4x + 1}{x - 2}$

21. $\dfrac{a + 6}{4} + \dfrac{a - 3}{5} = \dfrac{5a - 4}{8}$ $\qquad$ **22.** $\dfrac{6x + 7}{3x + 2} = \dfrac{4x + 5}{2x + 3}$

23. $\dfrac{3(1 - x) - 2(2x - 3)}{2 - 5x} = 1\dfrac{13}{17}$ $\qquad$ **24.** $\dfrac{4x - 5}{x + 2} - \dfrac{8x - 1}{2x + 1} = 0$

25. $\dfrac{2 + 15x}{3x - 1} - \dfrac{1 + 5x}{2 + x} = 0$ $\qquad$ **26.** $4x - \dfrac{1}{3}(x - 2) = 41$

27. $\dfrac{3x - 5}{2x + 3} = \dfrac{3}{5}$ $\qquad$ **28.** $\dfrac{4x + 9}{2x - 1} = \dfrac{6x + 5}{3x - 2}$

29. $\dfrac{3x - 1}{2x + 2} = \dfrac{5}{6}$ $\qquad$ **30.** $\dfrac{x + 5}{2x - 3} = \dfrac{3x + 1}{6x - 5}$

31. $\dfrac{3x - 1}{4} - \dfrac{5 + 2x}{3} = \dfrac{5}{2} - 2x$

32. $(a + 3)(a + 2) - (a - 1)(a + 4) = 5$

33. $\dfrac{2 + p}{3} - \dfrac{p - 6}{5} + \dfrac{2p - 1}{15} = 6$

PROBLEMS INVOLVING EQUATIONS

Problems can be solved using equations taking the following steps :

1. The unknown quantity is supposed to be x.
2. Then according to the conditions of the expression of the problem, an equation is created.
3. The equation is solved to find the value of x.
4. This value of x is the unknown quantity that had been supposed.

Let us now solve some examples :

Example 1. **Two numbers are in the ratio 7 : 8 and their difference is 3. Find the number.**

Solution :   Suppose the numbers are $7x$ and $8x$

∴   Their difference $= 8x - 7x$

But actual difference $= 3$

According the expression $= 8x - 7x = 3$

or $x = 3$

∴   Numbers $= (7 \times 3)$ and $8 \times 3 =$ **21, 24** *Ans.*

Example 2. **The numerator of a rational number is less than its denominator by 3. If the numerator is multiplied by 3 and the denominator is increased by 20, the new rational number is $\dfrac{1}{8}$. Find the original rational number.**

Solution :   Let the denominator of the number $= x$

∴   Its numerator $= x - 3$

∴   Number $= \dfrac{x - 3}{x}$

If we multiply its numerator by 3, it will be $3(x - 3)$

If we add 20 to its denominator, it will be $x + 20$

125

$\therefore$ New Rational number will be $\dfrac{3(x-3)}{x+20}$

According to the expression, the new number $= \dfrac{1}{8}$

$\therefore \quad \dfrac{3(x-3)}{x+20} = \dfrac{1}{8}$ or $8 \times 3(x-3) = 1(x+20)$

or $24(x-3) = x+20$

or $24x - 72 = x + 20$ or $24x - x = 20 + 72$

or $23x = 92$ or $x = 4$

$\therefore$ Denominator of the original number $= 4$

and Numerator $= 4 - 3 = 1$

$\therefore$ Reqd No. $= \dfrac{1}{4}$ Ans.

Example 3. **Mohan's father is four times as old as Mohan. After 5 years, his father will the thrice as old as Mohan will be. Find their present ages.**

Solution :   Suppose Mohan's present age $= x$ years

$\therefore$ His father's present age $= 4 \times x = 4x$

Mohan's age after 5 years will be $x + 5$ years

His father's age after 5 years will be $4x + 5$ years

According to the expression—

$4x + 5 = 3(x + 5)$

or $4x + 5 = 3x + 15$

or $4x - 3x = 15 - 5$ or $x = 10$

$\therefore$ Mohan's age $= $ **10 years**

His father' age $= 10 \times 4 = $ **40 years** $\Big]$ *Ans.*

Example 4. **The ten's digit of a number is thrice its unit's digit. The sum of this number and the number formed by reversing its digits is 88. Find the number.**

Solution :   Suppose the unit's digit $= x$

$\therefore$ ten's digit $= 3x$

$\therefore$ Number $= 10 \times$ ten's digit $+$ unit's number

$= (10 \times 3x) + x = 30x + x = $ **31x**

∴ If the digits are reversed x will become the ten's digit while 3x will be the unit's digit

∴ New number will 10 × New ten's digit + New unit's digit

$$= 10x + 3x = \textbf{13x}$$

Now according the expression

$$31x + 13x = 88 \text{ or } 44x = 88 \text{ or } x = 2$$

∴ Unit's digit is **2** and the ten's digit is $2 \times 3 = \textbf{6}$

Hence the Reqd. No. = **62** *Ans.*

PRACTICE EXERCISES 29

A. 1. The sum of the ages of a brother and his younger sister is 48 years. The ratio between their ages is 5 : 1. Find their ages.

2. Two numbers are in the ratio 3 : 8. If their difference is 50, find the numbers.

3. If the half of a number is added to it, we get 42. Find the number.

4. The numerator of a rational number is 7 less than its denominator. If we increase the numerator by 2 and the denominator by 9, we get the same rational number. Find the number.

5. The digit in the ten's place of a two-digit number is twice its unit's digit. If the digits change places, the new number is 18 less than the original number. Find the original number.

6. A girl's father is four times as old as she is. Five years back he was seven times as old as she was. Find their present ages.

7. One angle of a triangle is twice the other angle. The ratio of the third angle with the bigger is 10 : 3. Find the three angles.

8. A boat can move in still water at 10 kilometres an hour. It takes a certain time to sail 26 kilometres downstream. But in the same time, it can sail only 14 kilometres upstream. Find the speed of the flowing water.

9. 400 grams of milk contain 15% water. How much more water be added to it so that water in it becomes 32% ?

10. Three cash prizes were given in a contest. One of the prizes was the three-fourths of the other. The third prize was the three-fourths of the middling prize. If the total value of the prizes was Rs. 185. Find the value of each of them.

11. The breadth of a rectangle is shorter than its length by 7 cm. If the length is increased by 4 cm. and the breadth is decreased by 3 cm. The area of the new rectangle shall be 12 sq. cm. less than the area of the original rectangle. Find its length and breadth.

12. A boat covers a certain distance downstream in 5 hours. It cover the same distance upstream in 8 hours. If the speed of the flowing water be 3 kilometres an hour, find the speed of the boat.

13. The price of 2 chairs and 5 tables is Rs. 680. If the price of a table is Rs. 80 more than that of the chair, find the price of either of them.

14. Two numbers differ by 72. If we divide one of them by the other the quotient is 4. Find the number.

15. An alloy of copper and gold weighs 30 grams in air and 28 grams in water. Supposing that gold loses one-nineteenth of its weight in water while copper loses one-tenth of its weight in water, find the weight of either metal in the alloy.

16. The numerator of a fraction is larger than its denominator by 4. If 11 is added to the numerator and 1 is subtracted from the denominator, the new fraction becomes, $\frac{7}{3}$. Find the original fraction.

17. The distance between two places is 230 km. Two cars start from their places at the same time in opposite directions. After three hours they are 20 kilometres apart. If the speed of the one car is 10 kilometres less than the speed of the other car per hour, find the speed of the either car.

18. The sum of the two digits of a number is 15. If its digits change places, the new number so formed is less than the original number by 27. Find the original number.

19. There is a difference of 9 metres between the length and the breadth of a rectangle. If the length and also the breadth is increased by 3 metres, the area of the new rectangle will be more than the original area by 84 square metres. Find the length and the breadth of the original rectangle.

20. A boat goes downstream to cover a distance between two places in 4 hours. but it takes 5 hours to cover the same distance upstream. If the water is flowing at 2 kilometres an hour, find the speed of the boat in still water.

21. Two years back, a father was three times as old as his son. Two years hence, twice the father's age will equal five times that of his son. Find their present ages.

22. The sum of three consecutive odd number is 159. Find the numbers.

23. The sum of the three consecutive even numbers is 252. Find the numbers.

MISCELLANEOUS EXERCISES III

A. **1.** Add up : $3x^2 - 3xy + 5y^2$; $5x^2 + y^2$ and $7x^2 - 2y^2 + 4xy$

2. Subtract : $x^3 - xy^2 + 5x^2y - y^3$ from $y^3 - x^3 + 2xy^2 - 3x^2y$

3. Multiply : (a) $7x - 4x^2 + 2x^3 - 5$ by $3x - 2$

(b) $\left(\dfrac{x^2}{2} + \dfrac{x}{3} - 1\right)$ by $\left(\dfrac{3x^3}{4} - \dfrac{2x}{3} + \dfrac{1}{9}\right)$

4. Divide : (a) $x^5 - x^4 + 3x^3 + 4x^2 - 4x - 3$ by $x + 1$

(b) $x^5 + 3x^4 - 5x^3 + 14x^2 + 39x - 11$ by $x^3 - x^2 + x + 8$

B. **5.** Expand : $\left(3x - \dfrac{1}{2x}\right)^2$ **6.** Expand $\left(\dfrac{x}{5} - \dfrac{y}{6}\right)^2$

7. Expend : $(x - 2y - 5z)^2$ **8.** $(2p - 3q + z)^2$

C. **9.** If $2x + 3y = 8$ and $xy = 2$, find $4x^2 + 9y^2$

10. If $x + \dfrac{1}{x} = 5$, find $x^2 + \dfrac{1}{x^2}$ and $x^4 + \dfrac{1}{x^4}$

11. If $x + \dfrac{1}{x} = 4$, find $x^2 + \dfrac{1}{x^2}$ and $x^4 + \dfrac{1}{x^4}$

12. Find the value of $8x^3 - 27y^3$, if $2x - 3y = 20$ and $xy = 3$

13. If $x + y = 5$, $xy = 4$, find $x^3 + y^3$

D. Simplify :

14. $\dfrac{y^2 + y - 2}{4 + y} - \dfrac{4y - 1 + y^2}{2 - y}$

15. $\dfrac{1 + 4x}{12} \times \dfrac{2x - 1}{2x + 1} - \dfrac{2x + 1}{2x - 1}$

16. $\dfrac{2x^2 + 1}{x + 1} \times \dfrac{x + 1}{x - 1} \times \dfrac{x^2 - 1}{2x}$

17. $(a + 3b)^3 - (a - 3b)^3$

E. Solve :

18. $\left(3x + \dfrac{1}{2}y\right)\left(9x^2 - \dfrac{3}{2}xy + \dfrac{1}{4}y^2\right)$

19. $\left(\dfrac{2}{3}p - \dfrac{1}{3}q\right)\left(\dfrac{4p^2}{9} + \dfrac{2}{9}pq + \dfrac{1}{9}q^2\right)$

20. Factorize : (a) $4x^2 + y^2 + 9z^2 + 4xy + 6yz + 12zx$

(b) $x^2 - 3x - 54$ (c) $x^2 - 3xy + 2y^2$

(d) $27x^3 + 64y^3$ (e) $343x^3 - 64$

129

21. **Find the value of :**

(a) 136×107 (b) $(48)^3 - (30)^3 - (18)^3$

22. **Find the value of :**

(a) $a^3 + b^3 + c^3 - 3abc$, if $a + b + c = 9$ and $ab + bc + ca = 26$

(b) $x^3 + y^3 + z^3$, if $x + y + z = 0$

23. **Factorize :**

(a) $8x^3 - 343$ (b) $9x^2 - 22xy + 8y^2$

24. **Solve the equations :**

(a) $\dfrac{4x + 1}{3} + \dfrac{2x - 1}{2} - \dfrac{3x - 7}{5} = 6$

(b) $\dfrac{0 \cdot 5y + 4}{1 \cdot 2y + 8} = \dfrac{5}{3}$ (c) $\dfrac{2x - (7 - 5x)}{9x - (3 + 4x)} = \dfrac{7}{6}$

25. A steamer goes downstream to cover a distance in 4 hours. But it takes 5 hours to cover the same distance upstream. If the speed of the steamer is 18 kilometres per hour, find the speed of the flowing water.

26. The distance between A and B is 425 kilometres. Two buses start from these two stations on the same road in opposite directions to cross each other. The speed of one bus is 5 kilometres more than that of the other per hour. After 3 hours, they were still 20 kilometres apart. Find the speeds of both the buses.

MEMORABLE FACTS

1. $(a + b)^2 = a^2 + b^2 + 2ab$

2. $(a - b)^2 = a^2 + b^2 - 2ab$

3. $a^2 - b^2 = (a + b)(a - b)$

4. $(a + b + c)^2 = a^2 + b^2 + c^2 + 2ab + 2bc + 2ca$

5. $(a + b)^3 = a^3 + b^3 + 3ab(a + b)$

6. $(a - b)^3 = a^3 - b^3 - 3ab(a - b)$

7. $a^3 + b^3 = (a + b)(a^2 - ab + b^2)$

8. $a^3 - b^3 = (a - b)(a^2 + ab + b^2)$

9. $a^3 + b^3 + c^3 - 3abc = (a + b + c)(a^2 + b^2 + c^2 - ab - bc - ca)$

10. If $a + b + c = 0$, then $a^3 + b^3 + c^3 = 3abc$

UNIT IV

GEOMETRY

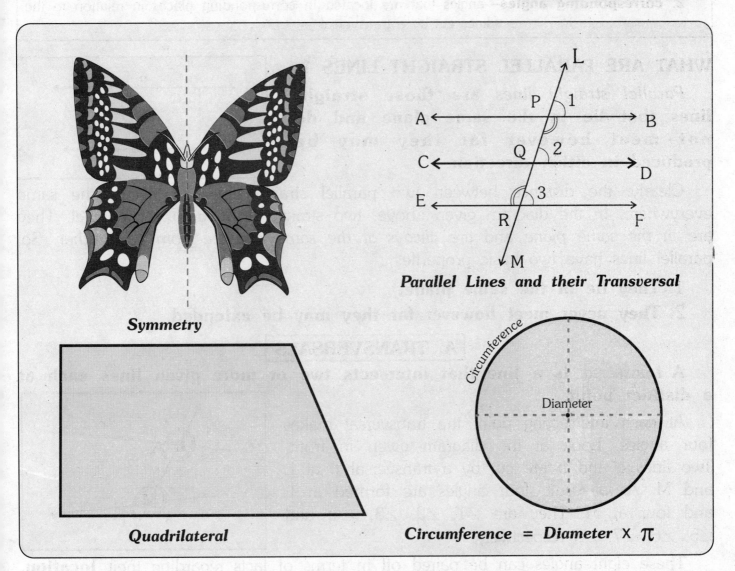

Symmetry

Quadrilateral

L

P 1

A ← → B

Q 2

C ← → D

E ← 3 → F

R

M

Parallel Lines and their Transversal

Circumference

Diameter

Circumference = Diameter × π

IN THIS UNIT—

16 PARALLEL STRAIGHT LINES

WHAT ARE PARALLEL STRAIGHT LINES ?

Parallel straight lines **are those straight lines that lie in the same plane and do not meet however far they may be produced in either direction.**

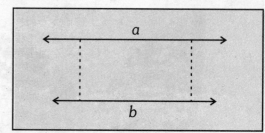

Clearly, the distance between two parallel straight lines is always the same everywhere. In the diagram given above, two straight lines a, b are parallel. They are *in the same plane* and *are always at the same distance from each other*. So, parallel lines have two basic properties :

1. **They lie in the same plane.**
2. **They never meet however far they may be extended.**

A. TRANSVERSALS

A *transversal* **is a line that intersects two or more given lines each at a distinct point.**

At each intersecting point the transversal makes four angles. Look at the diagram given in front. Two lines a and b are cut by a transversal t. at L and M. As a result, four angles are formed at L and four at M. They are $\angle 1$, $\angle 2$, $\angle 3$, $\angle 4$, and $\angle 5$, $\angle 6$, $\angle 7$, $\angle 8$ respectively.

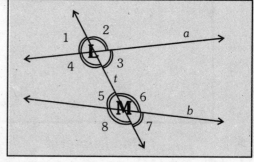

These eight angles can be paired off in terms of facts regarding their **location.** These pairs have been given separate names. Let us try to understand them.

[$\angle 1$ and $\angle 5$], [$\angle 2$ and $\angle 6$], [$\angle 3$ and $\angle 7$], [$\angle 4$ and $\angle 8$] are *four pairs of* **corresponding angles** because their location *corresponds* with each other.

[$\angle 1$ and $\angle 3$], [$\angle 2$ and $\angle 4$], [$\angle 5$ and $\angle 7$], [$\angle 6$ and $\angle 8$], are *four pairs of* **vertically opposite angles** because they are formed *opposite to each other* at the same vertex.

[$\angle 3$ and $\angle 5$], [$\angle 4$ and $\angle 6$], [$\angle 1$ and $\angle 7$], [$\angle 2$ and $\angle 8$] are *four pairs of* **alternate angles** because they are formed on the *alternate sides of the tranversal*.

[∠4 and ∠5], [∠3 and ∠6] are two pairs of **interior angles** because they are formed inside the parallel lines and on the same side of the transveral.

REMEMBER :

1. If a transversal cuts two **non-parallel lines**, all these pairs of angles are formed but they have no **relation** between themselves.

2. If a transversal cuts **two parallel lines**, these **angles are related** to each in terms of equality as under :

   (a) **The corresponding angles of each pair are equal to each other.**

   (b) **The alternate angles of each pair are equal to each other.**

   (c) **The vertically opposite angles of each pair are equal.**

   (d) **The interior angles of each pair are together equal to 180°.**

CONVERSELY,

Two lines cut by a transversal **are parallel** to each other if they make :

1. a pair of corresponding angles consisting of equal angles.

2. a pair of alternate angles consisting of equal angles.

3. If two of the interior angles formed on the same side of the transversal are together equal to 180°.

Let us now study **some facts** involving parallel lines and their properties.

| FACT 1 | **Two line-segments which are parallel to the same line-segment are parallel to each other.** |

Given : Two line-segments AB and EF are both parallel to line-segment CD

To prove : AB||EF

Construction : Draw a transversal LM that cuts AB at P, CD at Q and EF at R.

Proof : AB||CD and LM cuts them at P, Q

∴ ∠1 = corresponding ∠2

Again EF||CD and LM cuts them at Q, R

∴ ∠2 = corresponding ∠3

But ∠2 = ∠1 .....*(proved)*

∴ ∠1 = ∠3

But these are corresponding angles

∴ **AB||EF**

FACT 2	**Two line-segments perpendicular to the same line-segment in a plane are parallel to each other.**

Given : Two line-segments AB and CD are perpendicular to the line-segment EF

To prove : AB||CD

Construction : Produce AB to L and CD to M

Proof : AL and CM are two line-semgnets and line-segment EF cuts them as a transversal on B and D.

Also $\angle 1 = \angle 2$ ....(each = 90°)

But these are corresponding angles

∴ AL||CM or **AB||CD**

FACT 3	**Two intersecting line-segments cannot both be parallel to one and the same line-segment.**

Given : Two line-segments AB and CD intersect each other at P. CD is parallel to another line-segment EF.

To prove : AB is not parallel to EF

Construction : Draw a transversal LM through P cutting EF at Q

Proof : CD||EF and LM cuts them

∴ $\angle LPC = \angle 2$ ......(corresponding $\angle$s)

Now suppose that AB is also parallel to EF and LM cuts them as a transversal

∴ $\angle LPA$ must be = corresponding $\angle 2$

∴ $\angle LPA$ must be equal to $\angle LPC$ .... (∵ $\angle 2 = \angle LPC$)

But it is impossible because $\angle LPA$ is a part of $\angle LPC$ and a part can never be equal to the whole

∴ Our supposition is wrong.

Hence **AB is not parallel to EF**

 Such a proof is called an **indirect proof.**

DRAWING PARALLEL LINES

CASE 1 **drawing a line-segment CD parallel to a given line-segment AB through a given point P outside it.**

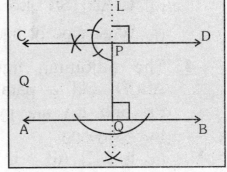

STEPS :
1. Draw PQ perpendicular to AB meeting it at Q
2. Produce QP to L
3. At P draw ∠QPC = 90°
4. Produce CP to D

Now AB and CD are both perpendicular to QPL

∴ They are parallel to each other.

∴ **Line-segment CD is the reqd. segment parallel to AB.**

CASE 2 **Drawing a line-segment CD parallel to a given line-segment AB at a given distance (say 3 cm.) from it.**

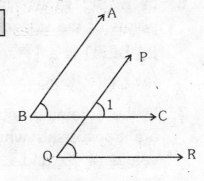

STEPS :
1. Take any point Q on AB.
2. Draw a line-segment QL perpendicular to AB.
3. Cut off QP = 3 cm. out of QL
4. Draw PC perpendicular to QL
5. Produce CP to D

Now AB and CD are both perpendicular to QL

∴ CD||AB

Hence CD is the reqd. line-segment parallel to AB

PRACTICE EXERCISES 30

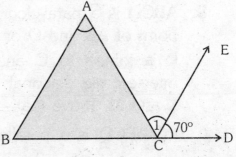

A. 1. In the figure given in front :

AB||PQ and BC||QR

Prove that ∠ABC = ∠PQR

Hint : ∠ABC = ∠1 .....(corr. ∠s)

∠1 = ∠PQR .....(∠corr. ∠s)

2. Given in front is ΔABC in which ∠A = 60°. BC is produced to D and CE is drawn parallel to BC.

If ∠ECD = 70°, find ∠ACB.

Hint : ∠1 = alt. ∠A = 60°

3. Given in front is a trapezium PQRS in which PQ||SR. Line-segment AB is drawn parallel to PQ. It meets SP in A and QR in B.

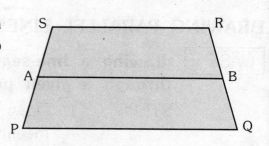

(a) Is AB||SR also ? If yes, why ?

(b) What type of figures are APQB, ABRS ?

4. The adjoining figure has a rectangle ABCD and a parallelogram DCFE. Also, FB and EA are joined. Answer each of the following :

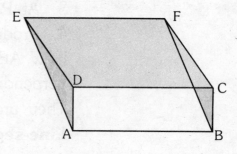

(a) Is DC||AB ? If yes, why ?

(b) Is EF||AB ? If yes, why ?

(c) Is EF = AB ? If yes, why ?

(d) Is ABFE a parallelogram ? If yes, why ?

(e) Can we say that rectangle ABCD is a parallelogram also ?

5. In the adjoining figure AB||CD and they are cut by a transversal EF at L and P respectively.

If LM bisects ∠ELC and PQ bisects ∠LPB, prove that LM||PQ.

Hint : ∠ELC = ∠LPB *(corr. ∠s)*

∴ ½∠ELP = ½∠LPB

In other words, ∠1 = ∠2

But they are corresponding ∠s.

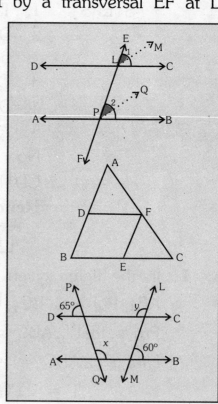

6. In ∆ABC shown in front D, E, F are middle-points of the sides AB, BC and CA. Prove that—

(a) BEFD is a ||^{gm}

(b) DF = ½BC

7. In the adjoining figure, AB||CD and PQ and LM are transversals which are not parallel. Find the values of ∠x and ∠y.

8. ABCD is a parallelogram in which P is the mid-point of AB and Q of CD.

P is joined to C and Q is joined to A. They intersect the diagonal BD of the parallelogram at L and M. Prove that—

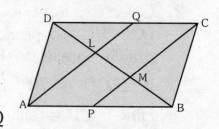

(a) APCQ is a parallelogram ?   (b) PB = DQ

9. Draw a line-segment AB = 6 cm. in length. Divide it into five equal parts through parallel lines.

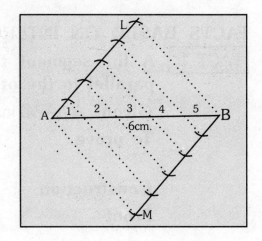

Hint : Make equal alternate angles at A and B respectively but in opposite directions

Mark on AL and BM five equal divisions using compasses. Join the division-marks as shown in front.

B. INTERCEPTS

The word—**intercept**—means *to stop a vehicle etc. on the way.* But in mathematics, it means *to mark off a line-segment between two points.*

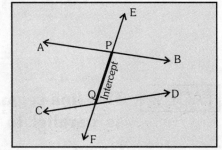

Observe the figure given in front. Two line-segments AB and CD intersect a third line-segment EF at P and Q. Clearly, **EF** *is a transversal.* As a result of its intersections by two different line-segments, its part PQ has been marked off. This part PQ is called an **intercept.** So, we can define an **intercept** as under :

An *intercept* **is a part of a line between two points on it at which two other lines intersect the given line.**

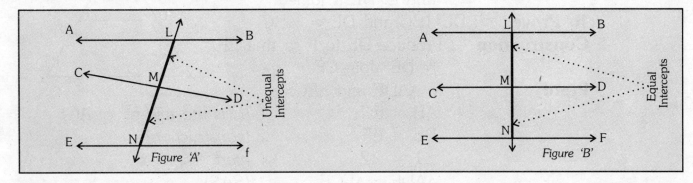

The two figures given above show two intercepts on each transversal. But these intercepts are different from one another.

In figure A, the line-segments intersecting the transversal are non-parallel. So, its **intercepts are unequal.** But in figure B, the line-segments intersecting the transversal are parallel and equidistant from one another. Also, the transversal is perpendicular to each of them. So, its **intercepts are equal.**

From the above discussion, it is clear that if three parallel lines mark off two equal intercepts on a transversal, they will make equal intercepts on any other transversal as well.

FACTS BASED ON INTERCEPTS

FACT 1 **A line-segment through the mid-point of one side of a triangle parallel to the other side bisects the third side.**

Given : A $\triangle ABC$ in which D is the mid-point of AB and DE is parallel BC

To prove : E is the mid-point of AC,
i.e. AE = EC

Construction : Draw PAQ||BC through A.

Proof : PAQ, DE and BC are three parallel lines. AB and AC are two transversals intersected by these lines.

∴ AD and DB are *intercepts* marked off on AB and AE and EC are *intercepts* marked off on AC.

But AD = DB   .....*(D is the mid-point of AB)*

∴ AE must be equal to EC *i.e.* E is the mid-point of AC

FACT 2 **The line-segment joining the mid-points of two sides of a triangle is parallel to the third side and is equal to half of it.**

Given : A $\triangle ABC$ whose sides AB and AC have their mid-points D and E. DE is joined.

To Prove : DE||BC and DE = ½BC

Construction : Produce DE to F so that EF = DE. Join CF

Proof : In $\triangle ADE$ and $\triangle ECF$

AE = EC   ....*(E is the mid-pt. of AC)*
DE = EF   ....*(construction)*
$\angle 1 = \angle 2$ ....*(vert. opp. $\angle$s)*

∴ $\triangle ADE \cong \triangle ECF$ ....*(SAS)*

∴ $\angle A$ = alternate $\angle 3$

∴ DA||CF or BD||CF

Also, DA = CF   .....*($\because$ DA = BD)*

or BD = CF   .....*($\because$ DA = BD)*

∴ BD = CF and also BD||CF

Thus BCFD is a parallelogram.

∴ DF||BC and DF = BC

or **DE||BC** and **DE = ½BC**   ......*($\because$ DE = ½DF)*

A. **1.** In the adjoining figure, D, E, F are the mid-points of the sides AB, BC and CA respectively. Prove that BEFD is a ||^{gm}.

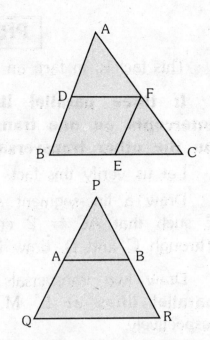

Hint : D, F are the mid-points of AB, AC

∴ DF||BE ; Similarly EF||BD

2. PQR is an isosceles Δ with PQ = PR. A is the mid-point of PQ and AB||QR meeting PR at B. Prove that PAB is also an isosceles Δ *i.e.* PA = PB

Hint : According to FACT 1, B is the middle point of PR ; *i.e.*

$$PB = \frac{1}{2}PR = \frac{1}{2}PQ \qquad ......(\because PR = PQ, given)$$

∴ PA = PB

3. ABCD is quadrilateral and E, F, G and H are the mid-points of the sides AB, BC, CD and DA respectively. EF, FG, GH and HE are joined. Then prove that EFGH is a parallelogram.

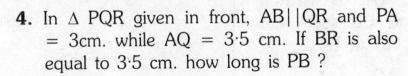

Hint : Join diagonal AC and prove—

EF||AC ; Also GH||AC ; EF||GH

Similarly by joining the diagonal BD, we can prove that HE||FG.

4. In Δ PQR given in front, AB||QR and PA = 3cm. while AQ = 3·5 cm. If BR is also equal to 3·5 cm. how long is PB ?

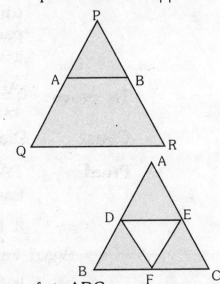

5. Draw a line-segment 7 cm. long and divide it into four equal parts.

6. In the adjoining figure, ABC is a triangle and D, E, F are the mid-points of its sides AB, BC and CA respectively. Prove that perimetre of Δ DEF = ½perimetre of Δ ABC.

Hint : Each side of Δ DEF = ½ one of the sides of Δ ABC

PROPORTIONAL INTERCEPTS

This fact is, in fact, an extension of the fact of **equal intercepts**. It states that—

If three parallel lines intersect two transversals, the ratio of the intercepts on one transversal is the same as the ratio of the intercepts on the other transversal.

Let us verify this fact.

Draw a line-segment AB. Take two points C, E such that AC = 2 cm. and CE = 1·5 cm. Through C and D, draw lines parallel to AB.

Draw two transversals intersecting these three parallel lines at L, M, N and at P, Q, R respectively.

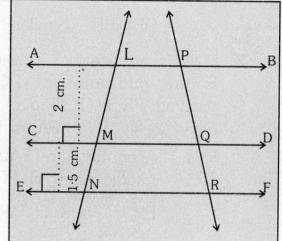

Measure LM, MN and also PQ, QR.

You will see that—

$$\frac{LM}{MN} = \frac{2}{1\cdot5} \quad \text{and} \quad \frac{PQ}{QR} = \frac{2}{1\cdot5}$$

In other words, $\dfrac{LM}{MN} = \dfrac{PQ}{QR} = \dfrac{2}{1\cdot5}$

Another fact based on this fact is as under :

FACT 1 **If a line is drawn parallel to one side of a triangle, it intersects the other side, in the same proportion as the first side.**

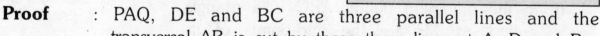

Given : A $\triangle$ABC. From a pt D on AB, DE is drawn parallel to BC such that it meets AC at E

To prove : $\dfrac{AE}{EC} = \dfrac{AD}{DB}$

Const : Draw PAQ∥DE through A

Proof : PAQ, DE and BC are three parallel lines and the transversal AB is cut by these three lines at A, D and B.

∴   It has two intercepts AD, DB

Again transversal AC is cut by the three lines at A, E, C

∴   It has two intercepts AE, EC

Now, according to the fact proved above—

Ratio of AD and DB = Ratio of AE, EC

or $\dfrac{AE}{EC} = \dfrac{AD}{BD}$

FACT 2 **DIVIDING A LINE-SEGMENT INTO A RATIO (2 : 3)**

STEPS :   1. Draw a line-segment AB = 7·6 cm.

2. Draw any ray making any acute angle with AB.

3. Starting from A mark off 2 + 3 = 5 equal arcs 1, 2, 3, 4, 5 of a proper radius.

4 Join arc 5 with B.

5. From arc 2 draw 2E parallel to 5B.

The point E will divide AB in the ratio 2 : 3

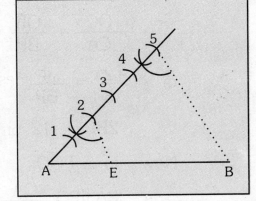

PRACTICE EXERCISES 32

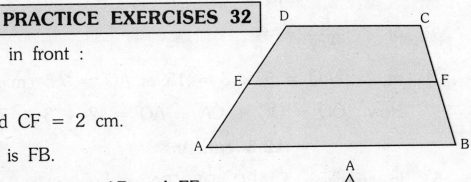

1.   In the figure given in front :

(a) CD ∥ EF ∥ AB

(b) EA = 2DE and CF = 2 cm.

Find how long is FB.

2.   In △ ABC, E is any point on AB and EF is drawn parallel to BC. If

(a) AE = 2·5 cm., EB = 5 cm. ; AF = 3 cm. find CF

(b) AE = 3·6 cm., EB = 5·4 cm., CF = 6 cm. ; found AF.

Hint : 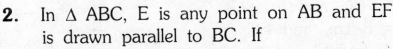 $\dfrac{AE}{EB} = \dfrac{AF}{CF}$

3.   Given in front is a △ PQR in which ∠PDE = ∠Q. Also, PE = 2 cm. and ER = 3 cm. If PD = 4 cm., find DQ and PQ

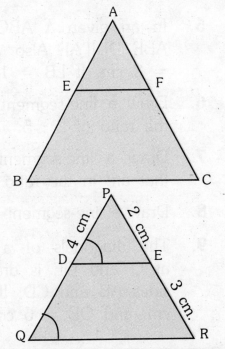

4. Given in front is a triangle POQ.

From a point B on PO, BC is drawn parallel to PA. Also BA∥PQ.

If OC = 2 cm., CA = 3 cm. and OB = 4 cm., find OQ

Hint : In Δ POA

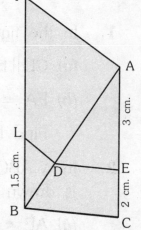

∵   BC∥PA

∴ $\dfrac{OC}{CA} = \dfrac{OB}{BP}$ or $\dfrac{2}{3} = \dfrac{OB}{BP}$

or $\dfrac{2}{3} = \dfrac{4}{BP}$

∴   2BP = 12 or BP = 6 cm.

Now,   in Δ POQ

∵   BA∥PQ, $\dfrac{OA}{AQ} = \dfrac{OB}{BP} = \dfrac{2}{3}$

or $\dfrac{2cm. + 3cm.}{AQ} = \dfrac{OB}{BP} = \dfrac{4}{6} = \dfrac{2}{3}$

or $\dfrac{5}{AQ} = \dfrac{2}{3}$

or   2AQ = 5 × 3 = 15 or AQ = 7·5 cm.

Now   OQ = OC + CA + AQ = (2 + 3 + 7·5) cm.

= **12·5 cm.** *Ans.*

5. In an given Δ ABC, DE∥BC and in Δ ABF, DL∥AF. Also, AE = 3 cm. and EC = 2 cm. If LB = 1·5 cm. find FL.

6. Draw a line-segment PQ = 7 cm. and divide it into two parts that are in the ratio of 2 : 5.

7. Draw a line-segment AB = 8·5 cm. in length. Divide it into three parts that are in the ratio 1 : 2 : 3

8. Draw a line-segment EF = 6·5 cm. Find a point P on it so that EP = $\dfrac{2}{5}$EF.

9. The diagonals of a trapezium ABCD intersect at O and OE is drawn parallel to the parallel sides AB and CD. If CO = 3 cm., AO = 4·5 cm. and OB = 6 cm. find OD.

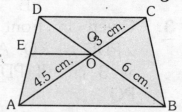

17 LINEAR SYMMETRY

WHAT IS SYMMETRY ?

Symmetry **means a balance/proportion between two halves of a body/ figure to create harmony and beauty.**

A body or figure with symmetry looks beautiful. It can be divided into two parts by a mere *point* or *along a line* or *plane*. These parts are *exactly the same* in **size** and **shape**. Also, they are **similar** in **position** in relation to the dividing point or line. Observe the follows figures and pictures etc.

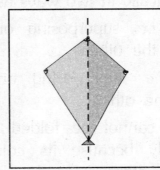

M W A
B E 8

All the pictures and letters shown above are symmetrical. Each of them can be divided into two congruent parts by drawing a line. This line is called the **axis of symmetry**.

Remember that figures, objects or letters etc. that have no axis of symmetry are called **non-symmetrical**. Given below are some pictures showing non-symmetrical figures, objects etc. :

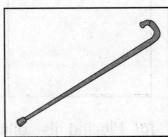

7   J   2   5

SYMMETRY IN TWO OR MORE DIMENSIONS

Imagine an **isosceles triangle** ABC whose side AB = side AC. We can fold it along **only one axis of symmetry** as shown in front because it has *only one pair of equal sides* and *one pair of equal angles.*

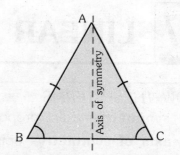

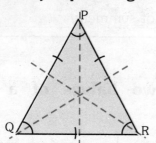

Now imagine an **equilateral triangle** PQR as shown in front. How many *axes of symmetry* has it ? Clearly, it can have **three axes of symmetry** because it has *three pairs of equal sides* and all the three of its angles are also equal.

IN THE CASE OF A RECTANGLE

A rectangle has two pairs of equal sides. So, it can be folded symmetrically in two ways as under :

(a) **Breadthwise**, *i.e.* superposing one of its breadths upon the other.

(b) **Lengthwise**, *i.e.* superposing one of its lengths upon the other.

Remember that it cannot be folded along its diagonals symmetrically because its corners will not coincide with each other.

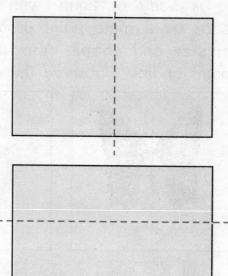

IN THE CASE OF A SQUARE

A square has all its **side** as well as **angles** equal. So, it can be folded symmetrically in four ways as under :

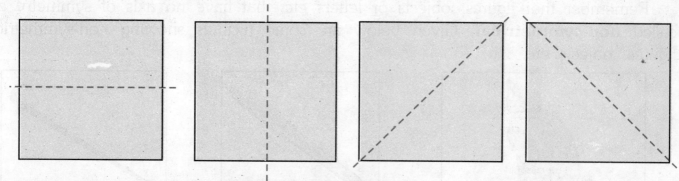

(a) Placing its one side upon the opposite side.
(b) placing the adjacent side upon its opposite side.
(c) Placing one corner upon the opposite corner.
(d) Placing the adjacent corner on its opposite corner.

IN THE CASE OF A RHOMBUS

Though a rhombus has all its sides equal but its angles are not equal. So, it has only **two axes of symmetry** as under :

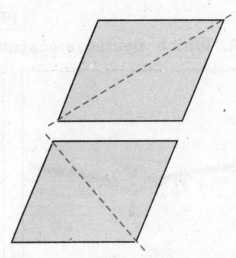

(a) one through its one pair of opposite angles.

(b) the other through its other pair of opposite angles.

IN THE CASE OF A TRAPEZIUM

Normally a trapezium has no axis of symmetry. But if its non-parallel sides happen to be equal, it has one axis of symmetry. The two figure given below explain this point.

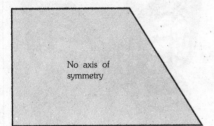

No axis of symmetry

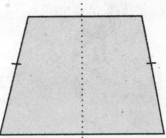

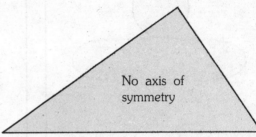

No axis of symmetry

Similarly a SCALENE TRIANGLE has no axis of symmetry. The reason is that it has all its sides of different lengths. Naturally its angles are also unequal. So, no symmetry is there in any of its parts.

IN THE CASE OF A CIRCLE

We know any diameter of a circle divides it into two identical parts **(semi-circles)**.

But we also know that a circle can have innumerable diameters. So, we can say that every diameter of a circle forms an axis of symmetry.

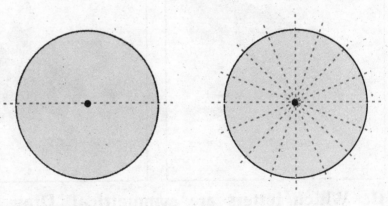

AXIS OF SYMMETRY

An *axis of symmetry* **is a** *point* **or** *line* **along which a figure or body can be folded to show its identical parts.**

Also remember :

Any two or more points equidistant from the axis of symmetry of a figure are called *symmetric points.*

A. Which figures are symmetrical. Draw the axis of symmetry also.

B. Which letters are symmetrical. Draw each axis of symmetry also.

B   L   O   J   S

W   R   A   V   M

C. Draw the *axis/axes* of symmetry in each of the following figures :

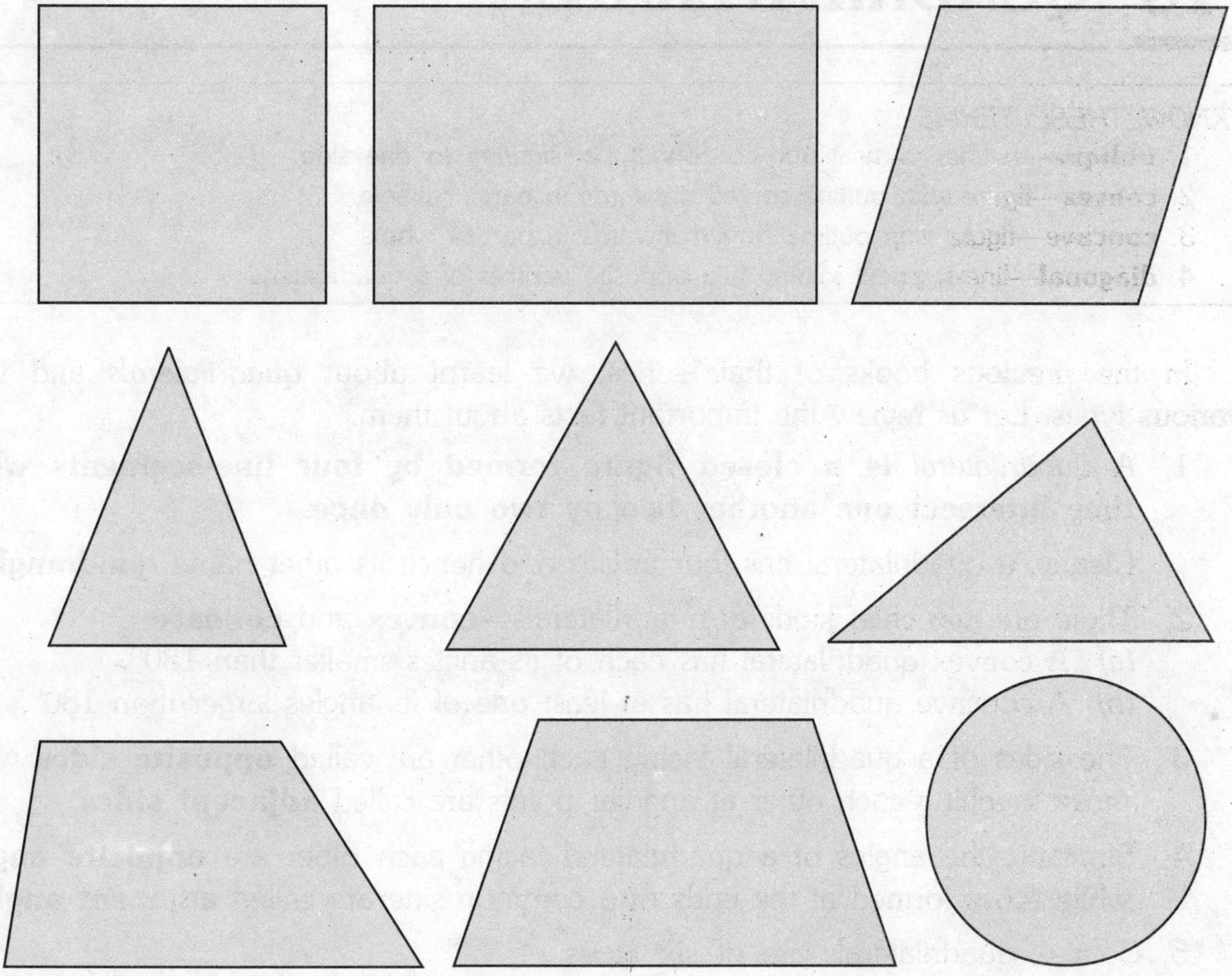

D. Define :

(a) symmetry :

....

....

(b) axis of symmetry :

....

....

(c) symmetric figures :

....

....

18 QUADRILATERALS

In the previous books of their series, we learnt about *quadrilaterals* and their various types. Let us review the important facts about them.

1. **A *quadrilateral* is a closed figure formed by four line-segments when they intersect one another two by two only once.**

   Clearly, a quadrilateral has four angles and hence its other name **quadrangle**.

2. There are two chief kinds of quadrilaterals—**convex** and **concave** :
   (a) A convex quadrilateral has each of its angles smaller than 180°.
   (b) A concave quadrilateral has at least one of its angles larger than 180°.

3. The sides of a quadrilateral facing each other are called **opposite sides** while those touching each other at angular points are called **adjacent sides**.

4. Similarly, the angles of a quadrilateral facing each other are **opposite angles** while those formed at the ends of a common side are called **adjacent angles**.

5. Convex quadrilaterals are of six types.

   (a) SQUARE

   A *square* is an equilateral quadrilateral with all its sides equal to each other and each of its angles = 90°.

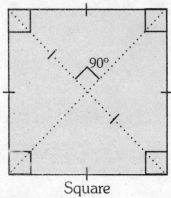
Square

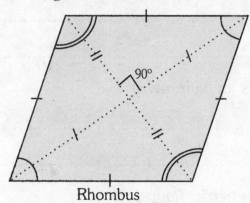
Rhombus

   (b) RHOMBUS

   A *rhombus* is a quadrilateral with all its sides equal to one another and two pairs of equal opposite angles.

Note : 1. The diagonals of a square are *equal* and they *bisect each other at 90°.*

2. The diagonals of a rhombus are *not equal* but they *bisect each other at 90°.*

3. As a rhombus has none of its angles = 90°, it is called an **oblique square** also.

(c) RECTANGLE

A *rectangle* is a quadrilateral with its opposite sides equal and each of its angles = 90°.

The diagonals of a rectangle are *equal* and they *bisect each other but not at right angles.* Each of them bisects the rectangle into two equal rt. Δs.

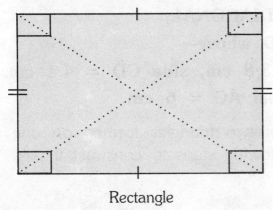

Rectangle

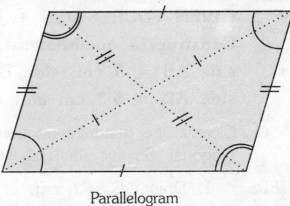

Parallelogram

(d) PARALLELOGRAM

A *parallelogram* is a quadrilateral with two pairs of opposite sides equal as well as parallel.

The opposite angles of a $||^{gm}$ are equal and its diagonals *bisect each other.* Also each diagonal divides the parallelogram into two congruent triangles.

(e) TRAPEZIUM

A *trapezium* is a quadrilateral with one pair of opposite sides *parallel* **and** *unequal.*

1. The other pair of sides is non-parallel.

2. If the non-paralllel sides are equal, the trapezium is called an **isosceles trapezium**.

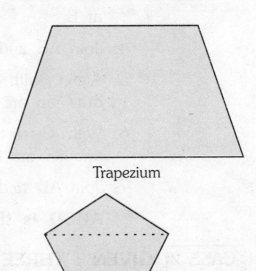

Trapezium

(f) KITE

A *kite* is quadrilateral with two pairs of adjacent sides equal but with opposite sides unequal.

A kite is formed when two unequal isosceles triangles are formed on a common base.

Kite

Also remember :

1. The sum of the angles of a quadrilateral is equal to 360°, *i.e.* 4 rt. ∠s.
2. A quadrilateral has ten chief elements.

   (a) four sides   (b) four angels   (c) two diagonals

3. Each quadrilateral can be divided into two triangles by drawing any of its diagonals.

CONSTRUCTING QUADRILATERALS

CASE 1   **GIVEN FOUR SIDES + ONE DIAGONAL**

Construct a quadrilateral ABCD whose—
side AB = 3 cm, side BC = 3·8 cm, side CD = 4·1 cm, side AD = 5·3 cm and diagonal AC = 6 cm.

Clearly, the quadrilateral consists of two triangles formed on one of its diagonal. So, we shall take the following steps to construct it.

STEPS :
1. Draw AC = 6 cm.

2. With A as centre and radius 3 cm. *(length of AB)* draw an arc on one side of AC.

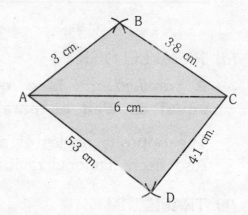

3. With C and centre and radius 3·8 cm. *(length of BC)* draw another arc cutting the first arc at B.

4. Join AB and BC

5. Again, with A as centre and radius = 5·3 cm. *(length of AD)* draw an arc on the other side of AC.

6. With C as centre and radius = 4·1 cm. *(length of CD)* draw another arc that cuts the first arc at D.

7. Join AD and CD

ABCD is the required quadrilateral.   Q.E.F

CASE 2   **GIVEN : THREE ANGLES + TWO CONTAINED SIDES**
Construct a quadrilateral ABCD whose—
side AB = 4 cm, side BC = 4·5 cm, ∠A = 90°, ∠B = 75° and ∠C = 120°

STEPS : 1. Draw the side AB = 4 cm.

2. At A draw ∠BAP = 90°

3. At B draw ∠ABQ = 75°

4. Out of BQ, cut off BC = 4·5 cm.

5. At C draw angle ∠BCD = 120° so that its arm CD cuts AP at D.

ABCD is the required quadrilateral Q.E.F.

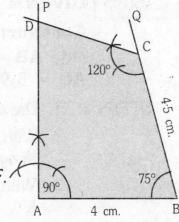

CASE 3 **GIVEN : FOUR SIDES + ONE ANGLE**

Construct a quadrilateral ABCD whose—
side AB = 3·7 cm, side BC = 3·8 cm, side CD = 4·3 cm,
side AD = 4·6 cm. and ∠D = 75°

STEPS : 1. Draw AD 4·6 cm.

2. At D draw ∠ADP = 75°

3. Cut off DC = 4·3 cm. out of DP.

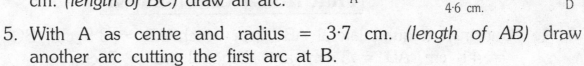

4. With C as centre and radius = 3·8 cm. *(length of BC)* draw an arc.

5. With A as centre and radius = 3·7 cm. *(length of AB)* draw another arc cutting the first arc at B.

6. Join AB and BC.

ABCD is the required quadrilateral. Q.E.F.

CASE 4 **GIVEN : THREE SIDES + TWO CONTAINED ANGLES**

Construct a quadrilateral ABCD whose—

side AB = 4 cm, side BC = 4·2 cm, side CD = 4·9 cm,

∠B = 75° and ∠C = 105°

STEPS : 1. Draw BC = 4·2 cm.

2. At B draw ∠B = 75°

3. At C, draw ∠C = 105°

4. Cut off BA = 4 cm. and CD = 4·9 cm.

5. Join AD.

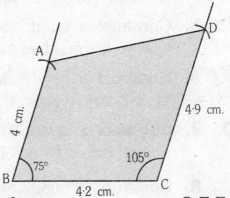

ABCD is the required quadrilateral. Q.E.F.

| CASE 5 | GIVEN : THREE SIDES + TWO DIAGONALS |

Construct a quadrilateral ABCD whose—
side AB = 4 cm, side BC = 4·7 cm, side AD = 4·2 cm, diagonal
AC = 5·9 cm. and diagonal BD = 6·7 cm.

STEPS :
1. Draw BC = 4·7 cm.

2. With B as centre and radius = 4 cm. *(length of AB)* draw an arc.

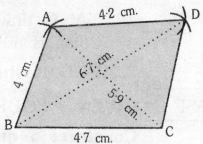

3. With C as centre and radius = 5·9 cm. *(length of diagonal AC)* draw another arc that cuts the previous arc at A.

4. Join AB and AC

5. Now with A as centre and radius = 4·2 cm. *(length of AD)* draw an arc.

6. With B as centre and radius = 6·7 cm. *(length of diagonal BD)* draw another arc that cuts the first arc at D.

7. Join AD, DC and BD.

ABCD is the required quadrilateral.   *Q.E.F*

| PRACTICE EXERCISES 34 |

A. 1. Construct a quadrilateral ABCD in which AB = 3·5 cm, BC = 5·4 cm CD = 4·8 cm, AD = 5 cm. and diagonal AC = 7 cm.

2. Draw a quadrilateral ABCD given that its side AB = 5·5 cm, BC = 4·8 cm, CD = 4·5 cm, AD = 3·2 cm. and diagonal BD = 4 cm.

B. 3. Construct a quadrilateral ABCD whose side AB = 3·5 cm, BC = 4·2 cm, CD = 4·5 cm, AD = 5 cm. and $\angle$B = 60°.

4. Construct a quadrilateral whose side AB = 3·8 cm, BC = 3·4 cm, CD = 4·5 cm, AD = 5 cm. and B = $\angle$75°.

C. 5. Construct a quadrilateral ABCD in which side BC = 4 cm., AD = 4·5 cm, CD = 5 cm, diagonal AC = 5·6 cm. and diagonal BD = 6·5 cm.

6. Construct a quadrilateral ABCD given that AB = 3·8 cm, BC = 3 cm, AD = 3·7 cm, diagonal AC = 5 cm and diagonal BD = 5·8 cm.

D. 7. Construct a quadrilateral ABCD in which AB = 4 cm, BC = 4·6 cm, CD = 5·1 cm, $\angle$B = 60° and $\angle$C = 135°

8. Construct a quadrilateral ABCD in which AB = 4·2 cm, BC = 5 cm, CD 5·3 cm, $\angle$B = $\angle$120° and $\angle$C = 75°.

E. 9. Construct a quadrilateral ABCD whose ∠A = 60°, ∠B = 105°, ∠C = 120°, side AB = 4·3 cm. and side BC = 5 cm.

10. Construct a quadrilateral ABCD given that ∠A = 105°, ∠B = 60°, ∠C = 135°, side AB = 5·2 cm. and side BC = 3·8 cm.

CONSTRUCTING REGULAR QUADRILATERALS

CASE 1 **PARALLELOGRAMS**

A. Construct a parallelogram whose adjacent sides AB, BC are 4 cm. and 5·2 cm. respectively and the angle contained by them is of 75°.

STEPS : 1. Draw the longer side BC = 5·2 cm.

2. At B draw ∠CBP = 75°

3. Out of BP, cut off BA = 4 cm.

4. With A as centre and radius = 5·2 cm. draw an arc.

5. With C as centre and radius = 4 cm. draw another arc cutting the first one at D.

6. Join AD and CD.

ABCD is the required parallelogram.   *Q.E.F.*

B. Construct a parallelogram whose two adjacent sides AB and AD are 5·2 cm. and 3 cm. respectively and diagonal BD is equal to 6·4 cm.

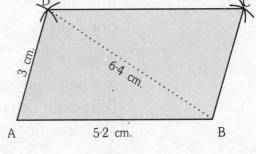

STEPS : 1. Draw AB = 5·2 cm.

2. With A as centre and radius = 3 cm. draw an arc.

3. With B as centre and radius = 6·4 cm. *(length of the diagonal BD)* draw another arc that cuts the previous arc at D.

4. Join BD.

5. Now with D as centre and radius = 5·2 cm. draw an arc.

6. With B as centre and radius 3 cm. draw another arc that cuts the previous arc at C.

7. Join CD and BC.

ABCD is the required parallelogram.   *Q.E.F*

C. Construct a parallelogram whose diagonals arc 3·8 cm. and 4·6 cm. respectively and an angle between them = 60°.

STEPS : We know that the diagonals of a parallelogram bisect each other. So, we shall take the following steps :

1. Draw AC = 4·6 cm.

2. Bisect AC at O.

3. At O, make ∠COP = 60°.

4. Produce PO to Q.

5. Out of OP, cut off OD = $\frac{1}{2}$ *(other diagonal)*, *i.e.* = 3·8 ÷ 2 = 1·9 cm.

6. Out of OQ, cut off OB = OD.

7. Join AB, BC, CD and AD to complete the parallelogram.

ABCD is the required parallelogram.   *Q.E.F.*

D. Construct a parallelogram whose one side is 4·4 cm. and both the diagonals arc 5·6 cm. and 7 cm. respectively.

STEPS : 1. Draw the given side AB = 4·4 cm.

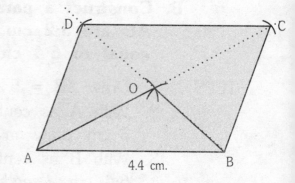

2. With A as centre and radius = half one diagonal, *i.e.* 2·8 cm., draw an arc.

3. With B as centre and the radius = half the other diagonal, *i.e.* 3·5 cm. Draw another arc that cuts the first arc at O.

4. Join OA, OB

5. Produce AO to C such that OC = AO

6. Produce BO to D such that OD = BO

7. Join BC, CD and AD to complete the parallelogram.

ABCD is the required $\parallel^{gm}$.   *Q.E.F.*

154

CASE 2 **SQUARES**

A. Construct a square ABCD given that its side = 3·8 cm.

STEPS :
1. Draw AB = 3·8 cm.

2. At A draw $\angle BAP = 90°$

3. Cut off AD out of AP = 3·8 cm.

4. At B draw $\angle ABQ = 90°$

5. Out of BQ, cut off BC = 3·8 cm.

6. Join CD to complete the square.

ABCD is the required square.   *Q.E.F.*

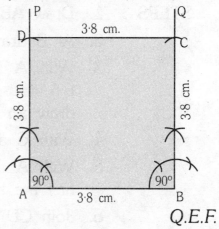

B. Construct a square ABCD whose diagonal AC = 6·2 cm.

STEPS :
1. Draw AC = 6·2 cm.

2. Draw PQ the right bisector of AC cutting it at O.

3. Cut off OB and OD = $\frac{1}{2}$ AC, *i.e.* 6·2 ÷ 2 = 3·1 cm. each out of the right bisector on both sides of AC.

4. Join AB, BC, CD and AD to complete the square.

ABCD is the required square.   *Q.E.F.*

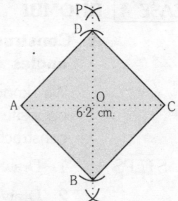

CASE 3 **RECTANGLES**

A. Construct a rectangle ABCD whose sides AB and BC are 4 cm. and 3·5 cm. respectively.

STEPS :
1. Draw AB = 4 cm.

2. At A draw $\angle BAP = 90°$

3. Cut off AD out of AP = 3·5 cm.

4. At B draw $\angle ABQ = 90°$

5. Out of BQ cut off BC = 3·5 cm.

6. Join CD to complete the rectangle.

ABCD is the required rectangle.   *Q.E.F.*

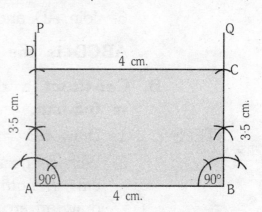

B. Construct a rectangle whose side AB = 5 cm. and the diagonal AC = 6·5 cm.

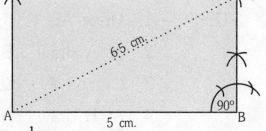

STEPS : 1. Draw AB = 5 cm.

2. At B draw ∠ABP = 90°

3. With A as centre and radius = 6·5 cm. (length of diagonal AC), draw an arc cutting BP at C.

4. With C as centre and radius 5 cm. draw an arc.

5. With A as centre and radius = BC draw another arc cutting the first arc at D.

6. Join CD and AD to complete the rectangle.

ABCD is the required rectangle.   *Q.E.F.*

CASE 4   **RHOMBI**

A. Construct a rhombus whose side is 4·5 cm. and one of the angles is 75°.

We know that all the sides of a rhombus are equal and also its opposite angles are equal. So, we shall take the following steps to construct the rhombus.

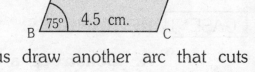

STEPS : 1. Draw BC = 4·5 cm.

2. Draw ∠CBP = 75°.

3. Cut off BA out of BP = 4·5 cm.

4. With centre A and radius = 4·5 cm. draw an arc.

5. With centre C and the same radius draw another arc that cuts the previous arc at D.

6. Join AD and CD to complete the rhombus.

ABCD is the required rhombus.   *Q.E.F.*

B. Construct a rhombus whose side = 4 cm. and a diagonal = 6·5 cm.

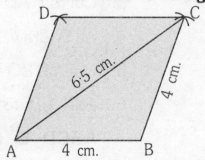

STEPS : 1. Draw AB = 4 cm.

2. With centre A and radius = 6·5 cm. (length of the diagonal) draw an arc.

3. With centre B and radius = 4 cm. *(length of the side)* draw another arc that cuts the previous arc at C.

4. Join AC and BC.

5. With centre A and radius = 4 cm. draw an arc.

6. With centre C and the same radius draw another arc that cuts the previous arc at D.

7. Join AD and CD to complete the rhombus.

ABCD is the required rhombus. *Q.E.F.*

C. Construct a rhombus ABCD whose diagonals AC and BD are 8·6 cm. and 6·4 cm. respectively.

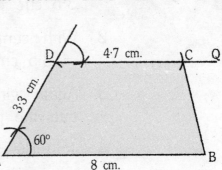

STEPS : 1. Draw AC = 8·6 cm.

2. Draw PQ the right bisector of AC cutting it at O.

3. Out of OP and OQ both, cut off OD and OB each = ½ BD, = 3·2 cm.

4. Join AB, BC, CD and DA to complete the rhombus.

ABCD is the required rhombus. *Q.E.F.*

CASE 5 **TRAPEZIUMS**

A. Construct a trapezium ABCD given its parallel sides AB and CD equal to 8 cm. and 4·7 cm. while side AD = 3·3 and ∠A = 60°

STEPS : 1. Draw AB = 8 cm.

2. At A make an angle of 60°.

3. Cut off AD = 3·3 cm. out the arm of the angle.

4. Through D, draw DQ parallel to AB.

5. Out of DQ, cut off DC = 4·7 cm.

6. Join BC

ABCD is the required trapezium. *Q.E.F.*

B. Construct a trapezium ABCD in which AB||CD and its sides AB = 10 cm, AD = 5 cm. and CD = 7 cm. respectively.

STEPS : 1. Draw AB = 10 cm.

2. Take a point P on AB (10 − 7) = 3 cm. away from A.

3. Draw a line-segment that is perpendicular to AB at P.

4. With centre A and radius = 5 cm. draw an arc cutting the perpendicular at D.

5. Join AD

6. Draw DQ||AB and out of it cut off DC = 7 cm.

7. Join BC to complete the trapezium.

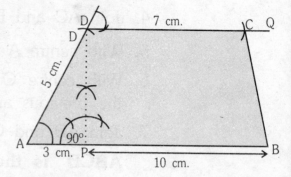

ABCD is the required trapezium.   *Q.E.F.*

C. Construct an isosceles trapezium whose parallel sides arc 10 cm. and 6·5 respectively and each of the non-parallel sides = 3·5 cm.

It is clear from the figure given in front that the difference between the lengths of the parallel sides is (10 − 6·5) cm. = 3·5 cm. Therefore we shall take the following steps to construct the required trapezium.

STEPS : 1. Take a line-segment AB = 10 cm. and cut off BE = 3·5 cm. out of it.

2. With centre E and radius = 3·5 cm. draw an arc.

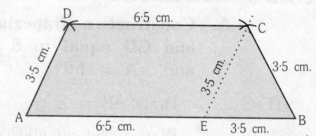

3. Again with centre B and the same radius draw another arc that cuts the previous arc at C.

4. Join BC and EC.

5. Now with centre C and radius = 6·5 cm. draw an arc.

6. Again, with A as centre and radius = 3·5 cm. draw another arc that cuts the previous arc at D.

7. Join CD and AD to complete the trapezium.

ABCD is the required trapezium.   *Q.E.F.*

PRACTICE EXERCISES 35

A. Write *true* or *false* against each statement :

1. A rhombus is an oblique square.
2. A square is an equilateral parallelogram.
3. A trapezium is a type of rhombus.
4. A kite is made up of two unequal isosceles $\triangle$s.
5. The diagonals of a rhombus bisect each other at $90°$.
6. The diagonals of a rectangle bisect each other at $90°$.
7. An isosceles trapezium has its parallel side equal.
8. The opposite sides of a parallelogram are equal and parallel.

B. Construct a *parallelogram ABCD* whose—

9. side AB = 6 cm, side BC = 4·5 and diagonal AC = 6·8 cm.
10. side AB = 5·2 cm. and its diagonals are 6 cm. and 6·4 cm. respectively.
11. diagonals are 5·4 cm. and 6·2 cm. respectively and one of the angles between them = $60°$.
12. side AB = 4 cm, side BC = 5·2 cm. and $\angle B = 75°$

C. Construct a *rectangle ABCD* whose—

13. side AB = 4·5 cm, side BC = 3·2 cm.
14. side AB = 4·8 cm. and the diagonal AC = 5·5 cm.

D. Construct a *square ABCD* whose—

15. side = 5 cm.
16. diagonal = 7 cm.

E. Construct a *rhombus* whose—

17. side AB = 5·2 cm. and an angle = $60°$.
18. side BC = 4·8 cm. and diagonal BC = 6 cm.
19. diagonals AC and BD are 7 cm. and 5 cm. long respectively.

F. Construct a *trapezium* whose—

20. parallel sides AB and CD are 6·2 cm. and 4 cm. respectively, AD = 3·5 cm. and $\angle A = 50$.
21. parallel sides AB and CD are 6·7 cm. and 10 cm. and each of the non-parallel sides = 3·3 cm.

19 SIMILARITY OF TRIANGLES

SIMILAR AND CONGRUENT FIGURES

The word—**similar**—refers to *shape* but **not size**.

We read about **congruence** in the previous book of this series. Two *congruent figures* have the same *shape* as well as *size*. But two *similar figures* **resemble in shape**. They may or may not be equal in size. Thus we can say that—

1. Two congruent figures are similar also.

2. Two similar figures are not essentially congruent.

The figures given below clarify the difference between *congruent* and *similar* figures.

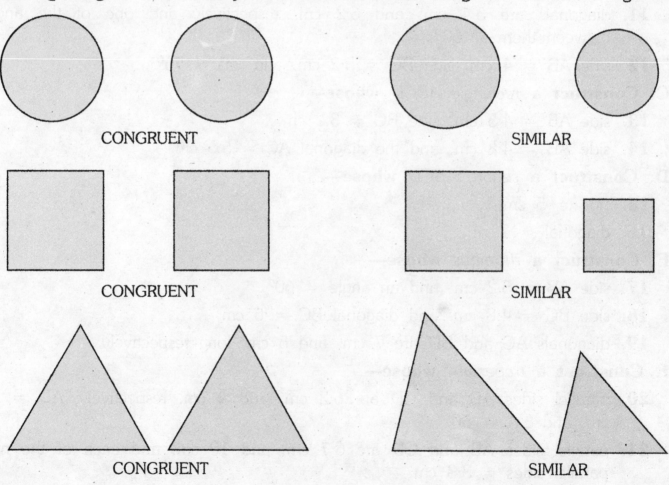

CONGRUENT   SIMILAR

CONGRUENT   SIMILAR

CONGRUENT   SIMILAR

It is clear from the above figures that if two figures are congruent, either of them can be super-imposed on the other. **Both of them will coincide with each other**—*part to part*.

But if two figures are similar, they **will not coincide** when one is super-imposed on the other.

Thus we see that similarity is based on the following two factors :

1. **To get a similar figure of a small figure, it is to be enlarged.**
2. **To get a similar figure of a large figure, it is to be diminished.**

SIMILARITY OF POLYGONS

Two polygons are said to be similar, if—

(a) **they have their corresponding angles equal.**

(b) **they have their corresponding sides proportional.**

Similar Circles

So, it is clear that—

1. Two squares are always similar.
2. Two circles are always similar.
3. Two equilateral triangles are always similar.

Similar Equilateral Triangles

Similar Squares

The word—**porportional**—means *to be in the same ratio.*

Two triangles ABC and PQR are similar if—

(a) $\angle A = \angle P$, $\angle B = Q$ and $\angle C = \angle R$

(b) $\dfrac{AB}{PQ} = \dfrac{AC}{PR} = \dfrac{BC}{QR}$

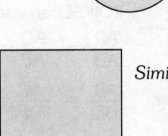

The symbol used to express similarity is (~).
It is read as : **is similar to**.

CASES OF SIMILARITY OF TRIANGLES

Just as there are *three general cases of the congruency of triangles,* there are **three case of similarity** of ∆s also.

Graded Maths-Part-8

CASE 1 — EQUIANGULAR △S ARE SIMILAR.

This case is called **AAA similarity** or **AA similarity** because if two angles of a △ are equal to two corresponding angles of another triangle each to each, their third angles are bound to be equal as the sum of the angles is to be 180° in either case.

Given : △ ABC and DEF are equiangular, *i.e.* $\angle A = \angle D$, $\angle B = \angle E$ and $\angle C = \angle F$

To prove : $\dfrac{AB}{DE} = \dfrac{AC}{DF} = \dfrac{BC}{EF}$, *i.e.* $\triangle ABC \sim \triangle DEF$

Const. : Out of AB, mark off AP = DE and out of AC, mark off AQ = DF. Join PQ

In △s APQ and DEF

AP = DE, AQ = DF   ......*(const.)*

cont. $\angle A$ = cont $\angle D$ ....*(given)*

∴   △ APQ ≅ △ DEF

∴ $\angle 1 = \angle E$ = corr. $\angle B$ ∵ ....($\angle B = \angle E$ ....*given*)

∴   PQ ∥ BC and so PQ will divide AB and AC in the same ratio.

∴ $\dfrac{AP}{AB} = \dfrac{AQ}{AC}$ or $\dfrac{AB}{AP} = \dfrac{AC}{AQ}$

or $\dfrac{AB}{DE} = \dfrac{AC}{DF}$ $(\because AP=DE,\ AQ=DF)$

Similarly we can prove that $\dfrac{AB}{DE} = \dfrac{BC}{EF}$

Hence $\dfrac{AB}{DE} = \dfrac{AC}{DF} = \dfrac{BC}{EF}$

or   △ **ABC** ∼ △ **DEF**

CASE 2 — ALL THE THREE SIDES ARE PROPORTIONAL

This case of similarity is called **SSS similarity**

Given : △ ABC and △ DEF are such that—

$$\dfrac{AB}{DE} = \dfrac{AC}{DF} = \dfrac{BC}{EF}$$

To prove : △s are similar.

Const. : Make $\angle 1 = \angle B$ and $\angle 2 = \angle C$ on EF on the opposite side of D. Let A take the position of P.

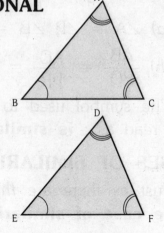

162

Proof : In Δ ABC and Δ PEF

$\angle B = \angle 1$, $\angle C = \angle 2$ ....*(const.)*

∴ Third $\angle A$ must be equal to $\angle P$

∴ Δ ABC and Δ PEF are similar

∴ $\dfrac{AB}{EP} = \dfrac{AC}{FP} = \dfrac{BC}{EF}$

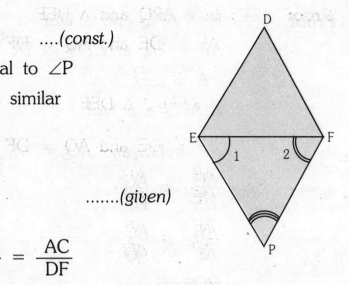

But $\dfrac{AB}{DE} = \dfrac{AC}{DF} = \dfrac{BC}{EF}$ ....*(given)*

∴ $\dfrac{AB}{EP} = \dfrac{AB}{DE}$ and $\dfrac{AC}{FP} = \dfrac{AC}{DF}$

∴ EP = DE and FP = DF   ....*(proved)*

Now in Δs PEF and DEF

EP = DE ; FP = DF   ....*(proved)*

and EF = EF   ....*(common)*

∴ Δ DEF ≅ Δ PEF

But Δ ABC and Δ PEF are equiangular

∴ Δ ABC and Δ DEF are also equiangular

Hence, Δ **ABC** ~ Δ **DEF**

CASE 3 **ANGLE = ANGLE AND CONTAINING SIDES PROPORTIONAL**

In this case, one angle of one triangle is equal to the corresponding angle of the other triangle and the sides containing these equal angles are proportional. This case of similarity is called **SAS similarity**.

Given : Δs ABC and DEF in which

$\angle A = \angle D$ and $\dfrac{AB}{DE} = \dfrac{AC}{DF}$

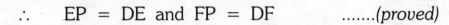

To prove : Δ ABC ~ Δ DEF

Const. : Out of AB, mark off AP = DE
Out of AC, mark off AQ = DF.
Join PQ.

Proof : In $\triangle$ APQ and $\triangle$ DEF

$$AP = DE \text{ and } AQ = DF \qquad ....(const.)$$

$$\angle A = \angle D \qquad\qquad ....(given)$$

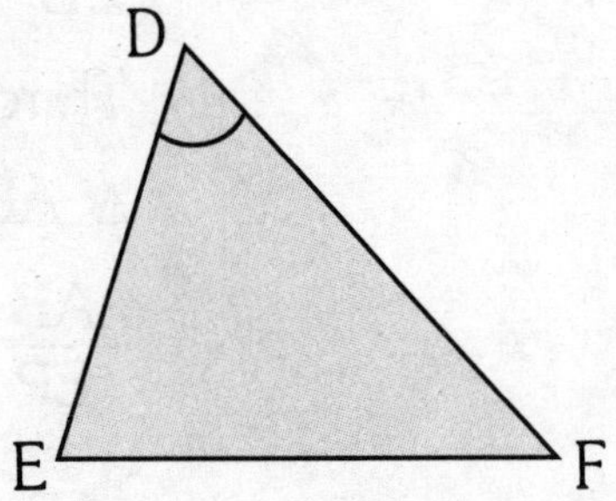

$\therefore \qquad \triangle$ APQ $\cong$ $\triangle$ DEF

$\therefore \qquad AP = DE$ and $AQ = DF$

Now, $\dfrac{AB}{DE} = \dfrac{AC}{DF} \qquad ....(given)$

$\therefore \qquad \dfrac{AB}{AP} = \dfrac{AC}{AQ} \qquad (\because AP=DE,\ AQ=DF\ .....\ proved)$

$\therefore \qquad$ PQ $\parallel$ BC

$\therefore \qquad \angle 1 = \angle B$ and $\angle 2 = \angle C$

$\therefore \qquad \triangle$ ABC and $\triangle$ APQ are equiangular.

Hence $\triangle$ ABC and $\triangle$ DEF are also equiangular.

$\therefore \qquad$ Their corresponding sides are proportional

$\therefore \qquad \triangle$ **ABC** ~ $\triangle$ **DEF**

PRACTICE EXERCISES 36

A. Answer :

1. Are any two equilateral triangles always similar ? ....
2. Are any two squares always similar ? ....
3. Are any two circles always similar ? ....
4. Are two rectangles always similar ? ....
5. Are two parallelograms always similar ? ....
6. Are two congruent triangles similar also ? ....
7. Are two similar triangle congruent also ? ....

B. 8. What are the two features of two similar figures :

(a) ....

(b) ....

9. Which two steps can be taken to draw a figure similar to a given figure ?

(a) ....

(b) ....

C. Define—

10. similarity
11. congruence
12. SSS similarity
13. AAA similarity
14. SAS similarity :

D. 15. Given on the right is a figure with measurements. Observe it carefully and find which two triangles are similar ? Also find the values of x and y.

16. A photographer prepared my photograph that was 10 cm. × 8 cm. I asked him to reduce it so that its width is only 5 cm. What will be the length of the new photograph ?

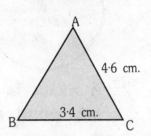

8 cm   4 cm

17. Two triangles ABC and PQR are similar and some of their sides are as under :

BC = 3·4 cm. CA = 4·6 cm.

PQ = 4·8 cm. QR = 5·1 cm.

Find AB and PR.

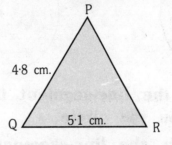

18. A vertical pole is 20 metres high. It casts a shadow 15 metres in length. Not away from it is a tower that casts a shadow 72 metres long. How high is the tower ?

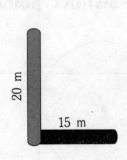
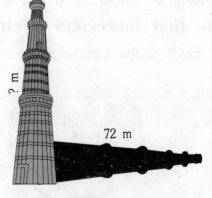

19. Given in front is a △ ABC in which DE is drawn parallel to BC. If AD = 4 cm, BD = 6 cm, AC = 12 cm. find AE and CE.

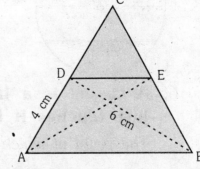

20 CIRCLES—I

> *KNOW THESE TERMS :*
> 1. **circle**—an endless curve equidistant from a central point
> 2. **radius**—distance of the curve of a circle from its centre
> 3. **diameter**—line-segment that is double the radius and passes through the centre
> 4. **secant**—line-segment intersecting the circle at two distinct points
> 5. tangent—line-segment that runs just touching a circle at one point only

We already know some basic facts about circles. Let us review them.

1. **A *circle* is an endless curved path made up of all those points in a plane each of which is at the same distance from a point lying inside the circle and called its *centre*.**

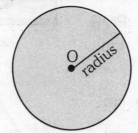
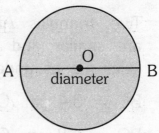

2. **A *radius* is the line-segment that joins the centre of a circle with any point on the circle.**

3. **A *diameter* is the line-saegment that passes through the centre of a circle and has its end-points on the circle.**

4. **A *chord* line-segment having its end-points on the circle.**

   A diameter is the longest chord of a circle.

5. **A *secant* is a line that intersects a circle at two distinct points.**

   A chord produced both ways becomes a secant.

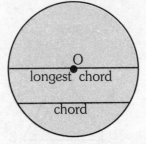
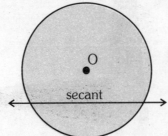
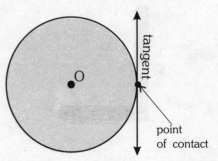

6. **A *tangent* is a line that meets a circle just at one point, *i.e.* that just touches it from outside.**

   *The point at which the tangent touches the circle is the **point of contact**.*

7. **An** *arc* **is the part of a circle marked off by any two points on it.**

(a) *An arc less than a semicircle is called a* **minor arc,**

(b) *An arc larger than a semicircle is called a* **major arc,**

(c) *The sign used for an arc is (⌢) eg.* $\overset{\frown}{AB}$.

8. **A** *sector* **is the region inside a circle which is bounded by an arc and two radii joining the centre with the ends of the arc.**

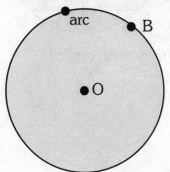 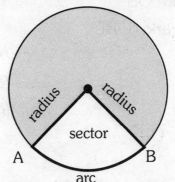 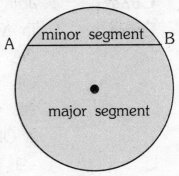

9. **A** *segment* **is a part of the region inside a circle :**

(a) *A segment smaller than half the entire region inside a circle is called a* **minor segment.**

(b) *A segment larger than half the entire region inside a circle is called a* **major segment.**

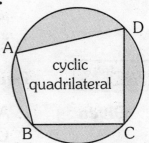

10. **A** *cyclic quadrilateral* **is the quadrilateral that lies inside a circle and has each of its four vertices on the circle.**

FACTS ABOUT CHORDS

FACT 1 **The perpendicular drawn from the centre of a circle to a chord bisects the chord.**

Given : A circle with centre O and a chord AB drawn in it. Also OL ⊥ AB

To prove : AL = BL

Const. : Join OA and OB

Proof : In rt. Δs OLA and OLB

Hyp. OA = Hyp OB   ....(*radii of the same circle*)

Side OL = side OL   ....(*common*)

∴   Δ OLA ≅ Δ OLB

∴   **AL = BL**

FACT 2	The line joining the centre of a circle to the mid-point of a chord is perpendicular to it.

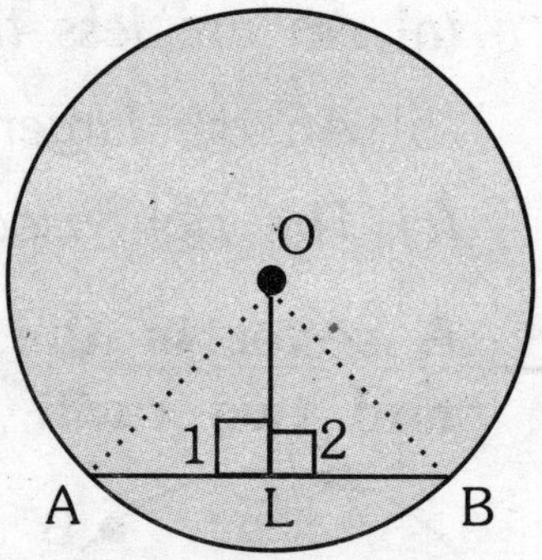

Given : A circle with centre O and a chord AB in it. L, the mid-point of AB is joined to O.

To prove : OL is perpendicular AB

Const. : Join OA and OB

Proof : In $\triangle$s OAL and OBL

OA = OB   ....(radii of the same circle)

OL = OL   ....(common)

AL = BL   ....(given)

$\therefore$ $\triangle$ OLA $\cong$ $\triangle$ OLB

$\therefore$ $\angle 1 = \angle 2$

But $\angle 1$ and $\angle 2$ are together 180°

$\therefore$ each of them is = 90°

Hence **OL is perpendicular to AB.**

FACT 3	Equal chords of a circle are equidistant from its centre.

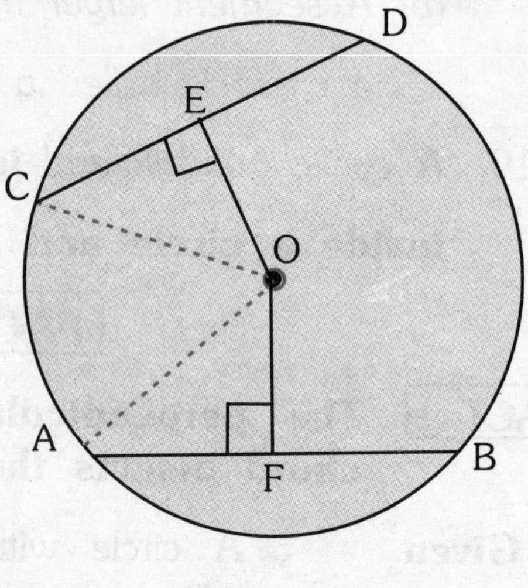

Given : A circle with centre O. AB and CD are two equal chords in it. OE $\perp$ CD and OF $\perp$ AB

To prove : OE = OF

Const. : Join OA and OC

Proof $\therefore$: AB is a chord and OF $\perp$ AB

$\therefore$ OF bisects AB, i.e. AF = — AB

Similarly CE = ½ CD

But, ½ AB = ½ CD   .....($\because AB = CD$)

or   AF = CE   .....($\because CE = ½ CD$)

Now in rt. $\triangle$s OAF and OCE

Hyp. OA = Hyp. OC   .....(radii of the same circle)

side AF = CE   .....(proved above)

$\therefore$ $\triangle$ OAF $\cong$ $\triangle$ OCE

$\therefore$ **OE = OF**

| FACT 4 | **Chords of a circle equidistant from the centre are equal.** |

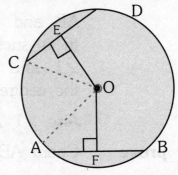

Given : A circle with centre O. AB and CD are two chords in it such that OF ⊥ AB = OE ⊥ CD

To prove : AB = CD

Const. : Join OA and OC

Proof : In rt. Δs OAF and OCE

Hyp. OA = Hyp. OC   .....*(radii of the same circle)*

side OF = side OE   .....*(given)*

∴   Δ OAF ≅ Δ OCE

∴   AF = CE

But   AF = ½ AB because OF being ⊥ AB from the centre bisects it

Similarly CE = ½ CD

∴   2AF = 2CE or **AB = CD**

| FACT 5 | **Equal chords of a circle subtend equal angles at the centre.** |

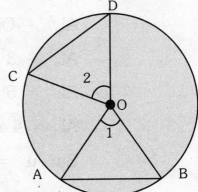

Given : A circle with centre O. AB, CD are two equal chords in it. AB subtends ∠1 at the centre and CD subtends ∠2.

To prove : ∠1 = ∠2

Proof : In Δs OAB and OCD

OA = OC   *(radii of the same circle)*

OB = OD   *(radii of the same circle)*

AB = CD   *(given)*

∴   Δ OAB ≅ Δ OCD

∴   **∠1 = ∠2**

| FACT 6 | **Chords of a circle that subtend equal angles at the centre are equal to each other.** |

Given : A circle with centre O.

AB and CD are two chords in it such that they subtend $\angle 1$ and $\angle 2$ respectively at the centre.

Also $\angle 1 = \angle 2$

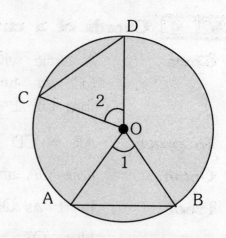

To prove : Chord AB = chord CD

Proof : In $\triangle$s OAB and OCD

OA = OC ....(*radii of the same circle*)

OB = OD ....(*radii of the same circle*)

cont. $\angle 1$ = cont. $\angle 2$ ....(*given*)

$\therefore \quad \triangle$ OAB $\cong \triangle$ OCD

$\therefore \quad$ **AB = CD**

PRACTICE EXERCISES 37

1. AB is a chord of a circle with centre O. OL is drawn perpendicular to AB. If OL = 3 cm. and radius OA = 5 cm. Find the length of the chord AB.

Hint : OAL is a rt. $\triangle$

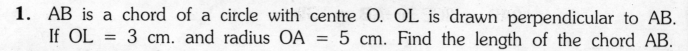

$AL^2 + OL^2 = OA^2$

$AL^2 + 3^2 = 5^2$

or $AL^2 = 5^2 - 3^2 = 25 - 9 = 16 = 4^2$

AL = 4 cm. $\because$

But AL $= \frac{1}{2}$ AB or AB = 2 × AL ....(OL $\perp$ AB from the centre)

$= 2 \times 4 =$ **8 cm.** *Ans.*

2. PQ is a chord in a circle with centre O. If the radius OP is 10 cm long and PQ = 16 cm. long, find OA the distance of the chord PQ from the centre.

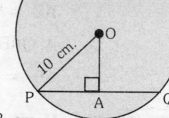

Hint : OPA is a rt triangle and PA = $\frac{1}{2}$ PQ = 8 cm.

$\therefore OA^2 = 10^2 - 8^2 = 100 - 64 = 36$ or OA = 6 cm.

3. A chord AB of a circle is 16 cm. in length and is at a distance of 6 cm. from the centre. Another chord of the same circle is at a distance of 8 cm. from the centre. How long is this chord.

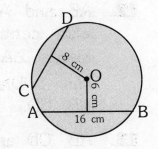

4. P, Q, R are three points on a circle whose centre is not shown. How will you find its centre ?

Hint : Join chords PQ and QR and draw their right bisectors. The point where these bisectors intersect is the centre of the circle.

5. Two circles with centres P and Q intersect at A and B such that AB is their common chord. L is the mid-point of AB. Answer :

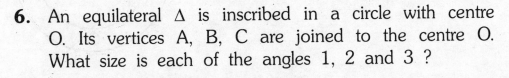

(a) What size is ∠ALP ?

(b) What size is ∠ALQ ?

(c) Are A, L, B in the same straight line ?

    Hint : AB is the common chord and L is its mid-point.

    ∴   PL is perpendicular to AB and also QL is perpendicular to AB

    ∴   All the three results follow.

6. An equilateral △ is inscribed in a circle with centre O. Its vertices A, B, C are joined to the centre O. What size is each of the angles 1, 2 and 3 ?

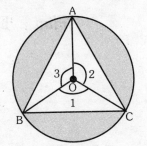

7. A square ABCD is inscribed in a circle with centre O. Its vertices are joined to the centre O. What size is each of ∠1, ∠2, ∠3 and ∠4 ?

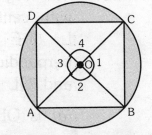

8. A regular hexagon is inscribed in a circle with centre O. What angle does each of its sides subtend at the centre ?

9. A regular polygon is inscribed in a circle with centre O. If each of its sides subtends an angle of 40° at the centre, how many sides has it ?

10. A regular polygon is inscribed in a circle. Each of its sides subtends an angle of 72° at the centre. How many sides has the polygon ?

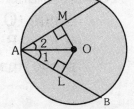

11. AB and AC are two equal chords of a circle with centre O. OA is joined and OL and OM are drawn perpendiculars to AB and AC respectively. Prove that OA bisects ∠A, *i.e.* ∠1 = ∠2.

12. AB and AC are two chords of a circle with centre O. If the diameter AOD bisects ∠A, prove that AB = AC.

Hint : Draw OL, OM perpendiculars to AB, CD.

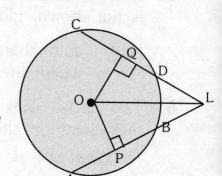

13. AB, CD are two equal chords of a circle with centre O. When produced outside the circle, the chords meet in L. OP is drawn perpendicular to AB and OQ to CD.

(a) Is OP = OQ ?   *(b)* Is PL = QL ?

(c) Is AL = CL ?   *(d)* Is △ OPL ≅ △ OQL ?

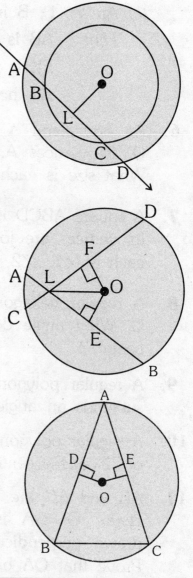

14. Two concentric circles are intersected by a line at A, B, C and D as shown in front. Prove that AB = CD

Hint : Draw OL perpendicular to the line.

15. Two equal chords AB, CD of a circle with centre O intersect inside the circle at L. OE and OF have been drawn perpendiculars to AB and CD respectively and OL is joined.

(a) Is OE = OF ?   *(b)* Is EL = FL ?

(c) Is BL = DL ?   *(d)* Is △ OLE ≅ △ OLF.

16. A triangle ABC is inscribed in a circle with centre O. OD is drawn perpendicular to its side AB and OE to AC. If OE = OD, prove that the △ is isosceles.

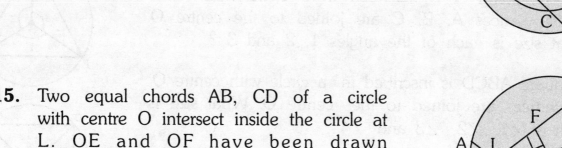

THE CENTRAL ANGLE

The *central angle* of a circle is the angle that has its vertex at the centre of the circle.

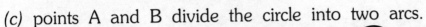

(a) ∠ AOB in the adjoining figure is the central angle of the circle.

(b) the part of the circle marked off by points A and B is the **intercepted arc**.

(c) points A and B divide the circle into two arcs.

(d) Both the arcs can be named arc AB (⌢AB).

(e) The arc intercepted by the angle is a **minor arc** because it is smaller than a semi-circle. It is in the **interior of the angle.**

(f) The remaining arc is larger than a semi-circle and it lies in the **exterior of the angle.**

(g) Points A and B are common to both the arcs.

(h) **Minor ⌢AB** subtends acute ∠O (∠1) at the centre

(i) **Major ⌢AB** subtends reflex ∠O (∠2) at the centre.

(j) Clearly the angle subtended by the major AB is larger than the angle subtended by the minor AB at the centre.

(k) If two arcs subtend equal angles at the centre, they are congruent.

So, we can compare two arcs of a circle using the angles subtended by them at the centre.

DEGREE MEASURE OF AN ARC

(a) The angular measure **of a circle** is 360° because the circle is an endless arc and it subtends an angle of 360° at the centre.

(b) The degree measure of a **semi-circle** is 360° ÷ 2 = 180° at the centre.

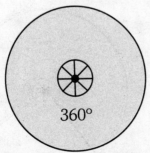

360°

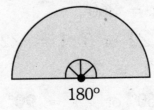

180°

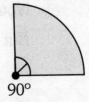

90°

(c) The degree measure of a **quarter circle** is 360° ÷ 4 = 90° at the centre.

(d) Similarly every arc has a **degree measure**. It is equal to the angle subtended by it at the centre. We write it as $m\widehat{\mathbf{AB}}$ and read it as *measure of arc AB.*

If arc AB is *minor*, we write its degree as m (minor $\widehat{AB}$)

If the arc AB is *major*, we write its degree as m (major $\widehat{AB}$)

Let us now solve some examples :

Example 1 : In the adjoining figure $\widehat{AOB}$ is a diameter and OC is a radius.

If $\angle BOC = 50°$, find—

    (a) $m(\widehat{AB})$ *(b)* $m(\widehat{AC})$ *(c)* m(Major $\widehat{BAC}$)

Solution : $m(\widehat{BC})$ = angle subtended by it at O.

It is given to be 50°

(a) $\widehat{AB}$ is a semicircle

     angle subtended by it is 180°

     So, $m(\widehat{AB})$ = **180°**

(b) $m(\widehat{AC})$ = $m(\widehat{AB})$ – $m(\widehat{BC})$

          = 180° – 50° = **130°**

(c) m(major $\widehat{BAC}$) = 360° – $m(\widehat{BC})$

          = 360° – 50° = **310°** *Ans.*

Example 2 : Two points on a circle mark off a minor and a major arc. The degree measure of the minor arc is one-third of that of the major arc. Find the measure of either arc.

Solution :   Let A and B be the two points on the circle. Then measure of minor $\widehat{AB}$ = $\angle 1$ and measure of major $\widehat{AB}$ = $\angle 2$

Now $\angle 1 + \angle 2 = 360°$

But $\angle 1$ is $\dfrac{1}{3} \angle 2$ or $3\angle 1 = \angle 2$

     $\angle 1 + 3\angle 1 = 360°$

or $4\angle 1 = 360°$ or $\angle 1 =$ **90°**

     So, m (minor AB) = 90°

and m (major AB) = 90° × 3 = **270°**

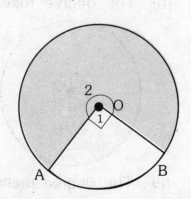

PRACTICE EXERCISES 38

1. AB is a diameter of a circle with centre O and OC is a radius of the circle. If angle AOC = 80°, find the degree measures of $\overarc{AC}$, $\overarc{BC}$ and $\overarc{ABC}$,

2. AB is a minor arc of a circle with centre O. If the degree measure of minor $\overarc{AB}$ be 72°, find m(major $\overarc{AB}$)

3. Two points on a circle divide it into a minor arc and a major arc. If the degree measure of the major arc be five times the degree measure of the minor arc, find the measure of each arc.

4. MN is a diameter and OC is radius of a circle with centre O. If angle MOC = 60°, find—

   (a) m (minor $\overarc{MC}$)   (b) m (major $\overarc{NC}$)   (c) m ($\overarc{MNC}$)

5. In a circle, the degree measure of a major arc is four times the degree measure of the minor arc. Find the measures of both the arcs.

6. AB and CD are two chords of a circle with centre O. If m(minor $\overarc{AB}$ = m(minor $\overarc{CD}$) prove that chord AB = chord CD.

7. In the adjoining figure AB and CD are two diameters of a circle with centre O. If $m(\overarc{AD})$ = 110°, find—

   (a) m(minor $\overarc{AC}$)   (b) m(minor $\overarc{BD}$)

   (c) m(minor $\overarc{BC}$)

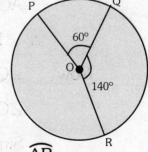

8. In the figure given in front, OP, OQ and OR are three radii of the circle such that angle POQ = 60° and angle QOR = 140°, find—

   (a) m(major $\overarc{PQ}$)   (b) m(major $\overarc{QR}$)

   (c) m(major $\overarc{PR}$)   (d) m(minor $\overarc{PR}$)

9. P is a point on a minor $\overarc{AB}$ of a circle with centre O. If $m(\overarc{AB})$ = 120° and $m(\overarc{AP})$ = 75°, find $m(\overarc{PB})$

10. Given a minor $\overarc{AB}$ of a circle with centre O. Bisect minor $\overarc{AB}$.

    Hint : We have to find a point P on $\overarc{AB}$ such that $m\,\overarc{AP}$ = $m\,\overarc{BP}$

11. Two points on a circle mark off a minor arc and a major arc. If the measures of both the arcs be in the ratio 3 : 4, find the degree measure of each arc.

INSCRIBED ANGLES

An angle is said to be **inscribed** in a circle if its vertex lies on the circle and either of its two arms meet/intersect the circle at two distinct points.

The figures given below show several inscribed angles.

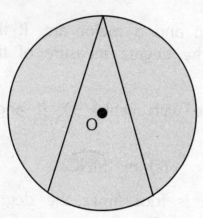 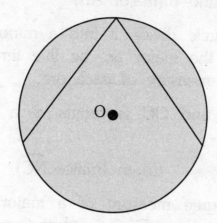 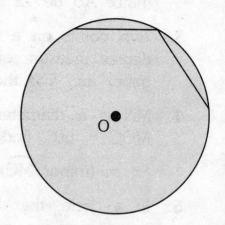

Let us now study some facts about inscribed angles.

FACT 1 | **The angle subtended by an arc of a circle at its centre is double the angle subtended by it at any point on the remaining part of the circle.**

Given : $\overarc{AB}$ subtends $\angle AOB$ at the centre and it subtends $\angle P$ on the remaining part of the O

To prove : $\angle P = \dfrac{1}{2} \angle AOB$

Const. : Join PO and produce it such that it meets the circle at Q.

Proof : In $\triangle$ AOP

$\qquad$ AO = OP $\qquad$ .....(radii)

$\qquad \therefore \angle 1 = \angle 2$

Now $\qquad \angle QOA$ is an exterior angle of $\triangle AOP$

$\qquad \angle QOA = \angle 1 + \angle 2 = 2\angle 1$

$\qquad$ Similarly $\angle QOB = 2\angle 3$

$\qquad \angle QOA + \angle QOB = 2\angle 1 + 2\angle 3$

$\qquad \angle AOB = 2\ (\angle 1 + \angle 3) = 2\angle P$

$\qquad$ **Hence $\angle P = \dfrac{1}{2} \angle AOB$**

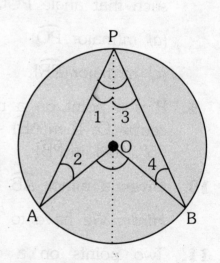

| FACT 2 | **An angle inscribed in a semi-circle is a right angle.**

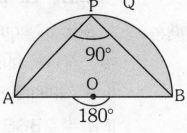

Given : A circle with centre O. Diameter AOB is drawn. P is a point on the circle and it is joined to A and B to form ∠APB.

To Prove : ∠APB = 180° × ½ = 90°

Proof : AOB is the diameter

AB subtends ∠AOB at the centre O.

But it is a straight angle

∴ ∠AOB = 180°

Now AB subtends ∠APB on the circle

∠APB = ½ ∠AOB

or   ∠APB = 180° × ½ = 90°

Let us now solve some examples based on these two facts.

Example 1 : **ΔABC is inscribed in a circle with centre O and its side BC passes through O. If ∠ACB = 30°, find ∠A and ∠B.**

Solution : BC passes through the centre O

BOC is a diameter

∠BAC is an angle in the semi-circle

∴   ∠BAC = **90°**

∴   ∠C = 30°

But ∠B + ∠BAC + ∠C = 180°

or   ∠B + 90° + 30° = 180° or ∠B = 180 – 90° – 30° = **60°**

Hence ∠A = **90°** and ∠B = **60° Ans.**

Example 2. ABC is an equilateral triangle inscribed in a circle with centre O. Find ∠BOC.

Solution : Δ ABC is equilateral with each of its angles = 60°

So, ∠A = 60°

It is subtended by $\overset{\frown}{BC}$ on the circle.

∴ It is $\frac{1}{2}$ ∠BOC that is subtended at the centre by $\overset{\frown}{BC}$

or ∠BOC = 2 ∠A = 2 × 60° = **120°** *Ans.*

PRACTICE EXERCISES 39

A. In each of the following figures, find the value of *x* if O is the centre of the circle :

1.   **2.**   **3.**

B. 4. Δ ABC is inscribed in a circle with centre O. Find ∠C if ∠B = 40° and BC is a diameter.

Hint : ∠BAC = 90° as it is an angle in a semi-circle

5. In a circle with centre O, AOB is the diameter and CD is a chord. AC and OD are joined. If ∠BOD = 80° find ∠ACD.

Hint : ∠ACD = $\frac{1}{2}$ ∠AOD

6. A circle with centre O has a chord BC which is equal to its radius in length. A is any point on the circle. Find ∠BAC.

Hint : ∠BOC = 60° as OB = OC = BC

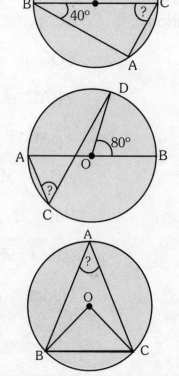

7. Δ ABC is inscribed in a circle with centre O such that side BC of the triangle is a diameter of the circle. If ∠B = 48°, find ∠C.

   Hint : ∠A = 90° as it is in a semi-circle.

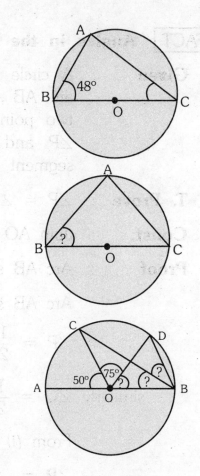

8. A circle with centre O in which BOC is a diameter and chord AB = Chord AC. Find ∠ABC.

   Hint : ∠A = 90° and ∠B = ∠C as AB = AC

9. In a circle with centre O, AOB is the diameter and there are two arcs AC and CD on the same side of the diameter. OC, OD, BC and BD have been joined. If $m(\widehat{AC}) = 50°$ and $m(\widehat{CD}) = 75°$, find the following angles :

   (a) ∠BOD   (b) ∠ABC   (c) ∠CBD

   Hint : ∠BOD = 180° – 50° – 75°

   ∠ABC = ½ ∠COA and ∠CBD = ½ ∠COD

10. Two circles with centres P, Q intersect each other at A and B. APL and AQM are respective diameters. Prove that the points L, B and M are collinear.

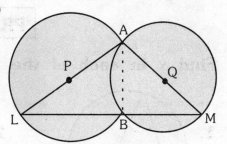

   Hint : Join the common chord AB. ∠LBA = 90°

   and ∠MBA = 90°   ......(∠s in semi = circles)

   ∴   They are together = 180°

   ∴   LBM is a st. line

11. Trapezium ABCD is inscribed in a circle and its diagonal AC is joined. Prove that $m(\widehat{AD}) = m(\widehat{BC})$

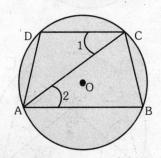

   Hint : ∠1 = alt. ∠2

ANGLES IN THE SAME SEGMENT

The angles subtended by one and the same arc at two different points on the circle are said to be *angles in the same segment.*

179

FACT **Angles in the same segment of a circle are equal.**

Given : A circle with centre O in which arc AB subtends two angles at two points P, Q respectively, *i.e.* ∠P and ∠Q are in the same segment.

T. Prove : ∠P = ∠Q

Const. : Join AO and BO

Proof : Arc AB subtends, ∠AOB at the centre   .....(const.)

Arc AB subtends ∠P on the remaining part of the circle

∴ $\angle P = \frac{1}{2} \angle AOB$ ....(i)

similarly $\angle Q = \frac{1}{2} \angle AOB$ ....(ii)

From (i) and (ii)

∠P = ∠Q

PRACTICE EXERCISES 40

A. Find x in each of the following :

1.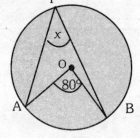

2.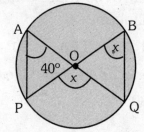

3.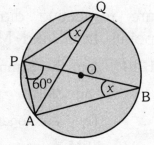

4.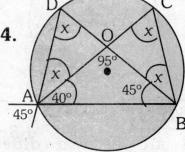

5.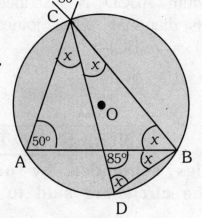

180

B. 6. Two chords AB and CD meet each other at P when produced outside the circle. AD and BC are joined. If ∠P = 45° and ∠BCP = 30°. Find ∠ADP.

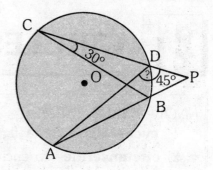

Hint : ∠A = ∠C = 30°

∠ADP = 180° – 30° – 45°

7. Δ ABC is inscribed in a circle and AD is drawn perpendicular to BC. It meets the diameter BC at D. AD, when produced, meets the circle at E.

If ∠ABC = 40°, find ∠ECD

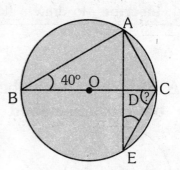

Hint : ∠E = ∠B = 40°   ....(∠s in the same segment)

∠D = 90°

∴ ∠ECD = 180° – 40° – 90°

8. A circle with centre O and ∠ABC is drawn in it in a semi-circle. B and C are joined to a point D on the other side of the diameter AOC. If ∠BDC = 40°, find ∠BCA.

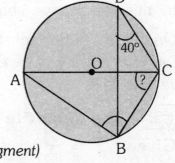

Hint : ∠A = ∠D = 40°   ....(∠s in the same segment)

∠ABC = 90°   ....(∠ in a semi-circle)

∴ ∠BCA = 180° – 40° – 90°

9. The extremities of two diameters AB, CD of a circle with centre O are joined. If ∠BAC = 45°. Find ∠ABD

Hint : ∠BDC = ∠BAC   ....(same segment)

= ∠ABD   .....(∵ radius OB = radius OD)

21 CIRCLES—II

CYCLIC FIGURES

A figure is said to be **cyclic** if **its vertices lie on a circle** *i.e,* **if a circle can be circumscribed round it touching its vertices.**

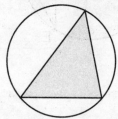 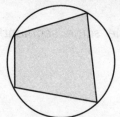 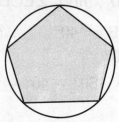 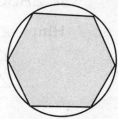

| Cyclic Triangle | Cyclic Quadrilateral | Cyclic Pentagon | Cyclic Hexagon |

In this lesson, we shall study **cyclic quadrilaterals.**

One very important fact about cyclic quadrilaterals is that their opposite angles are supplementary, *i.e.* each pair of opposite angles adds up to be 180°. Let us prove this fact.

FACT **The opposite angles of a cyclic quadrilateral are supplementary.**

Given : A cyclic quadrilateral ABCD

To Prove : $\angle A + \angle C = 180°$ and
$\angle B + \angle D = 180°$

Const. : Join AC and BD

Proof : AB is an arc. It subtends $\angle 1$ and $\angle 2$ in the same segment
∴ $\angle 1 = \angle 2$ ....(i)
Again BC is an arc and it subtends $\angle 3$ and $\angle 4$ in the same segment
∴ $\angle 3 = \angle 4$ ....(ii)
Adding (i) and (ii)
$\angle 1 + \angle 3 = \angle 2 + \angle 4 = \angle ADC$ .....($\angle 2 + \angle 4 = \angle ADC$)

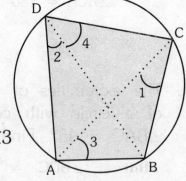

Adding ∠ABC to both sides—

$$∠1 + ∠3 + ∠ABC = ∠ADC + ∠ABC$$ ∵

But   ∠1 + ∠3 + ∠ABC = 180°   .....(∠s of △ABC)

∴   **∠ADC + ∠ABC = 180°**

Similarly **∠BAD + ∠BCD = 180°**

Another Proof :

Const   : Join AO, CO

Proof   : Arc AC subtends ∠1 at the centre and ∠D on the circle

∠D = ½ ∠1

Similarly ∠B = ½ ∠2

∴   **∠B + ∠D** = ½ (∠1 + ∠2) = ½ × 360° = **180°**

Similarly **∠A + ∠C = 180°**

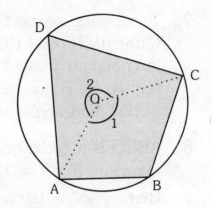

PRACTICE EXERCISES 41

A. 1. What is a *cyclic figure* ?

2. What important fact about cyclic quadrilaterals have you learnt ?

B. 3. Side AB of a cyclic quadrilateral has been produced to L. If ∠D = 120°, find ∠CBL ?

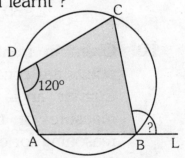

> ☞ **The exterior angle of a cyclic quadrilateral is equal to the interior opposite angle.**

4. In a cyclic quadrilateral ABCD, AD is parallel to BC. Prove that ∠A = ∠D.

Hint : Produce AB to E

∠A = ∠1   ......(corr. ∠s)

∠1 = ∠D   ......(ext. ∠ of a cyclic quad.)

∴   ∠A = ∠D

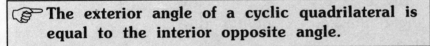
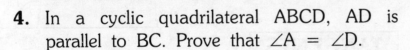

5. Two chords AB and DC of a circle are produced to meet at E outside the circle. If AE = DE, prove that AD||BC.

Hint : ∠A = ∠D   .....(∵ AE = DE)

∠1 = ∠D   .....(ext. ∠)

∴   ∠A = corr. ∠1 and AD||BC

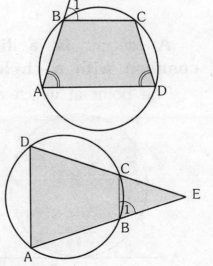

6. A cyclic parallelogram is always a rectangle or square. Is it true ?

Hint : *It is so because the opposite angles of a cyclic quadrilateral are supplementary. Rectangles and squares have all their angles = 90°. So, their opposite angle add up to be 180°.*

7. Two circles intersect each other at P and Q. Quadrilaterals PQAD and PQBC are inscribed in these circles such that D, P, C and A, Q, B are collinear. If ∠D = 85°, ∠1 = 95°, find angles x, y, z.

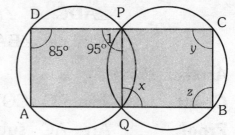

8. ABCD is a cyclic quadrilateral whose base BC is a diameter. If ∠A = 120° find ∠CBD.

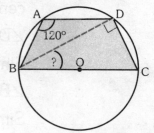

Hint : ∠C = 180° – 120° = 60°

∠BDC = 90°   .....(∠ *in a semi-circle*)

∴   ∠CBD = 180° – 60° – 90°

9. ABCD is a cyclic quadrilateral whose side AB is a diameter and ∠C = 125°. BD is joined. Find ∠ABD.

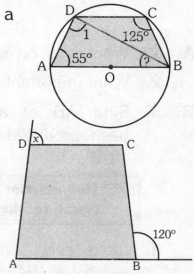

Hint : ∠A = 180° – 125° = 55° and ∠1 = 90°

∴   ∠ABD = 180° – 90° – 55°

10. Given in front is a quadrilateral whose angular points are concyclic. Side AB is produced and the exterior angle so formed is of 120°. Find the measure of the angle marked x giving due reasoning for each step.

TANGENTS

A *tangent* is a line-segment that has one and only one point in common with a circle however far it may be produced.

The point at which a tangent touches a circle is called the **point of contact**.

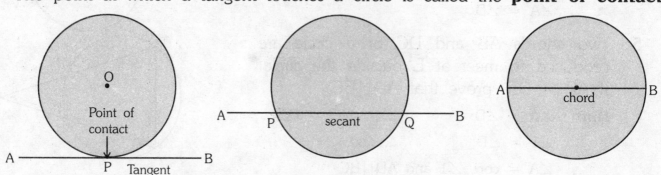

We must bear in mind the difference between a **tangent,** a **secant** and a **chord**. Remember :

1. A **tangent** touches the circle from outside at one point only.
2. A **secant** has its end-points outside the circle but it intersects the circle at two distinct points.
3. A **chord** lies inside the circle and has its two end-points on the circle itself.

COMMON TANGENT

If a tangent touches two circles—each at a point, it is called their *common tangent.*

The tangent shown in front is a common tangent to two circles with centres P and Q respectively. It touches them at A and B respectively.

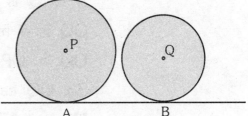

Let us study two important facts above tangents.

| FACT 1 | **The radius joining the centre of a circle to the point of contact of its tangent is perpendicular to the tangent.** |

Given : A circle with cenre O. A tangent AB is drawn to it. Pt. O is joined to L, the point of its contact.

To prove : OL ⊥ AB

Proof : If OL is not ⊥ AB, let us suppose that OQ ⊥ AB

Now Q = 90°

∴ OQ is the shortest line from O to AB

∴ It must be shorter than OL

So, Q is certainly inside the circle and OQ, when produced will cut the circle at another point.

But it is not possible at all

∴ OQ is not perpendicular to AB

Hence OL is ⊥ to AB

☞ *Note—Such a proof is called an* **Indirect Proof.**

| FACT 2 | **A line drawn through the end-point of a radius of a circle perpendicular to the radius is a tangent to the circle.** |

Given	:	A circle with centre O and OP is a radius. A line AB ⊥ OP is drawn through P.

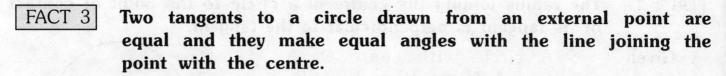

To prove : APB is a tangent.

Proof : If P is not the point of contact, let Q be another point on AB so that Q may be the point of contact,

        Now OP ⊥ AB   ....(given)

∴   Δ OPQ is a rt. Δ at P.

∴   OQ is a hypotenuse

∴   OQ > OP which is a radius

So, OQ can neither be a radius nor be the point of contact

Hence APB is a tangent.

FACT 3   **Two tangents to a circle drawn from an external point are equal and they make equal angles with the line joining the point with the centre.**

Given : A circle with centre O and a point P outside it. From P are drawn two tangents PA and PB to the circle. Also PO is joined.

To prove : (a) PA = PB

        (b) ∠1 = ∠2

Const. : Join OA and OB

Proof : ∵ OA is a radius and PA is a tangent at A

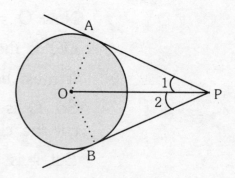

∴   ∠OAP = 90°

    Similarly ∠OBP = 90°

∴   In rt. Δs AOP and BOP

    Hyp. OP = Hyp. OP   ......(common)

    Side OA = OB   ......(radii of the same circle)

∴   ΔAOP ≅ ΔBOP

∴   **AP = BP and ∠1 = ∠2**

A. Define :

1. a *chord* **2.** a *secant* **3.** a *tangent*

B. 4. Given in front is a circle with centre O. Some line-segments are also drawn. Name—

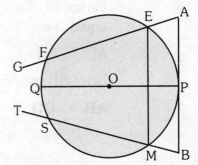

(a) a tangent : ....

(b) two secants : ...., ...

(c) a diameter : ....

(d) two chords : ...., ...

(e) point of contact : ....

C. Answer :

5. Is the diameter of a circle a chord also ?

6. Can a tangent touch a circle at two different points ?

7. Can a secant have its end-points on the circle itself ?

8. What will you do to make a secant out of a chord ?

D. 9. Given in front is a circle with centre O and APB is a tangent drawn to it at P. Find the value of ∠OPB.

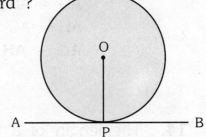

10. Prove that tangents drawn at the end-points of a diameter of a circle are parallel.

Hint : int. angles ∠1 + ∠2 = 180°

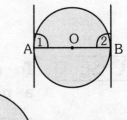

11. A circle with centre O and radius = 6 cm. is drawn. From a point P 10 cm. away from O is drawn a tangent PQ to the circle. Find the length the tangent PQ.

Hint : Δ POQ is rt. ∠d at ∠Q

Hyp. OP = 10 cm. and side OQ = 6 cm.

Now $OQ^2 + PQ^2 = OP^2$ or $6^2 + PQ^2 = 10^2$ or $PQ^2 = 10^2 - 6^2$

$= 100 - 36 = 64 = (8)^2$ or **PQ = 8 cm.** *Ans.*

12. A circle with centre O is inscribed in a quadrilateral ABCD such that its sides AB, BC, CD, DA are tangents to the circle at E, F, G, H respectively. Prove that AB + CD = BC + AD

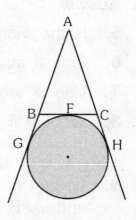

Hint : Two tangents are there from each vertex of the quadrilateral. So, they are equal, *i.e.*

AE = AH   BE = BF   CF = CG   DG = DH

Now AB = AE + BE and CD = CG + DG

∴ **AB + CD** = AE + BE + CG + DG = AH + BF + CF + DH

= (BF + CF) + (AH + DH) = **BC + AD**

13. A circle touches the side BC of a ∠ABC externally at F. Its sides AB, AC are produced and they touch the circle at G and H respectively. Prove that (AG + AH) = (AB + BC + AC)

Hint : AG = AH ; BF = BG and CF = CH

AG = AB + BG = AB + BF

AH = AC + CH = AC + CF

AG + AH = AB + BF + AC + CF

= AB + (BF + CF) + AC

= **AB + BC + AC**

14. The length of a tangent drawn to a circle from a point 20 cm. away from its centre is 16 cm. Find the radius of the circle.

DRAWING TANGENTS

CASE 1 **To draw a tangent to a circle at a point on it.**

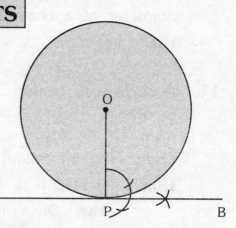

STEPS : 1. Draw the circle with the given radius.

2. Take a point P on the circle.

3. Join OP

4. At P draw BP ⊥ OP and produce it to A

5. **APB is the required tangent :**

To draw a tangent to a circle from a point outside it.

STEPS : 1. Draw the circle with the given radius.

2. Take a point P outside the circle and join OP.

4. With OP as diameter draw a semi-circle that cuts the given circle at A.

5. Join PA and produce it to B.

PAB is the reqd. tangent. *Q.E.F.*

PRACTICE EXERCISES 43

1. Draw a circle with radius 2·5 cm. Take a point P on the circle. At P draw a tangent to the circle.

2. Draw a circle with radius 3 cm. Take a point P outside it. From P draw a tangent to the circle.

3. Draw a circle with radius 2·8 cm. Take a point A outside it. From A draw two tangents to the circle.

4. In the above construction measure the two tangents. Are they equal ?

5. Draw a circle with radius 8 cm. Take a point P outside the circle at a distance of 10 cm. from the centre of the circle. From P draw two tangent to the circle. Measure the lengths of the tangents.

   (a) How long is either of them ?

   (b) Verify their lengths by calculation.

MISCELLANEOUS EXERCISES IV

A. Define :

1. *parallel straight lines*   2. *a transversal*   3. *symmetry*

4. an *intercept*   5. a *quadrilateral*   6. a *circle*   7. a *cyclic figure*

B. Prove that—

8. the line-segment joining the mid-points of any two sides of a triangle is parallel to the third side.

9. two lines perpendicular to the same line in a plane are parallel to each other

10. the figure formed by joining the mid-points of a the four sides of a quadrilateral is a parallelogram.

11. the triangle formed by joining the mid-points of the sides of a triangle has a perimeter equal to half the perimeter of the bigger triangle.

12. the line joining the centre of a circle to the mid-point of a chord is perpendicular to the chord.

13. equal chords of a circle subtend equal angles at the centre and they are equidistant from the centre.

14. the angle subtended by an arc of a circle at the centre is twice the angle subtended by it on any point on the remaining part of the circle.

15. the angle in a semi-circle is always a right angle.

16. angles in the same segment of a circle are equal.

17. sum of the opposite angles of a cyclic quadrilateral is equal to 180°.

18. two tangents drawn to a circle for an external point are equal.

C. Draw :

19. a line parallel to a given line at a distance of 3 cm. from it.

20. a line-segment = 7·6 cm. and then divide it into 6 equal parts.

21. a line-segment = 6 cm. and divide it in the ratio 3 : 4.

22. a quadrilateral ABCD whose sides BC, CD, AD are 4 cm., 5 cm. and 4·5 cm. while its diagonals AC, BD are 5·6 cm. and 6·5 cm.

23. a quadrilateral whose sides AB, BC are 4·5 cm. and 5 cm. while its ∠A = 60°, ∠B = 100° and ∠C = 120°.

24. a tangent at a point taken on a circle with radius 2·5 cm.

MEMORABLE FACTS

1. Lines parallel to the same straight line are **parallel to each other.**

2. If three parallel lines make three equal intercepts on any tranversal, they make equal intercepts on any other transversal too.

3. If three parallel lines are intercepted by two transversals, the ratio of the intercepts on one of the transversals is the same as this ratio is on the other.

4. The **opposite angles** of a **cyclic quadrilateral** are **supplementary**.

5. Equal arcs subtend **equal angles** at the centre.

6. A **cyclic figure** can have a circle passing through all its vertices.

7. Angles formed in the **same segment** of a circle are **equal.**

8. Two tangents to a circle from an external point are equal.

9. A tangent can touch a circle at one point only.

10. The point where a tangent touches a circle is called the **point of contact.**

UNIT V
MENSURATION

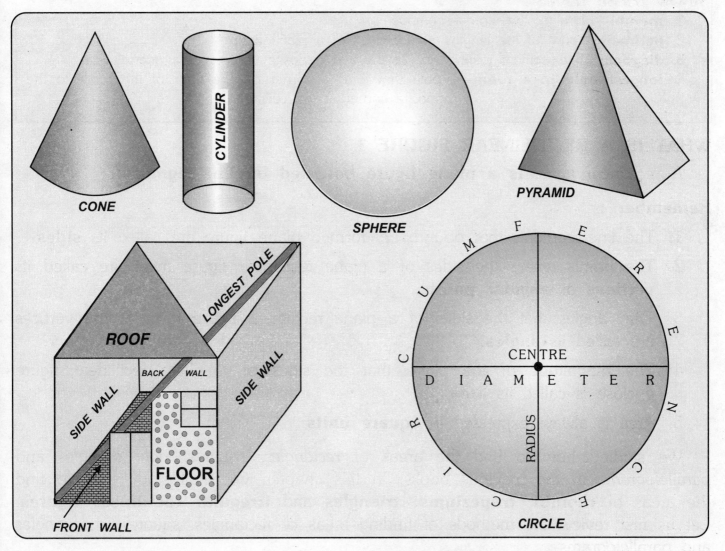

CONE

CYLINDER

SPHERE

PYRAMID

ROOF

LONGEST POLE

BACK WALL

SIDE WALL

SIDE WALL

FLOOR

FRONT WALL

CIRCUMFERENCE

CENTRE

DIAMETER

RADIUS

CIRCLE

IN THIS UNIT—

22 MEASUREMENT OF AREA—I
(RECTILINEAR FIGURES)

WHAT IS A RECTILINEAR FIGURE ?

A *rectilinear figure* **is a plane figure bounded by line-segments.**

Remember :

1. The line-segments that bound, *i.e.* form a plane figure are called its **sides**.

2. The points where the sides of a plane rectilinear figure meet are called its **vertices** or **angular points**.

3. The angles that the sides of a plane rectilinear figure form at the vertices are called its **angles**.

4. The magnitude of the plane that the sides of a plane rectilinear figure enclose is called its **area**.

5. Area is always expressed in **square units**.

We studied how to find the areas of *rectangles, squares, right triangles* and *parallelograms* in the previous books. In this chapter, we shall study how to find the areas of **rhombi, trapeziums, triangles** and **irregular rectilinear figures**. Let us first review the methods of finding areas of rectangles, squares, rt. triangles and parallelograms.

RECTANGLES

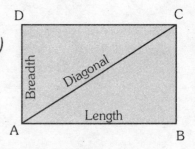

1. Area of a Rectangle $\quad = Length \times Breadth\ (L \times B)$
2. Length of a Rectangle $\quad = Area \div Breadth\ (A \div B)$
3. Breadth of a Rectangle $\quad = Area \div Length\ (A \div L)$
4. Diagonal of a Rectangle $= \sqrt{L^2 + B^2}$
5. Perimeter of a Rectangle $= 2\ (L + B)$
6. Area of Four Walls of a Room $\ = 2\ (Length + Breadth) \times Height$
$$= 2\ (L + B) \times H$$
7. The Longest Pole in a Room $\quad = \sqrt{L^2 + B^2 + H^2}\ or \sqrt{Diagonal^2 + H^2}$

SQUARES

1. Area of a Square   = $(Side)^2$
2. Side of a Square   = $\sqrt{Area}$
3. Diagonal of Square   = $\sqrt{2} \times Side$
4. Area of a Square   = $\frac{1}{2} \times (Diagonal)^2$
5. Perimeter of a Square = $4 \times Side$

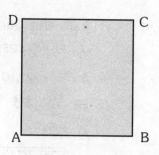

AREA OF A TRIANGLE

1. Area of a Rt. Δ = $\frac{1}{2} \times Base \times Height$
2. Height (Altitude) = $(Area \times 2) \div Base$
3. Base = $Area \times 2 \div Altitude$

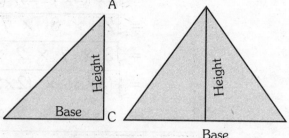

If the lengths of the sides of a triangle are given, then its area

$= \sqrt{s(s-a)(s-b)(s-c)}$ **where** a, b, c **are sides and** $s = \frac{1}{2}(a+b+c)$

Example 1. Find the area and perimeter of a rectangular field whose diagonal = 50 m and side is 48 m.

Solution :   ABC is a rt. Δ

$\therefore$ $AB^2 + BC^2 = AC^2$

or $48^2 + BC^2 = 50^2$

or $BC^2 = 50^2 - 48^2$

$= 2500 - 2304 = 196$

$\therefore$ $BC = \sqrt{196} = 14$

$\therefore$ Breadth of the field = 14 metres

$\therefore$ Its Area = (48×14) sq. m. = **672 sq. m.**

And   its perimeter = 2 (L + B) = 2 (48 + 14)m = **124 m.** *Ans.*

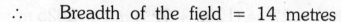

Example 2. Find the area of a square whose diagonal measures 18·2 m.

Solution :   Diagonal of the square = 18·2 m. = $\frac{182}{10}$m = $\frac{91}{5}$m

$\therefore$ Area of the square

$= \frac{1}{2} \times (Diagonal)^2$

$= \frac{1}{2} \times \frac{91}{5} \times \frac{91}{5}$ sq. m. = $\frac{8281}{50}$ sq. m.

$= \frac{828·1}{5}$ sq. m. = **165·62 sq. m.** *Ans.*

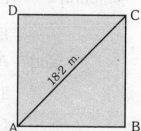

Example 3. Find the area of a triangle whose sides are 13 m, 14 m and 15 m respectively.

193

Solution :   Let the sides of the Δ ABC be
a, b, c respectively

$\therefore$ $s = \frac{1}{2}(a + b + c)$

      $= \frac{1}{2}(13 + 14 + 15)$ m $= \textbf{21 m}$

$\therefore$ Δ ABC $= \sqrt{s\,(s - a)\,(s - b)\,(s - c)}$

      $= \sqrt{21\,(21 - 13)\,(21 - 14)\,(21 - 15)}$ sq. m.

      $= \sqrt{21 \times 8 \times 7 \times 6}$ sq. m.

      $= \sqrt{3 \times 7 \times 2 \times 2 \times 2 \times 7 \times 2 \times 3}$ sq. m.

      $= \sqrt{(3 \times 3) \times (2 \times 2) \times (7 \times 7) \times (2 \times 2)}$ sq. m.

      $= 3 \times 2 \times 7 \times 2$ sq. m. $= \textbf{84 sq. m.}$ *Ans.*

☞ This formula is known as **Hero's Formula.**

Example 4. **The legs of a right triangular park are in the ratio 3 : 4 while its area is 486 sq. m. Find its hypotenuse.**

Solution :   Let the legs AB and AC of the park be 3x and 4x

$\therefore$ Its area $= \frac{1}{2} \times 3x \times 4x = 6x^2$

But   Actual Area $= 486$ sq. *m*

$\therefore$ $6x^2 = 486$ or $x^2 = 81$

or $x = \sqrt{81} = 9$

$\therefore$ Legs of the Park $= (9 \times 3) = \textbf{27 m}$ and $(9 \times 4) = \textbf{36 m}$

Now $(\text{Hyp. BC})^2 = AB^2 + AC^2$

          $= 36^2 + 27^2 = (1296 + 729)$ m $= 2025\, m = (45)^2\, m$

Hence **Hyp. BC = 45 m** *Ans.*

Example 5. **A hall is 15 m long, 9 m wide and 4 m high. Find the area of its walls and also the cost of white-washing them at Rs 2 per sq. m along with the ceiling.**

Solution :   Length of the hall $= 15$ m, Width $= 9$ m, Height $= 4$m

$\therefore$ Its area $= L \times B = (15 \times 9)$ sq. m $= \textbf{135 sq. m}$

and   Area of Walls $= 2\,(L + B) \times H = 2 \times (15 + 9) \times 4 = \textbf{192 sq. m}$

$\therefore$ Total area to be white-washed $= (135 + 192)$ sq. m $= \textbf{327 sq. m}$

      Cost of white-washing per sq. m $= Rs\, 2$

$\therefore$ Total cost of white-washing $= Rs\, 2 \times 327 = \textbf{Rs. 654}$ *Ans.*

A. Fill up the blanks :

1. Area of a Rectangle = ... × ..... 2. Area of a Square = (........)^2

3. Area of a Triangle = $\sqrt{......... (....... - ....) (...... - ....) (...... - ......)}$

B. 4. The area of a rectangular field is 27000 sq. metres and its sides are in the ratio of 6 : 5. Find the cost of fencing it at Rs. 700 per kilometre.

5. A triangular park has its sides 60 m, 56 m and 52 m respectively. Find its area. Also find its altitude corresponding to its longest side.

6. The length and breadth of a rectangular field are in the ratio 3 : 2 and its area is 3456 sq. m. Find the cost of fencing it at Rs. 3·50 per metre.

7. Find the area of a rectangular park whose one side is 35 metres long and one diagonal 37 metres long.

8. Find the area of a square whose diagonal is 2·9 metres.

9. A room is 9 metres long, 8 metres wide and 6·5 metres high. It has one door (2 m × 1·5 m) and four windows each (1·5 m × 1 m). Find the cost of plastering its walls at Rs. 3·75 per sq. metre.

10. A room measures 7 metres and 5 metres. It has one door (2 m × 1·5 m) and two windows each (1·5 m × 1 m). The cost of plastering it at 7·50 per square metre is Rs. 495. Find the height of the room.

11. The length and breadth of a rectangular field are in the ratio 5 : 3. The cost of fencing it at Rs. 7·50 per metre is Rs. 3000. Find its dimensions.

12. The base of a triangular field is thrice its altitude. If the cost of cultivating it at Rs. 246·80 per hectare is Rs. 3331·80. Find its base and height.

13. The area of an equilateral triangle is 43·25 sq. m. Find the length of its side.

    Hint : Area of an equilateral $\Delta = \frac{\sqrt{3}}{4} \times$ side and $\sqrt{3} = 1·73$

14. Find the area of a triangle whose sides are 78 cm., 50 cm. and 112 cm.

15. Find the area of an isosceles triangle with base = 48 cm. and side = 30 cm.

16. A rectangular field is 112 m long and 78 m broad. A path 2·5 metres wide runs round it on its inside. Find the area of the path and the cost of paving it at Rs. 1·80 per square metre.

17. A lawn is 60 metres by 45 metres. It has two cross-roads in its middle each of which is 5 metres wide—one parallel to the length and the other parallel to the width. Find the cost of paving the roads at Rs. 3·50 per m^2.

AREAS OF RHOMBI AND TRAPEZIUMS

AREA OF A RHOMBUS

A *rhombus* **is a parallelogram having all its sides equal and with its diagonals bisecting each other at right angles.**

It is clear from the rhombus given in front that its diagonals divide it into four triangles that are congruent and so equal an area.

Area of the rhombus = Total area of the 4 Δs

$\qquad\qquad\qquad$ = 4 × Area of one Δ

Area of one Δ (say AOB) = ½ × OA × OB

Area of 4 Δs $\quad$ = 4 × ½ × OA × OB

$\qquad\qquad\qquad$ = 2 × OA × OB

$\qquad\qquad\qquad$ = 2 × ½ AC × ½ BD = 2 × ¼ × AC × BD

$\qquad\qquad\qquad$ = ½ × AC × BD $\quad$ = ½ **(Product of Diagonals)**

AREA OF A PARALLELOGRAM

Given in front is a parallelogram ABCD. Draw DL $\perp$ AB and join BD

Area of Parallelogram ABCD = Δ ABD + Δ BCD

$\qquad\qquad\qquad\qquad$ = 2 Δ ABD ($\because \Delta$ *ABD* = Δ *BCD)*

$\qquad\qquad\qquad\qquad$ = 2 × ½ AB × DL = AB × DL

$\therefore$ $\quad$ **Area of a ||^{gm} = Base × Height**

AREA OF A TRAPEZIUM

Given in front is a trapezium ABCD in which AB||CD. Draw DL and CM both perpendicular to AB.

Area of trapezium ABCD

= Δ DAL + Rect. LMCD + Δ MBC

= (½ AL × DL) + (LM × DL) + (½ MB × CM)

Let us use the word *height (h)* for DL and CM

Trapezium ABCD $\quad$ = (½ AL × h) + (LM × h) + (½ MB × h)

$\qquad\qquad\qquad\qquad$ = ½h × AL + LM × h + ½h × MB

$\qquad\qquad\qquad\qquad$ = ½h × AL + ½h × 2LM + ½h × MB

$\qquad\qquad\qquad\qquad$ = ½h (AL + 2LM + MB) = ½h (AL + LM + LM + MB)

$\qquad\qquad\qquad\qquad$ = ½h [(AL + LM + MB) + LM] $\quad$ = ½h (AB + LM)

$\qquad\qquad\qquad\qquad$ = ½h **(AB + CD)** $\qquad\qquad$ ($\because$ *LM = CD)*

$\therefore$ **Area of a Trapezium = ½ × Height × Sum of the Parallel Sides**

AREA OF A QUADRILATERAL

Every quadrilateral can be divided into two triangles by joining one of its diagonals. If perpendiculars are drawn on this diagonal from the other two vertices, they can be used as **heights** for finding the areas of the two triangles formed by joining the diagonal. The sum of these two areas will be equal to the area of the quadrilateral. Let us have some examples :

Example 5. A quadrilateral ABCD has its diagonal AC = 26 cm. while the perpendiculars from B and D on AC are 15 cm and 10 cm. Find the area of the quadrilateral.

Solution :

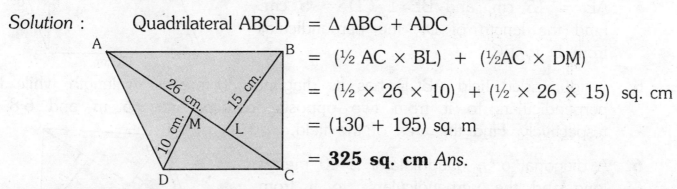

Quadrilateral ABCD $= \triangle$ ABC + ADC

$= (\frac{1}{2}$ AC $\times$ BL) + ($\frac{1}{2}$AC $\times$ DM)

$= (\frac{1}{2} \times 26 \times 10) + (\frac{1}{2} \times 26 \times 15)$ sq. cm

$= (130 + 195)$ sq. m

$= $ **325 sq. cm** Ans.

Example 6. A quadrilateral ABCD has its sides AB = 28 cm. BC = 26 cm. CD = 50 cm. and AD = 40 cm. and diagonal AC = 30 cm. Find the area of the quadrilateral.

Solution :   Diagonal AC divides the quadrilateral into two $\triangle$s ABC and ADC

Area of a triangle $= \sqrt{s\,(s-a)\,(s-b)\,(s-c)}$

s for $\triangle$ ABC $= \frac{1}{2}$ (28 + 26 + 30) cm.

$= \frac{1}{2} \times 84$ cm. $=$ **42 cm.**

s for $\triangle$ ADC $= \frac{1}{2}$ (30 + 50 + 40) cm.

$= \frac{1}{2} \times 120$ cm. $=$ **60 cm.**

Quad. ABCD $= \triangle$ ABC + $\triangle$ ADC

$\triangle$ ABC $= \sqrt{42\,(42-28)\,(42-26)\,(42-30)} = \sqrt{42 \times 14 \times 16 \times 12}$ sq. cm

$\triangle$ ADC $= \sqrt{60\,(60-30)\,(60-50)\,(60-40)} = \sqrt{60 \times 30 \times 10 \times 20}$ sq. cm.

$\triangle$ ABC + $\triangle$ ADC $= (336 + 600)$ sq. cm. $= 936$ sq. cm.

Hence area of Quad. ABCD = 936 sq. cm. Ans.

1. A parallelogram has its one side = 14 cm. and its height is 16·5 cm. Find its area.

2. The length of a parallelogram is twice its height. If its area be 512 sq. cm, find its base and height.

3. The base of a parallelogram is thrice its height. If its area be 300 square metres, find its base and height.

4. In a parallelogram ABCD, BC = 10 cm., AB = 15 cm. and BE ⊥ CD = 5 cm. Find the length of DF, the perpendicular from D to BC.

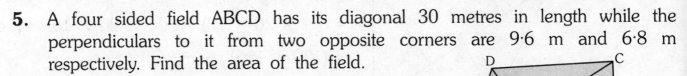

5. A four sided field ABCD has its diagonal 30 metres in length while the perpendiculars to it from two opposite corners are 9·6 m and 6·8 m respectively. Find the area of the field.

6. A diagonal of a quadrilateral is 40 metres long and the perpendiculars to it from the opposite corners are 8 m. and 10 m. respectively. Find its area.

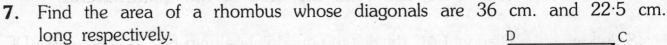

7. Find the area of a rhombus whose diagonals are 36 cm. and 22·5 cm. long respectively.

8. Find the area of a rhombus whose side is 15 cm. long while one of the diagonals is 24 cm. long.

   Hint : Join BD that cuts AC at O.
   Find DO using Pythagoras Theorem
   and then find the area.

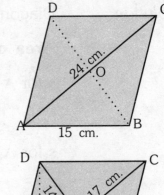

9. The perimeter of a rhombus ABCD is 40 cm. and its diagonals are 17 cm. and 14 cm. long respectively. Find its height DL corresponding to its side AB.

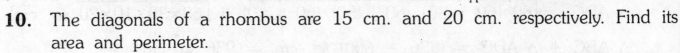

10. The diagonals of a rhombus are 15 cm. and 20 cm. respectively. Find its area and perimeter.

11. Find the area of a rhombus who side is 13 cm. and altitude is 2 cm.

12. The diagonals of a rhombus are 8 cm. and 6 cm. respectively. Find its area.

13. The area of a rectangular field is 27000 square metres and its sides are in the ratio 3 : 10. Find the cost of fencing it at Rs. 750 per kilometre.

14. The parallel sides of a trapezium are 15 metres and 8 metres while its height is 12 metres. Find its area.

15. Find the area of a trapezium whose parallel sides are 57 m and 39 m and the distance between them is 28 m.

16. A trapezium has its parallel sides AB and CD equal to 66 metres and 40 metres in length respectively. If AD = 28 m and BC = 30 m long find the area of the trapezium.

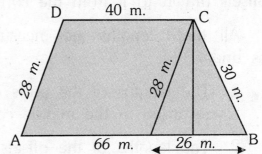

Hint : Draw CE||AD and CF ⊥ AB

Then CE = 28 m BE = 66 – 40 = 26 m

Find the area of Δ CEB by Hero's Formula and then find the height CF). Finally find the area of a the trapezium.

17. The area of a trapezium is 12 sq. m. If its height be 3 m and also one of the parallel sides be 3 m, find the length of the other parallel side.

18. The area of a trapezium is 248 sq. m. If its height be 8 m and one of the parallel sides be 30 m, find the other parallel side.

19. The lengths of the parallel sides of a trapezium are in the ratio 4 : 7. If the height of the trapezium be 14 m and its area be 385 sq. m, find the lengths of its parallel sides.

20. A trapezium has its parallel sides 25 cm. and 13 cm. respectively. If each of its non-parallel side be 10 cm. long, find its area.

AREAS OF IRREGULAR FIGURES

Various fields, farms, parks and plots etc. are irregular in shape. In order to find their areas, we use the **field methods**. Let us study how to do it. This method is called so because the dimensions of such pieces of land are recorded in a book called the **field book.**

Suppose we have an irregular field ABCDEF as shown in page 236. In order to find its area, its corners are marked (say A, B, C, D, E, F). Then the mutually farthest two corners are joined by a *line-segment*. This line-segment is called the **base-line**.

Next, a perpendicular is drawn to the base line from each of the other corners of the field. Each perpendicular is called an **offset**.

The figure in front has six corners A, B, C, D, E, F. Out of them A and C are the two corners farthest apart. So, AC has been drawn as the *base-line* while BL, DM, EN and FP are the offsets drawn to it from the corners B, D, E, F.

All these lengths are measured and recorded as under :

1. The lengths of the parts of the base line are recorded in the middle column.

2. The lengths of the offsets of one side of the base-line are recorded on the right while those of the other side are recorded on the left.

	Metres	
	To C	
	220	
70 to D	180	
	160	40 to B
60 to E	140	
80 to F	80	
	From A	

The plan of recording is shown on the right.

We can easily read the various measurements from this plan. From the above plan, it is clear that—

AP = 80 m

AN = 140 m   and   PF = 80 m

AM = 160 m   NE = 60m

AL = 180 m   DM = 70m

AC = 220 m   BL = 40m

Clearly, the base line and the offsets divide the field into a number of right triangles and trapezia. Their respective areas are found and added up to find the total area of the field as under :

Rt. $\triangle$ FAP $= \frac{1}{2} \times$ AP $\times$ PF $= \frac{1}{2} \times 80 \times 80$

$\qquad\qquad\qquad\qquad\qquad\qquad$ = **3200 sq. m**

$\qquad \triangle$ ABC $= \frac{1}{2} \times$ AC $\times$ BL $= \frac{1}{2} \times 220 \times 40$

$\qquad\qquad\qquad\qquad\qquad\qquad$ = **4400 sq. m**

Rt. $\triangle$ CDM $= \frac{1}{2} \times$ CM $\times$ DM $= \frac{1}{2} \times 60 \times 70$

$\qquad\qquad\qquad\qquad\qquad\qquad$ = **2100 sq. m**

Trapezium PNEF $= \frac{1}{2} \times$ PN (FP + EN) $= \frac{1}{2} \times 60 (60 + 80)$ sq. m

$\qquad\qquad\qquad\qquad\qquad\qquad$ $= (\frac{1}{2} \times 60 \times 140)$ sq. m

$\qquad\qquad\qquad\qquad\qquad\qquad$ = **4200 sq. m**

Trapezium DENM = ½ × NM (EN + DM)　= ½ × 20 (60 + 70) sq. m

= ½ × 20 × 130 sq. m

= **1300 sq. m**

Area of the total field　= (3200 + 4400 + 2100 + 4200 + 1300) sq. m²

= **15200 sq. m** *Ans.*

Example 7.　From the following field-plan draw the rough figure of the field and find its area.

Solution :　　　The figure shall be as under :

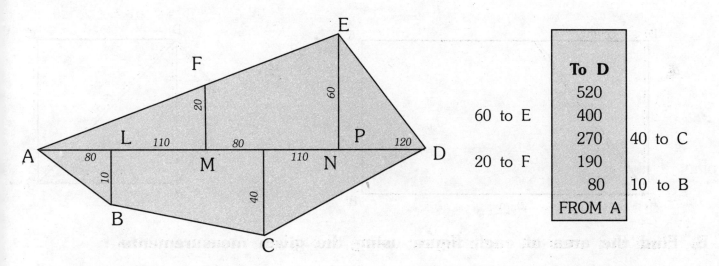

The figure has come to be divided into 4 triangles and 2 trapezia

Rt ΔALB = ½ × AL × BL = (½ × 80 × 10) sq. m = **400 sq. m**

Rt ΔAFM = ½ AM × FM = (½ × 190 × 20) sq. m = **1900 sq. m**

Rt ΔPED = ½ × PD × PE = (½ × 120 × 60) sq. m = **3600 sq. m**

Rt ΔCDN = ½ × DN × CN = (½ × 250 × 40) sq. m = **5000 sq. m**

Trapezium BCLN　= ½ × LN (BL + CN) = ½ × 190 (10 + 40) sq. m

= (½ × 190 × 50) sq. m = **4750 sq. m**

Trapezium EFMP　= ½ × MP (EP + FM) = ½ × 210 (20 + 60) sq. m

= (½ × 210 × 80) sq. m = **8400 sq. m**

Total area of the field　= (400 + 1900 + 3600 + 5000 + 4750 + 8400)m²

= **24050 sq. m** *Ans.*

A. Calculate the area of the shaded part of each figure from the measurements given with the figure itself :

1.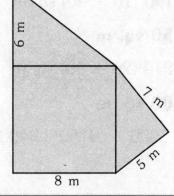

2.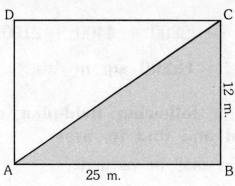

3.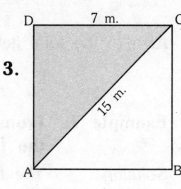

4.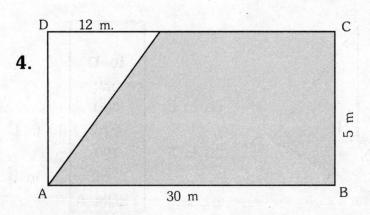

5.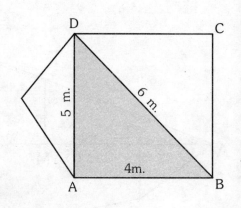

B. Find the area of each figure using the given measurements :

6.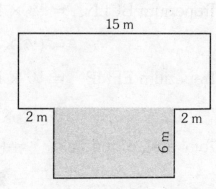

7.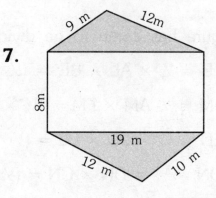

8.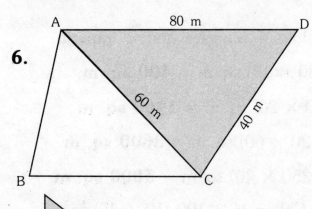

9.

C. Prepare the figure of the field from each plan and find its area :

10.

	To D	
	210	
60 to E	180	40 to C
70 to F	160	
	120	
	80	60 to B
	From A	

11.

	To D	
	140	
	80	
70 to F	40	60 to C
	25	40 to B
	From A	

12.

	To D	
	220	
50 to D	160	
40 to C	120	60 to E
	80	
	0	20 to F
	From A	

13.

	To D	
	200	
30 to Q	160	50 to N
40 to P	120	40 to M
	80	
	60	25 to L
	From A	

14.

	To D	
	140	
	100	50 to C
40 to E	90	
	60	45 to B
30 to F	45	
	From A	

15.

	To D	
	200	
	120	
	90	45 to F
50 to D	60	
	0	40 to F
	From A	

23 MEASUREMENT OF AREA—II
(CIRCLES, CYLINDERS, SPHERES, CONES)

We have been using the word circle for the boundary of a circle so far. The correct word for it is **circumference**.

We have also read about the **radius** and the **diameter**. We know that **diameter = 2 × radius.**

DIAMETER AND CIRCUMFERENCE

The **diameter** (D) and the *circumference* of a circle have a certain ratio which is **constant**.

We can check up this ratio by measuring the diameters and circumferences of various circles using a thread.

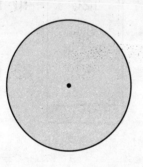 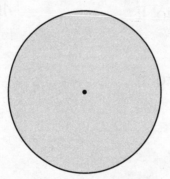 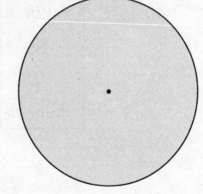

You will see that the ratio of the circumference to the diameter is a little above 3 every time. To be exact, it is **3·14 nearly.**

As a fraction, this ratio is written to be $\frac{22}{7}$ **nearly**

The term used for this ratio is a Greek letter **pi** and this very letter is used as a symbol for this ratio. This symbol is π

In short, we write the word circumference as O^{ce}

So, we can write that $\dfrac{O^{ce}}{D} = \dfrac{22}{7}$

or $O^{ce} = \dfrac{22}{7} \times$ **Diameter**

So, in order to find the circumference of a circle, we *multiply* the **diameter** by π, *i.e.* by $\frac{22}{7}$ or **3·14.**

Let us now solve some examples :

Example 1. **Find the circumference of a circle if its**

        (*a*) **diameter = 14 cm.**   (*b*) **radius = 3·5 cm.**

        (*c*) **diameter = 4·9 cm.**   (*d*) **radius = 2·1 cm.**

Solution :   (*a*) diameter of the circle = 14 cm.

$$O^{ce} = D \times \frac{22}{7} = \left(14 \times \frac{22}{7}\right) \text{ cm.} = \textbf{44 cm. } \textit{Ans.}$$

(*b*) Radius of the circle = 3·5 cm.

$$\therefore \quad \text{Diameter} = 2 \times 3\text{·}5 \text{ cm.} = 7 \text{ cm.}$$

$$\therefore \quad O^{ce} = \left(7 \times \frac{22}{7}\right) \text{ cm.} = \textbf{22 cm. } \textit{Ans.}$$

(*c*) Diameter = 4·9 cm. = $\frac{49}{10}$ cm.

$$\therefore \quad O^{ce} = \frac{49}{10} \times \frac{22}{7} = \frac{154}{10} \text{ cm.} = \textbf{15·4 cm. } \textit{Ans.}$$

(*d*) Radius = 2·1 cm., so Diameter = (2·1 × 2) = 4·2 cm.

$$\therefore \quad O^{ce} = 4\text{·}2 \times \frac{22}{7} = \frac{42}{10} \times \frac{22}{7} = \frac{132}{10}$$

$$= \textbf{13·2 cm. } \textit{Ans.}$$

Example 2. **Find the diameter of a circle whose circumference is 33 cm.**

Solution : O^{ce} = 33 cm.   Diameter = ?

$$\text{Diameter} \times \frac{22}{7} = O^{ce}$$

$$\therefore \quad \text{Diameter} = O^{ce} \times \frac{7}{22}$$

$$= 33 \times \frac{7}{22} = \frac{21}{2}$$

$$= \textbf{10·5 cm. } \textit{Ans.}$$

Example 3. **The radii of two circles are in the ratio 2 : 3. What is the ratio of their circumference.**

Solution :   Let the radii be 2 cm. and 3 cm.

∴ O^{ce} of the first circle $= 2 \times \dfrac{22}{7}$ cm. $= \dfrac{44}{7}$ cm.

and O^{ce} of the second circle $= 3 \times \dfrac{22}{7}$ cm. $= \dfrac{66}{7}$ cm.

∴   Ratio of circumferences $= \dfrac{44}{7} : \dfrac{66}{7} = 44 : 66 = $ **2 : 3** *Ans.*

Example 4. **There is a circular moat round a fort. A man walks round it. His step is 66 cm. long and he has to take 1000 steps to complete the round. Find the diameter of the moat.**

Solution :   The man walks along the circumference of the moat

He take 1000 steps each 66 cm. long

∴ O^{ce} of the moat $= 66 \times 1000$ cm. $= 66000$ cm.

Now   Diameter $\times \dfrac{22}{7} = O^{ce}$

or   Diameter $\times \dfrac{22}{7} = 66000$ cm.

or   Diameter $= \dfrac{66000 \times 7}{22} = 21000$ cm. $=$ **210 metres** *Ans.*

Example 5. **The moon is 385000 km. away from the earth. It takes a round of the earth every month. How much distance does it travel ?**

Solution :   Distance of the moon from the earth

= 385000 kilometres

Clearly it is the radius of the circle that the moon travels along

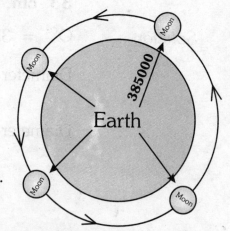

∴   Diameter $= 385000 \times 2 \times \dfrac{22}{7}$ km.

$= 55000 \times 2 \times 22$

$= 110000 \times 22$ km. $=$ **2420000 km nearly.**

PRACTICE EXERCISES 47

A. Define :

1. *Circumference* of a circle :

....

....

2. The *ratio* of the circumference to the diameter of a circle :

....

....

B. Find the *circumference* **if :**

3. Diameter = 42 cm.   4. Diameter = 28 cm.

5. radius = 63 cm.   6. radius = 10·5 cm.

7. radius = 1·75 m   8. diameter = 19·6 cm.

C. Find the *diameter* **and the** *radius* **if :**

9. circumference = 330 metres   10. O^{ce} 132 cm.

11. O^{ce} = 15·4 cm.   12. O^{ce} = 88 cm.

13. The diameter of a wheel is 1·4 meter. Find its circumference.

14. The diameter of the wheel of a car is 63 cm. How much distance will it transverse in 1000 revolutions ?

15. A piece of wire is in the form of a rectangle 8·4 cm. long and 2·6 cm. wide. It is reshaped into a circle. Find the radius of the circle.

16. The radius of a wheel of an engine is 1·75 metres. How many revolutions will it make in covering 22 kilometres ?

17. The minute-hand of a clock is 4·2 cm. long. How much distance does its tip move in 45 minutes ?

18. Given in front is a figure made up of a rectangle and two semi-circles. Find its perimeter. The measurements are given.

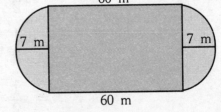

19. The diameter of a circular park is 140 metres. Around it on the outside a 7 metres wide path is there. Find the cost of at fencing the path from inside and outside at Rs. 7 per 100 metres.

AREA OF A CIRCLE

Observe the figure given below. It shows a circle divided into 16 parts by drawing its eight diameters. These 16 parts have been cut out and arranged as shown below.

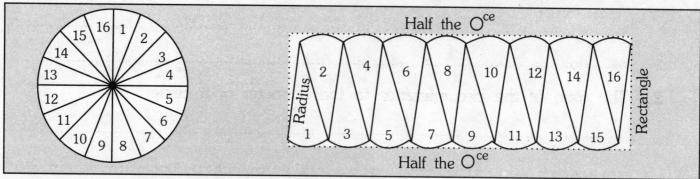

Observe the figure formed above by placing the sixteen parts of the circle in a row. This row has divided the entire circumference of the circle into two equal parts. Half the circumference is there in the form of small arcs on the upper side while the other half is in the form of small arcs on the lower side. The entire arrangement has resulted in a figure that almost resembles a **rectangle**.

If the circle is divided into 360 parts and then arranged in the manner shown above, the rectangle formed will have its upper and lower sides almost straight.

What is the *length* of this rectangle ?

Clearly, it is as long as **half the O^ce**.

What is the *breadth* of this rectangle ?

It is equal to the **radius** of the circle.

So, *Area of this Rectangle* will be equal to the *Area of the Circle*.

$$\textbf{\textit{Area of the Circle}} = \text{Area of the Rectangle}$$

$$= \text{Length} \times \text{Breadth}$$

$$= \frac{1}{2} \text{ O}^{ce} \times \text{radius } (r)$$

$$= \frac{1}{2} (\text{diameter} \times \pi) \times r \quad (\because \text{O}^{ce} = Diameter \times \pi)$$

$$= \frac{1}{2} \times \text{Diameter} \times \pi \times r$$

$$= \frac{1}{2} \times 2r \times \pi \times r \quad (\because Diameter = 2r)$$

$$= \pi \times r \times r = \pi r^2$$

$$\therefore \quad \textbf{\textit{Area of a Circle}} = \pi r^2$$

Let us solve some examples :

Example 1.   **Find the area of a circle whose—**
   (a) **radius = 21 cm.**   (b) **diameter = 63 m**
   (c) **circumference = 264 metres**

Solution : (a)   Radius of the circle = 21 cm.

Area of the circle $= \pi r^2 = \pi \times r \times r$

$$= \frac{22}{7} \times 21 \times 21 \text{ sq. cm.} = \textbf{1386 sq.cm}\quad Ans.$$

(b)   Diameter of the circle = 63 m

∴   Radius of the circle $= \frac{1}{2} \times$ Diameter $= \frac{1}{2} \times 63$ m $= \frac{63}{2}$ m

∴   Area of the circle $= \pi r^2 = \frac{22}{7} \times \frac{63}{2} \times \frac{63}{2}$ sq. m

$$= \textbf{3118·5 sq. metres}\ Ans.$$

(c)   Circumference = 264 m

∴   Diameter $= O^{ce} \div \frac{22}{7} = O^{ce} \times \frac{7}{22}$

$$= 264 \times \frac{7}{22} = 84 \text{ m}$$

∴   Radius $= 84 \div 2 = \textbf{42 m}$

∴   Area of the circle $= \pi r^2 = \pi \times r \times r$

$$= \frac{22}{7} \times 42 \times 42 \text{ sq. m.}$$

$$= \textbf{5544 cm}^2\ Ans.$$

Example 2.   **The area of a circle is 2464 sq. cm. Find its O^{ce}**

Solution :   Area of the circle = 2464 sq. cm.

or $\pi r^2 = 2464$ sq. cm   or $\frac{22}{7} \times r^2 = 2464$ sq. cm

or $r^2 = 2464 \times \frac{7}{22}$ sq. cm = 7 × 112 sq. cm = 784 sq. cm

∴ $r = \sqrt{784} = 28$ cm.   or   Diameter = 28 × 2 cm. = 56 cm.

Now, $O^{ce} =$ Diameter $\times \frac{22}{7}$

$$= 56 \times \frac{22}{7} \text{ cm.} = \textbf{176 cm.}\ Ans.$$

Example 3. The diameter of a circular field is 56 metres. Around it there is a path 3·5 metres wide running on its outside. Find the area of the path and the cost of paving it at Rs. 8 per square metre.

Solution :

Diameter of the field = 56 m

$\therefore$ Radius of the field = $56 \div 2$ = 28 m

$\therefore$ Area of the field $= \pi r^2 = \dfrac{22}{7} \times 28 \times 28$ sq. m = **2464 sq.m**

Width of the path = 3·5 m

$\therefore$ Radius of the (field + path) = $(28 + 3.5)$ m

$$= 31.5 \text{ m} = \dfrac{63}{2} \text{ m}$$

$\therefore$ Area of the (field + path) $= \pi r^2 = \dfrac{22}{7} \times \dfrac{63}{2} \times \dfrac{63}{2}$ sq. m

$$= \dfrac{6237}{2} \textbf{ sq. m}$$

Now Area of the path

= Area of the (field + path) – (Area of the field)

$= \left(\dfrac{6237}{2} - 2464\right)$ sq. m $= \dfrac{6237 - 4928}{2}$ sq. m

$= \dfrac{1309}{2}$ sq. m = **654·5 sq. metres** *Ans.*

Cost of paving per sq. m = Rs. 8

$\therefore$ Total cost of paving = Rs. $8 \times \dfrac{1309}{2}$ = **Rs. 5236** *Ans.*

PRACTICE EXERCISES 48

A. Complete the following relations :

1. O^{ce} = ... $\times \dfrac{22}{7}$ 2. Diameter = ... $\div \dfrac{22}{7}$

3. Area of a Circle = $\pi \times$ ....   4. Radius = ... $\div 2$

B. Find the area of a circle whose radius is :

5. 4·9 cm.   6. 2·1 cm.   7. 3·5 cm.

8. 21 cm.   9. 14 cm.   10. 7·7 cm.

C. Find the area of a circle whose diameter is :

11. 4·2 cm.   **12.** 70 cm.   **13.** 4 m. 20 cm.

14. 12·6 cm.   **15.** 11·2 m   **16.** 84 m.

D. Find the area of a circle whose circumference is :

17. 44 cm.   **18.** 88 cm.   **19.** 220 m

20. 154 metres   **21.** 264 cm.   **22.** 792 m

E. 23. The area of a circular field is 38·5 sq. metres. Find its circumference.

24. The area of a circular lawn is 154 square meters. Find its circumference.

25. Find the area of a circular running course whose outer and inner radii are 20 metres and 15 metres respectively.

26. A circular garden has a path running around it on its outside. The garden has a circumference of 396 m and the path is 3·5 m. wide. Find the area of the path.

27. A circular ground has 7-metre wide road running round it on its inside. If the radius of the ground is 56 m., find the area of the road.

28. The diameter of a circular park is 84 metres. A 3·5-metre wide path runs round it on its inside. Find the cost of paving the path at Re. 1 per sq. m.

29. A circular plot has its diameter to be 770 metres. Find its value at Rs. 570 per square metre.

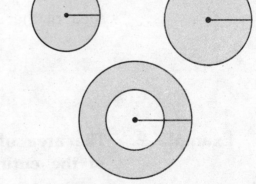

30. The diameters of two silver discs are in the ratio 2 : 3. What will be the ratio of their areas ?

31. The radius of the inner boundary of a circular path is 14 m. While its area is 176 metres. Find the radius of its outer boundary.

32. The area of a circle is equal to the area of a rectangle with sides 112 metres and 88 metres respectively. Find the circumference of the circle.

33. A garden is 120 m long and 80 m broad. Just in its middle is a circular tank with radius 14 m. Find the cost of turfing the remaining garden at Rs. 1·25 per sq. m.

211

AREA OF A SECTOR

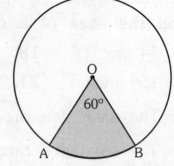

We know that **a *sector* is the part of a circular region enclosed between two radii.**

Every sector has its vertex at the centre where the radii enclosing it make an angle. It is called the **sector angle**.

We also know that if the entire circular region is taken as a sector, it makes an angle of **360°** at the centre.

Clearly, the area of a sector is directly proportional to its angle at the centre.

If a sector OAB makes an angle of **60°** at the centre, its area will be $\frac{60}{360}$ of the area of the circular region.

Area of a Sector $= \dfrac{\textbf{Sector Angle}}{\textbf{360}} \times \pi r^2$

Example 1. Find the area of a sector of a circle having radius = 35 cm., if its sector angle = 72°.

Solution :   Radius of the circle = 35 cm.

∴   Area of the circle $= \pi r^2 = \dfrac{22}{7} \times 35 \times 35$ sq. cm

Angle of the sector = 72°

∴   Area of the sector $= \dfrac{72}{360} \times$ area of the circle

$= \dfrac{72}{360} \times \dfrac{22}{7} \times 35 \times 35$ sq. cm

$= \textbf{770 sq. cm }$ *Ans.*

Example 2. The area of a sector of a circle is one-sixth of the area of the entire circle. Find the angle of the sector.

Solution : $\dfrac{\text{Sector Angle}}{360} \times \pi r^2 = $ Area of the Sector

or $\dfrac{\text{Sector Angle}}{360} = \dfrac{\text{Area of the sector}}{\pi r^2}$

or $\dfrac{\text{Sector Angle}}{360} = \dfrac{\text{Area of the sector}}{\text{Area of the circle}} = \dfrac{1}{6}$

or   Sector Angle $= \dfrac{360 \times 1}{6} = \textbf{60° }$ *Ans.*

Example 3. **The length of the minute-hand of a clock is 7 cm. Find the area covered by it on the dial in 24 minutes.**

Solution : The length of the minute-hand = radius of the dial, *i.e.* the circular face of the clock.

∴ radius = 7 cm.

Total area of the circular face = $\pi r^2 = \dfrac{22}{7} \times 7 \times 7$

$$= \textbf{154 sq. cm}$$

Now, angle described by the minute-hand in 60 minutes = 360°

∴ angle described by the minute-hand in 1 minute = $\dfrac{360°}{60}$

∴ angle described by the minute-hand in 24 minutes = $\dfrac{360°}{60} \times 24°$

$$= \textbf{144°}$$

∴ Area covered by the minute-hand = $\dfrac{144}{360} \times 154$ sq. cm

$$= \dfrac{308}{5} \text{ sq. cm}$$

$$= \textbf{61·6 sq. cm} \; Ans.$$

AREA OF A SEGMENT

We know that **a** *segment* **is a part of a circular region bounded by an arc and its corresponding chord.**

Every segment has its own arc that bounds it from outside. If we join the ends of its chord to the centre, we shall see that the segment becomes part of the sector that is formed by doing so. We know how to find the area of a sector So, we can find the area of the segment by subtracting the area of the triangle that covers the remaining part of the sector.

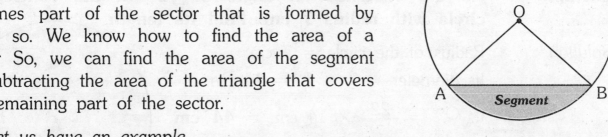

Let us have an example.

Example 1. **A chord AB divides the circle into two segments—minor and major. Find the areas of both the segments if the chord subtends an angle of 90° at the centre and the circle has a radius = 42 cm.**

213

Solution :   Sector OAB has an angle of 90° at the centre.

So, its area $= \dfrac{90}{360} \times$ area of the circle

$$= \dfrac{90}{360} \times \dfrac{22}{7} \times 42 \times 42 \text{ sq.cm} = \mathbf{1386\ sq.\ cm}$$

Now **minor segment** OAB

= Area of Sector OAB – Area of rt. Δ OAB

= 1386 sq. cm – rt. Δ OAB

= 1386 sq. cm $-\left(\dfrac{1}{2} \text{ OA} \times \text{OB}\right)$

= 1386 sq. cm $-\left(\dfrac{1}{2} \times 42 \times 42\right)$ sq. cm

= 1386 sq. cm – 882 sq. cm = **504 sq. cm** *Ans.*

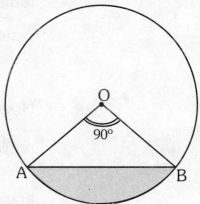

Area of **major segment OAB** = Area of the circle – Area of minor segment OAB

$$= \left(\dfrac{22}{7} \times 42 \times 42\right) - 504 \text{ sq. cm}$$

= 5544 sq. cm – 504 sq. cm = **5040 sq. cm** *Ans.*

FINDING LENGTH OF AN ARC

An arc is a part of the circumference of a circle that subtends an angle of 360° at the centre. So, the length of an arc is proportional to the angle that it subtends at the centre. In other words—

Length of an arc = circumference $\times$ $\dfrac{\text{angle subtended by the arc}}{360}$

Example 1.   An arc subtends an angle of 42° at the centre of a circle with radius 7 cm. Find its length.

Solution :   Radius of the circle = 7 cm.

∴   Its diameter = 7 × 2 = 14 cm.

∴   Its O^{ce} = $\dfrac{22}{7} \times 14$ cm. = **44 cm.**

∵   Arc subtends an angle of 42° at O

∴   Its length = $\dfrac{42}{360} \times$ circumference

$$= \dfrac{42}{360} \times 44 \text{ cm.} = \dfrac{77}{15} \text{ cm.} = \mathbf{5 \cdot 13\ cm.}\ Ans.$$

Example 2. **Find the angle subtended at the centre of a circle with radius 14 cm. by an arc 11 cm. long.**

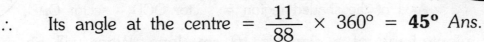

Solution :   Radius of the circle = 14 cm.

∴   Its diameter = 2 × 14 = 28 cm.

∴   Its O^{ce} = $\dfrac{22}{7}$ × 28 = **88 cm.**

Length of the arc = 11 cm.

∴   Its angle at the centre = $\dfrac{11}{88}$ × 360° = **45° Ans.**

PRACTICE EXERCISES 49

A. Define—

1. a *sector* of a circle :

   ....

   ....

2. an *arc* of a circle :

   ....

   ....

3. a minor segment of a circle :

   ....

   ....

4. a major segment of a circle :

   ....

   ....

B. 5. Find the area of a sector of a circle with radius = 6·3 cm. if it has an angle of 100° at the centre.

6. Find the area of a sector of a circle with radius 16 cm. cut off by an arc 18·5 cm. long.

   Hint : First find the angle subtended by the arc at the centre.

7. Find the area of a sector with 36° angle in a circle with radius 7 metres.

8. Find the area of a sector of a circle with radius 4·9 cm. and with a sector angle of 60°.

9. Find the area of the shaded region between two concentric circles.

> **Hint :** Clearly, we have two sectors of two circles : sector OAB and sector OCD that subtend an angle of 60° at the centre and have radii = 3 cm. and 3 + 2 = 5 cm. respectively.
>
> ∴ Area of the shaded region = sector OCD − sector OAB.

10. The minute-hand of a clock is 10 cm. long. What will be the area of the face of the clock swept by it between 9·00 a.m. and 9·35 a.m. ?

C.11. The radius of the inner boundary of a circular path is 14 cm. and the area of the path is 100 sq. cm. Find the radius of its outer boundary.

12. A 5280 metre race is to be run on a circular track with radius 140 metres. How many times will the runners have to run round it ?

13. The perimeter of a quadrant of a circle is 165 cm. Find its radius.

14. A garden has its dimensions 120 m × 80 m. In its middle is a circular tank with radius 14 m. Find the cost of tilling the remaining portion of the garden at Rs. 1·20 per sq. meter.

15. A rectangular park is bounded by semi-circles of diameter = 28 m. at its shorter ends. Find the perimeter and area of the total park if the rectangular part has a length of 80 metres.

D. 16. Find the lengths of two arcs of a circle with radius 6 cm., if the arcs subtend angles of 36° and 60° at the centre respectively.

17. Find the area of a segment of a circle with radius 14 cm. if its arc subtends an angle of ∠60°. **Hint.** equilateral $\triangle OAB = \frac{\sqrt{3}}{4} \times side^2$

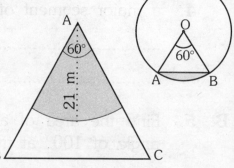

18. A cow is tied to the vertex of a field, which is an equilateral triangle, with a rope 21 metres long. Over what area can it graze ?

19. Find the areas of the shaded parts of each figure :

14 cm.

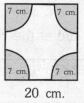

20 cm.

21 cm.

24 VOLUMES AND SURFACE AREAS—I
(CUBES, CUBOIDS, CYLINDERS)

KNOW THESE TERMS :
1. **solid**—something that occupies space
2. **dimensions**—measurable extents of a plane or solid figure
3. **capacity**—measure that shows how much liquid a vessel can contain
4. **surface area**—sum total of the areas of all the faces of a solid

Till now we have studied only *plane figures*. But in this chapter, we shall study **solids** in regard to their **surface areas** and **volumes**.

WHAT IS A SOLID ?

In mathematical terms, **a *solid* is something that takes up space.**

We see various types of solids around us—*bricks, soap-cakes, pens, pencils, boxes, jars, balls* and *bats*—that are all solids. A solid has **three dimensions**—*length, breadth* and *height*. Moreover, some solids have straight edges that bound **flat surfaces** while others have **curved surfaces**. Still others have a combination of these two types of surfaces—*flat* and *curved*. The solids that we are going to study in this chapter and the following one are—

1. Cubes and Cuboids
2. Right Circular Cylinders
3. Right Circular Cones
4. Spheres

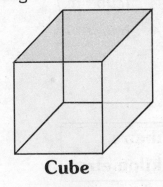

Cube

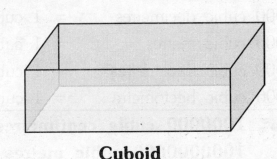

Cuboid

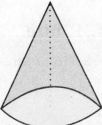

Right Circular Cylinder

Right Circular Cone

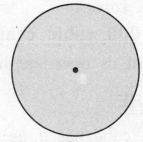

Sphere

Given above are the shapes of these various types of solids.

WHAT IS SURFACE AREA ?

The *surface area* **of a solid is the sum of the areas of all its faces whether flat or curved.**

1. *Remember that area is always expressed in* **square units.**
2. *Square units are* **two dimensional units.**
3. *Area needs* **two dimensions** *to be calculated.*

WHAT IS VOLUME ?

The volume of a solid means the amount of space enclosed within its faces.

In case of hollow solids, we call the *volume* by another name **capacity** which means **how much it can contain** in its hollow part. For example :

1. A bucket may have the *capacity* to contain 16 litres of water.
2. A room may have the capacity to contain 50 cubic metres of air in it.

> ☞ **Remember :**
> 1. Volume or capacity is always expressed in *cubic units*.
> 2. Cubic units are three dimensional units.
> 3. Volume needs three dimensions to be calculated.

LEARN THESE MEASURES OF VOLUME

1000 cubic millimetres	= 1 cubic centimetre	*(cu. cm.)*
1000 cubic centimetres	= 1 cubic decimetre	*(cub. m.)*
1000 cubic decimetres	= 1 cubic metre	*(cu. m.)*
1000 cubic metres	= 1 cubic decametre	
1000 cubic dacametres	= 1 cubic hectometre	
1000 cubic hectometre	= 1 cubic kilometre	

> ☞ **1000000 cubic centimetres = 1 cubic metre**
> **1000000000 cubic metres = 1 cubic kilometre**

In capacity

1000 cubic centimetres = 1 litre

Let us now find how to find surface areas and volumes of various solids.

CUBE

A cube has *three* **equal dimensions** and **six equal surfaces**. So,—

Surface Area of a Cube = 6 × area of 1 surface = **6 × (Side)²**

Volume of a Cube = Area of Base × Height = (Side)² × Height = **(Side)³**

CUBOID

A cuboid has three different dimensions—**length, breadth** and **height**. It has **three pairs of equal surfaces**. So,

Surface area of a Cuboid = 2 (sum of the areas of the three surfaces)

$$= 2 \text{ (LB + BH + LH)}$$

Volume of a Cuboid = Area of the Base × Height

$$= \text{Length × Breadth × Height}$$

Let us now solve some examples :

Example 1. **Find the volume and total surface area of—**

(a) **a cube whose side is 6 cm.**

(b) **a cuboid whose length = 8 cm.,**
breadth = 5 cm. and height = 3 cm.

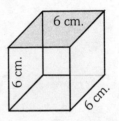

Solution : (a) side of the cube = 6 cm.

∴ *Its surface area* = 6 × (Side)^2

$$= 6 × (6 × 6) = \textbf{216 cu. cm.}$$

Its volume = (Side)^3 = (6)^3 = **216 cu. cm.** *Ans*

(b) Length of the cuboid = 8 cm.

Breadth of the cuboid = 5 cm.

Height of the cuboid = 3 cm.

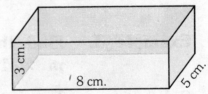

∴ Its *Surface Area* = 2 [(L × B) + (B × H) + (L × H)]

$$= 2 [(8 × 5) + (5 × 3) + (8 × 3)] \text{ cu. cm}$$

$$= 2 (40 + 15 + 24) \text{ cu. cm}$$

$$= 2 × 79 \text{ cm}^3 = \textbf{158 cu. cm.} \textit{ Ans.}$$

Its *Volume* = Length × Breadth × Height

$$= 8 × 5 × 3 \text{ cu. cm} = \textbf{120 cu. cm.} \textit{ Ans.}$$

Example 2. **A wall is to be constructed with dimensions 15 m length 3 dm width and 4 metres height. If $\frac{1}{12}$ of its total volume is the mortar used to build it, how many bricks will be required to build it when a brick measures 22 cm. × 12·5 cm. × 7·5 cm. ?**

Solution :   Length of the wall = 15 m

Width of the wall = 3 dm. = $\frac{3}{10}$ m

Height of the wall = 4 m

∴   Volume of the wall = $\left(15 \times \frac{3}{10} \times 4\right)$ cu. m = 18 cu. m

Volume of the mortar = $18 \times \frac{1}{12}$ cu. m = 1·5 cu. m

∴   Volume of the brick portion = (18 – 1·5) cu. m = 16·5 cu. m

Volume of a Brick   = 22 × 12·5 × 7·5 cu. cm

$$= 22 \times \frac{125}{10} \times \frac{75}{10} \text{ cu. cm}$$

$$= \frac{11 \times 75 \times 5}{2} \text{ cu. cm} = \frac{4125}{2} \text{ cu. cm}$$

$$= \frac{4125}{2} \times \frac{1}{1000000} \text{ cu. m} = \frac{165}{80000} \text{ cu. m}$$

∴   Reqd. No. of Bricks = $\dfrac{\text{Volume of the Wall}}{\text{Volume of a Brick}}$

$$= \frac{31}{2} \times \frac{80000}{165} = \textbf{8000} \text{ Ans.}$$

Example 3.   **Find the longest pole that can be placed in a room 10 m × 10 m × 5 m.**

Solution :   The longest pole will be from one corner of the floor to the opposite corner at the ceiling.

∴   The longest pole = $\sqrt{L^2 + B^2 + H^2}$

$$= \sqrt{10^2 + 10^2 + 5^2} \text{ m}$$

$$= \sqrt{100 + 100 + 25}$$

$$= \sqrt{225} \text{ m} = \textbf{15 m} \text{ Ans.}$$

Example 4.   **Find the capacity of a iron box 12·5 m × 8 m × 4·2 m. How much sheet will be needed to make it ?**

Solution :   Dimensions of the box = 12·5 m × 8 m × 4·2 m

∴   Its volume = $\frac{125}{10} \times 8 \times \frac{42}{10}$ cu. m = 420 cu. m

$$= 420 \times 1000000 \text{ cu. cm} = 420000000 \text{ cu. cm}$$

We know that 1000 cu. cm = 1 litre

Its capacity = $\dfrac{420000000}{1000}$ = **420000 litres** Ans.

Area of the sheet used for it = 2 (LB + BH + LH)

= 2 [(12·5 × 8) + (8 × 4·2) + (12·5 × 4·2)] sq. m

= 2 $\left(100 + \dfrac{336}{10} + \dfrac{5250}{100}\right)$ sq. m

= 2 $\left(\dfrac{10000 + 3360 + 5250}{100}\right)$ sq. m

= $\dfrac{37220}{100}$ m² = **372·2 sq. m** Ans.

PRACTICE EXERCISES 50

A. Complete the following relations :

1. Volume of a Cube = (.........................)³

2. Surface Area of a Cube = ... × (Side)²

3. Volume of a Cuboid = ... × .... × ....

4. Surface Area of a Cuboid = $\sqrt{....................}$ × (LB + BH + LH)

5. Longest Pole in a Cuboid = (.........)² + (...........)² + (.........)²

B. Find the *volume* **and** *total surface area* **of a cube whose side is :**

6. 8 m　　　　7. 6·5 cm.　　　　8. 9 m　　　　9. 3·5 cm.

C. Find the *volume* **and** *total surface area* **of a cuboid whose dimensions are :**

10. Length = 5 m　; Breadth = 3 m　Height = 2·5 m

11. Length = 8 m　; Breadth = 6 m　Height = 3·5 m

12. Length = 20 m　; Breadth = 6 m　Height = 3 m

D. 13. The total surface area of a cube is 384 sq. cm. Find its volume.

14. Find the total surface area of a cube whose volume is 729 cu. cm ?

15. A wall, 24 metres long, 8 metres high and 30 cm. thick, is to be built. How many bricks will be required for it if the dimensions of a brick are 24 cm. × 12 cm. × 8 cm. ?

16. A wall is 8 metres long ; 6 metres high. It needs 64000 bricks to be built. Find the thickness of the wall if the dimensions of each brick are 2·5 cm. × 11·25 cm. × 6 cm.

17. An open cuboidal cistern is 1·35 m long, 1·08 m wide and 90 cm. deep from outside. The iron-sheet used to make it is 2·5 cm. thick. Find the capacity of the cistern in litres and the total iron-sheet used to make it.

18. A field is 80 metres long and 50 metres wide. In one of its corners is dug is pit 10 m × 7·5 m × 8 m. The earth thus taken out is evenly spread over the remaining field. Find the rise in the level of this part of the field.

19. A field is 500 metres long and 30 metres wide. In its centre is dug a tank with dimensions 50 m × 20 m × 14 m. The earth taken out of it is spread evenly on the remaining field. How much will its level rise ?

RIGHT CIRCULAR CYLINDER

A *right circular cylinder* **is a solid bounded by a curved surface and two congruent circles at the bottom and at the top of the curved surface.**

The line joining the centres of these circles is called the **axis of the cylinder**.

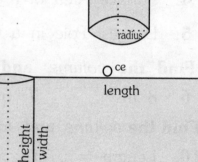

(a) *Volume of a cylinder = Area of the Base × Height*

∵   Base of the cylinder is circle

∴   Its area = πr^2

∴   **Volume of the Cylinder = $\pi r^2 h$**

Total surface Area of a cylinder = Area of the circles on the base and on the top + Area of the curve surface

Now Area of the base = πr^2 ....(i)
And Area of the top = πr^2 ....(ii)

(b) **Area of the Curved Surface**

If we cut the cylinder open and spread it, it will take the shape of a rectangle whose—

Length will be = circumference of the circle at either end and

Breadth will be = height of the cylinder

∴   **Area of the Curved Surface** = O^{ce} of the Base × Height = **$2\pi r \times h$** ....(iii)

∴   **Total Surface Area of a Cylinder** = (i) + (ii) + (iii)

$$= \pi r^2 + \pi r^2 + 2\pi rh$$

$$= 2\pi r^2 + 2\pi rh = 2\pi r (r + h)$$

(c) *Area of the Curved Surface (Lateral Surface)*

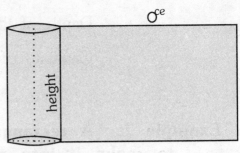

We have already learnt that if a cylinder is cut along its axis and spread out, it will take the shape of a rectangle as shown in front. The **height** of the cylinder will become the *breadth* of the rectangle and its $\circ^{ce}$ will become length of the rectangle. So,

Area of the Curved Surface = Area of the Rectangle

$\qquad\qquad$ = Length × Breadth

$\qquad\qquad$ = Circumference × Height

$\qquad\qquad$ = 2 πr × h = **2 πrh**

Example 5. **Find the volume, total surface area and area of the curved surface of a right circular cylinder whose height (altitude) is 15 cm. and the radius of the base = 7 cm.**

Solution : $\qquad$ Height of the Cylinder = 15 cm.

$\qquad\qquad$ Radius of its Base = 7 cm.

$\qquad\qquad \therefore$ Its Volume $= \pi r^2 h = \dfrac{22}{7} \times (7)^2 \times 15$ cu. cm

$\qquad\qquad\qquad = \dfrac{22}{7} \times 7 \times 7 \times 15$ cu. cm = **2310 cu. cm** *Ans.*

$\qquad\qquad$ Total Surface Area $= 2 \pi r\ (r + h)$

$\qquad\qquad\qquad = 2 \times \dfrac{22}{7} \times 7\ (7 + 15)$ sq. m

$\qquad\qquad\qquad = (44 \times 22)$ sq. cm = **968 sq. cm** *Ans.*

$\qquad\qquad$ Area of the Curved Surface $= 2 \pi rh$

$\qquad\qquad\qquad = 2 \times \dfrac{22}{7} \times 7 \times 15$ sq. cm

$\qquad\qquad\qquad = $ **660 sq. cm** *Ans.*

Example 6. **A water tank is cylinderical in shape and the diameter of its base is 28 m. If it is 7 metres deep, how many kilolitres of water can it hold ?**

Solution : $\qquad$ Base-diameter of the tank = 28 m

$\qquad\qquad \therefore$ Its radius = 28 ÷ 2 = 14 m

Depth of the tank = 7 metres

$\therefore$ Capacity of the tank $= \pi r^2 h = \dfrac{22}{7} \times 14 \times 14 \times 7$ cu. m

= **4312 cu. m 4312 kilolitres** *Ans.*

Example 7. **A rectangular sheet of metal is rolled along its length to make it into a cylinder. The sheet is 33 cm. long and 16 cm. wide. Find the capacity of the cylinder so formed.**

Solution :

Clearly, the length of the sheet will become the *circumference* of the cylinder and its breadth will become the *height* of the cylinder.

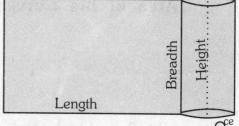

$\therefore$ $\bigcirc^{ce}$ of the Cylinder = Length of the Rectangle = 33 cm.

$\therefore$ Its Diameter $= 33 \times \dfrac{7}{22}$ cm. $= \dfrac{21}{2}$ cm.

$\therefore$ Its Radius $= \dfrac{21}{2} \times \dfrac{1}{2}$ cm. $= \dfrac{21}{4}$ cm.

Height of the Cylinder = Breadth of the Rectangle = 16 cm.

$\therefore$ Capacity of the Cylinder $= \pi r^2 h$

$= \dfrac{22}{7} \times \dfrac{21}{4} \times \dfrac{21}{4} \times 16$ cu. cm.

$= 22 \times 63$ cu. cm $= 1386$ cu. cm.

$= \dfrac{1386}{1000} = $ **1·386 litres** *Ans.*

PRACTICE EXERCISES 51

A. Complete each relation :

1. Volume of a Cylinder = ... × .... × ....

2. Lateral Surface of a Cylinder = ... × .... × .... × ....

3. Total Surface of a Cylinder = ... × .... × .... (....... + ...)

B. Find the *volume, lateral surface* **and** *total surface* **of a cylinder, if its :**

4. Height = 18 cm. ; Radius = 10·5 cm.

5. Height = 16 metres ; Diameter = 7 metres

6. Height = 21 cm. ; Circumference of the Base = 22 cm.

7. Height = 50 cm. ; Area of the Base = 154 cm².

C. 8. How many cubic metres of earth must be dug out to sink a well 16 metres in depth and 7 metres in diameter. If the dug out earth is spread over a square plot with its side 20 metres long, how much will the level of the plot rise ?

9. The diameter of the base of a cylinderical oil can is 16 metres. Find its height if it can contain 5632 kilolitres of oil.

10. A cylinderical tube, open at one end, is internally 10 cm. in diameter. The material of which it is made is 1 cm. thick. If the height of the tube is 7 cm, find its *capacity* and *volume of the metal used.*

11. The diameter of a roller is 2·5 m and its length is 1·4 m. It takes 400 complete revolutions to level a plot. If the levelling costs 50 paise per sq. metre, find the total cost.

12. The volume of a cylinder is 448π cu. cm. and its height is 7 cm. Find the areas of its *total surface* and its *lateral surface.*

13. A rectangular piece of paper is 22 cm. in length and 10 cm. in width. It is rolled into a cylinder along its length. Find the *volume* and the *total surface area* of this cylinder.

14. A closed metallic cylinder has its base diameter = 56 cm. and it is 2·25 meters high. Find the cost of the metal used to make it if it costs Rs. 80 per square metre. Also find its capacity in kilolitres.

15. A face-powder is sold in two types of packs—a *four-sided tin-can* with each side of its base = 5 cm. and height = 14 cm. and a *cylinderical plastic pack* with a base diameter of 7 cm. and height = 12 cm. which pack has the larger capacity and by how much ?

16. Two solids of right cylinderical shape are 49 cm. and 35 cm. high and their base diameters are 16 cm. 14 cm. respectively. Both are melted and moulded into a single cylinder 56 cm. high. Find its base diameter.

17. A cylinderical bucket is half filled with water. Its diameter is 21 cm. A solid cuboid stone 14 cm. × 11 cm. × 9 cm. is put in the bucket. By what height will the level of water rise ?

18. A well was dug 12 metres deep. Its internal diameter is 14 metres. The dug out earth was spread out around the well to a width of 7 metres to form an embankment. Find the height of the embankment.

25 VOLUMES AND SURFACE AREAS—II
(RIGHT CIRCULAR CONES, SPHERES)

> *KNOW THESE TERMS :*
> 1. **slant height**—line-segment joining the top of a cone to its base-edge
> 2. **sphere**—a round solid with every point on it equidistant from its centre (*core*)
> 3. **hemisphere**—half portion of a sphere

RIGHT CIRCULAR CONE

A *right circular cone* **is a solid figure with a** *circular plane base* **and lateral curved surface tapering towards its top to a point called its** *vertex.*

The line-segment that joins the *vertex* of a cone to the *centre* of its circular base is called its **height**. Any line-segment joining the vertex of a cone to any point on the circumference of its base is called its **slant-height**.

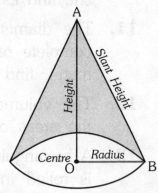

In the figure of a right circular cone given in front—

(a) AO is its **height** (*h*) and AB is its **slant-height** (*l*).

(b) O is its **base-centre** and OB is its **base-radius** (*r*).

(c) AOB is a △ right-angled at O. ∴ $l^2 = r^2 + h^2$

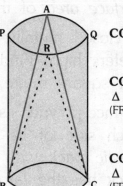

CONE I = △ABC (IN FRONT)

CONE II = △ AQC + △ RQC (FRONT)   (BACK)

CONE III = △ APB + △ RBP (FRONT)   (BACK)

Observe the figure given in front. It shows that the **cone** is one-third of the *Right Circular Cylinder* formed on the same base. Two parts are partially visible in the plane figure shown in front while the third part is hidden behind them. We know that

Volume of a Rt. Circular Cylinder = $\pi r^2 h$

∴ **Volume of a Right Circular Cone** = $\dfrac{1}{3}\pi r^2 h$

Area of the Curved Surface = Circumference of the Base × ½ Slant Height

$$= \pi \times 2r \times \tfrac{1}{2} l = \pi r l$$

Total Surface Area = Area of Base + Area of Curved Surface

$$= \pi r^2 + \pi r l = \pi r\,(r + l)$$

Let us solve some examples :

Example 1. **Find the** *volume, curved surface* **and** *total surface* **of a right circular cone with radius = 5 cm. and height =12 cm.**

Solution : We will find the slant height *(l)* first of all.

Radius of the Cone = 5 cm.

$\therefore$ In rt. $\triangle$ AOB, l^2 $= r^2 + h^2$

$$= 5^2 + 12^2 = 25 + 144$$

$$= 169 = (13)^2$$

or l = **13 cm.**

Now Volume of the Cone $= \frac{1}{3} \pi r^2 h$

$$= \left(\frac{1}{3} \times \frac{22}{7} \times 25 \times 12\right) \text{cu. cm}$$

$$= \frac{2200}{7} \text{cu. cm} = \mathbf{314\frac{2}{7}} \textbf{ cu.cm } Ans.$$

Curved Surface $= \pi r l$ $= \frac{22}{7} \times 5 \times 13$ cu. cm

$$= \frac{1430}{7} \text{cu. cm} = \mathbf{204\frac{2}{7}} \textbf{ cu.cm } Ans.$$

Total Surface $= \pi r (r + l)$ $= \frac{22}{7} \times 5 (5 + 13)$ cu. cm

$$= \left(\frac{22}{7} \times 5 \times 18\right) \text{cu. cm}$$

$$= \frac{1980}{7} \text{cu.cm} = \mathbf{282\frac{6}{7}} \textbf{ cu. cm } Ans.$$

Example 2. **Find the volume of a cone with the circumference of its base = 132 cm and its height = 15·5 cm.**

Solution : Circumference of the Base = 132 cm. or $2\pi r$ = 132 cm.

or $2r \times \frac{22}{7}$ = 132 cm. or $2r = 132 \times \frac{7}{22}$ cm. = 42 cm.

or r = 21 cm. Height = 15·5 cm. = $\frac{31}{2}$ cm.

$\therefore$ Volume $= \frac{1}{3} \pi r^2 h = \frac{1}{3} \times \frac{22}{7} \times 21 \times 21 \times \frac{31}{2}$ cu. cm

$$= 11 \times 21 \times 31 \text{ cu. cm} = \mathbf{1761} \textbf{ cu. cm } Ans.$$

Example 3. **A conical vessel has is inner radius = 24 cm. and its depth = 42 cm. How much water can it hold if one cu. cm of water weighs 1 gram.**

Solution :

Inner radius of the vessel = 24 cm.

Inner depth of the vessel = 42 cm. *i.e.* its *height* = 42 cm.

∴ It can hold $\frac{1}{3} \times \pi \times r^2 \times h$ of water

or Volume of water $= \frac{1}{3} \times \frac{22}{7} \times 24 \times 24 \times 42$ cu. cm

$= 25344$ cu. cm

∴ Weight of water $= 25344$ gm $= \frac{25344}{1000}$ kg. = **25·344 kg.** *Ans.*

Example 4. **A tent has a cylinderical form surmounted by a conical roofing. The diameter of the cylinder is 24 metres while the height of the cylinderical portion is 11 metres. The vertex of the conical roofing is at a height of 16 metres from the ground. Find the area of the canvas used to make the tent.**

Solution :

As for the Lower Cylinderical Portion

Diameter = 24 m or Radius = 12 m

Height = 11 m

∴ Area of the curved surface $= 2\pi rh$

$= (2 \times \frac{22}{7} \times 12 \times 11)$ sq. m $= \dfrac{\mathbf{5808}}{\mathbf{7}}$ **sq. m**

As for the Upper Conical Roofing—

Radius = 12 m

Height = 16 – 11 = 5 m

∴ Slant Height $= \sqrt{12^2 + 5^2}$ m $= \sqrt{169}$ m = 13 m

Area of the curved surface $= \pi rl$

$= \frac{22}{7} \times 12 \times 13$ sq. m $= \dfrac{\mathbf{3432}}{\mathbf{7}}$ **sq. m**

Total curved Area $= \left(\frac{5808}{7} + \frac{3432}{7}\right)$ sq. m $= \frac{9240}{7}$ sq. m

$= $ **1320 square metres** *Ans.*

∴ **Total cloth used to make the tent is 1320 sq. m** *Ans.*

Example 5. **The volume of a conical tent is 9856 cu. m and the area of its base is 616 sq. m. How much cloth has been used to make it ?**

Solution :
Volume of the Tent $= \frac{1}{3} \pi r^2 h = 9856$ cu. m

Base area of the Tent $= \pi r^2 = 616$ sq. m

Dividing the *Volume* by the *Base-area*

$\frac{1}{3} h = 9856$ cu. m $\div 616$ sq. m $= 16$ m

∴ **Height** of the Tent $= 16 \times 3 =$ **48 m**

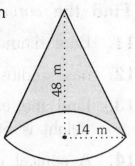

Now we are to calculate the curved surface of the cone

∴ We have to find out **radius** *(r)* and **slant height** *(l)*

$\pi r^2 = 616$ sq. m or $r^2 = 616 \times \frac{7}{22}$ sq. m $= 196$ sq. m

or $r =$ **14 m**

∴ $l = \sqrt{14^2 + 48^2}$ m $= \sqrt{196 + 2304}$ m $= \sqrt{2500}$ m $=$ **50 m.**

∴ Area of curved surface $= \pi r l$

$$= \left(\frac{22}{7} \times 14 \times 50 \right) \text{sq. m} = 2200 \text{ sq. m}$$

∴ **Cloth needed to make the tent = 2200 sq. m** *Ans.*

PRACTICE EXERCISES 52

A. Complete each relation :

1. Volume of a Cone $=$ .... × .... × .... × ....

2. Curved Surface of a Cone $=$ .... × .... × ....

3. Total surface of a Cone $= \pi \times$ .... × (............ + ...)

B. Find the *volume* of a cone whose—

4. base diameter $= 28$ cm. ; height $= 48$ cm.

5. base radius $= 10 \cdot 5$ cm. ; height $= 18$ cm.

6. base radius $= 15$ cm. ; height $= 35$ cm.

C. Find the *slant height* of a cone whose—

7. base radius $= 6$ cm. ; height $= 8$

8. base radius $= 14$ cm. ; height $= 48$ cm.

9. base radius $= 5$ cm. ; height $= 12$ cm.

10. base radius $= 3$ m ; height $= 4$ m.

D. Find the *curved surface* **and** *total surface* **of a cone whose—**

11. Base diameter = 70 cm. ; height = 84 cm.

12. base radius = 10·5 m ; height = 25·2 m

E. 13. Find the *volume, curved surface* and *total surface* of a cone whose slant height is 50 cm. and diameter of the base is 28 cm.

14. A conical cup has a circular base with diameter = 21 cm. and height = 18 cm. How much water can it contain ? If this water is poured into a cylinderical jar with internal diameter = 7 cm, find the height to which water will rise.

15. How much convas is needed to make a conical tent 10 metres in diameter and 6·3 metres in slant height ? The width of the canvas is 1·5 metres. If it costs Rs. 18·25 per metre, find the cost of making the tent as well.

16. A right-angled triangle has its sides other than the hypotenuse 20 cm. and 15 cm. in length. It is rotated on its longest side to form a cone. Find the volume of the cone. Also find its curved surface.

17. A conical vessel whose internal radius is 15 cm. and height is 72 cm is full of water. How much water is there in it. If this water is poured into a cylinderical vessel with internal radius of 30 cm., find the height of water in it.

18. Two solid cylinders are 12 cm. and 18 cm. in height. Their diameters are 12 cm. and 16 cm. respectively. Both the cylinders are melted and the material is moulded into a solid right circular cone of height = 33 cm. Find its diameter.

19. The area of the base of a right circular cone is 28·26 sq. m. If its height be 4 m, find its volume and the curved surface. (use π = 3·14)

20. The surface area of a cone is 4070 sq. cm and diameter is 70 cm. Find its slant height.

SPHERE

A *sphere* **is a solid figure generated by the revolution of a semi-circle round its diameter such that every point on its surface is equidistant from its centre (core).**

Clearly—

A sphere is a solid enclosed by one curved surface with every point on it equidistant from an inner fixed point.

A marble, a cricket ball, a dumb-bell are examples of a sphere. If a sphere is cut into two halves, either of the parts is a *hemisphere*.

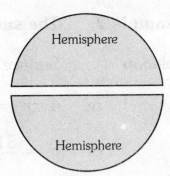

We know that the earth has its northern and southern hemispheres separated by the *equator*.

Volume of a Sphere

Cut a sphere into four equal parts. Each part will be a solid cone with its height equal to the radius of the sphere.

$$\therefore \quad \text{Volume of a Cone} \quad = \frac{1}{3}\,\pi r^2 h$$

$$\therefore \quad \text{Volume of } \frac{1}{4} \text{ Sphere} \quad = \frac{1}{3}\,\pi r^2 \times r = \frac{1}{3}\,\pi r^3 \qquad \left[\begin{array}{l} \because \text{ height of the cone} \\ = \text{ radius of the sphere} \end{array} \right.$$

$$\therefore \quad \textbf{Volume of the Sphere} \quad = 4 \times \frac{1}{3}\,\pi r^3 = \frac{4}{3}\,\pi r^3$$

Surface Area of a Sphere

Divide the surface of the sphere into four parts as shown in front. The top and the bottom parts are like circles. The two middle portions can also be made into circles. Each of the four circles has the same diameter as that of the sphere.

Clearly, the curved surface of the sphere = sum of the areas of the 4 circles explained above.

Now area of a circle = πr^2

Curved Surface of the Sphere = Area of 4 circles = $4\,\pi r^2$

Let us solve some examples :

Example 6. **The diameter of a sphere is 21 cm. Find its volume and the area of its surface.**

Solution : Diameter of the sphere = 21 cm.

$$\therefore \quad \text{Radius of the sphere} \quad = \frac{21}{2} \text{ cm.}$$

$$\therefore \quad \text{Volume} = \frac{4}{3}\,\pi r^3 \; = \frac{4}{3} \times \frac{22}{7} \times \frac{21}{2} \times \frac{21}{2} \times \frac{21}{2} \text{ cu. cm}$$

$$= \textbf{4851 cu. cm } Ans.$$

$$\text{and Surface Area} \; = 4\,\pi r^2 = 4 \times \frac{22}{7} \times \frac{21}{2} \times \frac{21}{20} \text{ sq. cm}$$

$$= \textbf{1386 sq. cm } Ans.$$

Example 7. The surface area of a sphere is $452\frac{4}{7}$ sq. cm. Find its volume.

Solution : Surface Area $= 452\frac{4}{7}$ sq. cm $= \frac{3168}{7}$ sq. cm

or $4\pi r^2 = \frac{3168}{7}$ sq. cm.

or $r^2 = \frac{3168}{7} \times \frac{1}{4} \times \frac{7}{22}$ sq. cm $= 36$ sq. cm

or $r = 6$ cm.

$\therefore$ Reqd. Volume $= \frac{4}{3}\pi r^3$

$= \frac{4}{3} \times \frac{22}{7} \times 6 \times 6 \times 6$ cu. cm $= \frac{6336}{7}$ cu. cm

$= 905\frac{1}{7}$ cu. cm *Ans.*

Example 8. The diameter of a metal sphere is 14 cm. It is beaten into a wire of radius 0·2 cm. How long will the wire be ?

Solution : Diameter of the Sphere $= 14$ cm.

$\therefore$ Its Radius $= 14 \div 2 = 7$ cm.

$\therefore$ Volume of the sphere $= \frac{4}{3} \times \frac{22}{7} \times 7 \times 7 \times 7$ cu. cm

Now the wire will be a cylinder with radius 0·2 cm. We have to find its height.

Base Area of the Wire $= \pi r^2 = \frac{22}{7} \times \frac{2}{10} \times \frac{2}{10}$

$\therefore$ Length of the Wire = Volume $\div$ Base Area

$= \frac{4}{3} \times \frac{22}{7} \times 7 \times 7 \times 7 \times \frac{7}{22} \times \frac{10}{2} \times \frac{10}{2}$ cm.

$= \frac{34300}{3}$ cm $= \frac{34300}{300}$ m $= 114\frac{1}{3}$ m *Ans.*

Example 9. How many lead shots each with radius 1 cm. can be made out of a sphere whose radius is 8 cm.

Solution : Radius of the sphere $= 8$ cm.

$\therefore$ Its Volume $= \frac{4}{3}\pi r^3 = \frac{4}{3} \times \frac{22}{7} \times 8 \times 8 \times 8$ cu. cm

Radius of a Lead shot $= 1$ cm.

$\therefore$ Its Volume $= \dfrac{4}{3} \times \dfrac{22}{7} \times 1 \times 1 \times 1$ cu. cm $= \dfrac{4}{3} \times \dfrac{22}{7}$ cu. cm

$\therefore$ No. of lead-shots = Volume of the sphere ÷ Volume of a Lead-shot

$= \dfrac{4}{3} \times \dfrac{22}{7} \times 8 \times 8 \times 8 \times \dfrac{3}{4} \times \dfrac{7}{22} = \mathbf{512}$ *Ans.*

Example 10. **A conical cup is full of ice-cream and has a hemispherical open end. The diameter of the open end is 6 cm. and the slant height of the cup is 5 cm. How much ice-cream does it contain ?**

Solution :   Radius of the cup's mouth = 6 ÷ 2 = 3 cm.

Slant Height of the Cup = 5 cm.

$\therefore$ Its height $= \sqrt{5^2 - 3^2}$ cm. $= \sqrt{16}$ cm. = 4 cm.

Volume of the Cone $= \dfrac{1}{3}\,\pi r^2 h$

$= \dfrac{1}{3} \times \dfrac{22}{7} \times 3 \times 3 \times 4$ cu. cm $= \dfrac{\mathbf{264}}{\mathbf{7}}$ **cu. cm**

Volume of the Hemisphere $= \dfrac{2}{3}\,\pi r^3$

$= \dfrac{2}{3} \times \dfrac{22}{7} \times 3 \times 3 \times 3$ cu. cm $= \dfrac{\mathbf{396}}{\mathbf{7}}$ **cu. cm**

$\therefore$ Total Volume $= \dfrac{264}{7} + \dfrac{396}{7}$ cu. cm $= \dfrac{660}{7}$ cu. cm

$= \mathbf{94\dfrac{2}{7}}$ **cu. cm** Ans.

PRACTICE EXERCISES 53

A. Complete the relations :

1. Volume of a Sphere   = ... × .... × ....

2. Surface of a Sphere   = ... × .... × ....

3. Volume of a Hemisphere   = ... × .... × ....

4. Curved Surface of Hemisphere = ... × .... × ....

5. Total Surface of a Hemisphere = ... × .... × ....

B. Find the *volume* and the *surface area* of a sphere whose—

  6. diameter = 21 cm   **7.** radius = 7 cm   **8.** radius = 5·6 cm.

C. 9. The area of the curved surface of a sphere is 616 sq. m. Find its volume.

10. The volume of a sphere is 38808 cu. cm, find its surface.

11. A spherical shot-put has its surface area equal to 1386 sq. cm. Find its volume.

12. The volume of a sphere is 4851 cu. cm. Find its surface area.

13. The surface area of a sphere is 2464 sq. cm. Find its diameter.

D. 14. A solid consists of a cylinder surmounted by a hemisphere at one end and by a cone at the other. Its measurements are shown in front. Find its total volume.

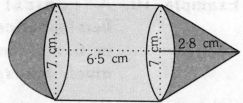

15. A hemispherical bowl has its inner radius = 5·6 cm. Find the volume of the water that it can hold.

16. How many lead-shots each with diameter = 0·3 cm. can be made out of a solid 9 cm. × 11 cm × 12 cm ?

17. The diameter of a metal sphere is 6 cm. It is to be melted and then drawn into a long wire 36 cm. long. Find the radius of the wire.

18. A toy is in the shape of a cone and it is mounted on a hemisphere of radius 3·5 cm. The height of the toy is 12 cm. Find the total surface area of the toy and the hemisphere.

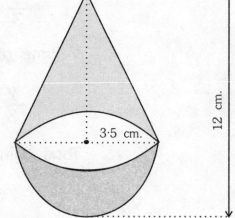

19. A right circular cone is 4·1 cm. high and has a radius = 2·1 cm. Another right circular cone is 4.3 cm. high and has a radius = 2·1 cm. Both the cones were melted and moulded into a sphere. Find the diameter of the sphere.

20. Find the total surface and weight of a hemispherical copper bowl 12 cm in external diameter and 1 cm in thickness if 1 cu. cm of copper weighs 8·88 grams.

MISCELLANEOUS EXERCISES V

A. Define :

 1. *area*   2. *volume*   3. a *diagonal*   4. *perimeter*

B. Complete each relation :

 5. Area of a Rectangle .... × ....

 6. Area of a △ = ... × .... × ....

 7. Area of a △ = $\sqrt{....... (........ - ....) (........ - ....) (........ - ....)}$

8. Area of a Square = (.............)²

9. Area of a||^{gm} = ... × ....

10. Area of Rhombus = ... × .... × ....

11. Area of a Trapezium = ... × .... × ....

12. Area of a Circle = ... 13. Area of a Sector = $\dfrac{.........}{.........}$ × ....

14. Length of an Arc = ... × $\dfrac{\angle\ ....}{360}$

15. Volume of a Cube = ...

16. Volume of a Cuboid = ... × .... × ....

17. Volume of a Cylinder = ... 18. Curved Area of a cylinder = ...

19. Volume of a Cone = ... × .... × ....

20. Curved Surface of a Cone = ... × ....

21. Volume of a Sphere = ... × .... × ....

22. Surface of a Sphere = 4 × ....

C. 23. The sides of a triangle are 13m, 14m and 15m respectively. Find the length of the perpendicular from its largest angle to the opposite side.

24. A field has two parallel sides measuring 173m and 227 m. The perpendicular distance between them is 85 m. Find the cost of tilling it at Rs. 2·50 per sq. metre.

25. How much canvas will be needed to make a conical tent with slant height 16 m and with a base area of 154 sq. m.

26. A hall is 16 metres × 10 metres and its volume is 640 cu. m. A semi-circular bow was added at one of its shorter ends. Find its total volume now.

27. The radius of the inner boundary of a circular race-course is 14 metres and its area is 110 square metres. Find the radius of its outer boundary.

28. A rt. triangle has its sides measuring 15 cm. and 20 cm. Find the length of the perpendicular from the right angle to the hypotenuse.

29. The diameter of a sphere is 6 metres. Find the side of the largest cube that can be cut out of it ?

30. A cylinderical vessel was partly filled with water. An iron sphere with 12 cm. diameter was put into the vessel. By how much will the water-surface go up, if the diameter of the vessel is 24 cm. ?

31. A hollow metal cylinder has its outer radius = 4·3 cm. and the inner radius = 1·1 cm. The length of the cylinder is 4 cm. It was melted and recast into a 12 cm. long solid cylinder. Find the radius of the new cylinder.

32. A solid right circular cone of ice has its base-diameter = 50 cm. and height = 60 cm. Find its weight if the weight of ice is 0·918 of the weight of the same volume of water.

33. Find the total surface area of a hemispherical copper bowl whose external diameter is 12 cm. and whose thickness is 1 cm. Find its weight if 1 cu. cm of copper weighs 5·15 grams.

34. A circular plate has a diameter of 24 centimetres. The air-pressure on the plate is acting at the rate of 140 grams per square centimetre. Find the total pressure on the plate.

MEMORABLE FACTS

1. **Area** means the total measurement of a surface in square units.

2. **Volume** means the total space enclosed within the faces of a solid.

3. **Surface Area of a** *Cube* = **6 ×** **(side)** and its **Volume** = **(side)³**

4. **Surface Area of a** *Cuboid* = **2 (LB + BH + LH)**

5. **Volume of a Cuboid** = **Length × Breadth × Height**

6. **Capacity** is the measure that shows how much of a liquid a vessel can contain.

7. 1000 cubic centimetres = **1 litre**

8. **Volume** of a Right Circular Cone = $\frac{1}{3}\pi r^2 h$

9. **Slant Height** of Right Circular Cone = $\sqrt{r^2 + h^2}$

10. **Curved Surface** of a Right Circular Cone = $\pi r l$

11. **Total Surface** of a Right Circular Cone = $\pi r\,(r + l)$

12. **Volume** of a Sphere = $\frac{4}{3}\pi r^2 h$

13. **Surface** of a Sphere = $4\pi r^2$

14. Volume of a Hemisphere = $\frac{2}{3}\pi r^2 h$

15. Curved Surface of a Hemisphere = $2\pi r^2$

16. Total Surface of a Hemisphere = $3\pi r^2$

17. The Longest Pole in a Room = $\sqrt{L^2 + B^2 + H^2}$

18. Units of area are **two dimensional units.**

19. Units of volume are **three dimensional units.**

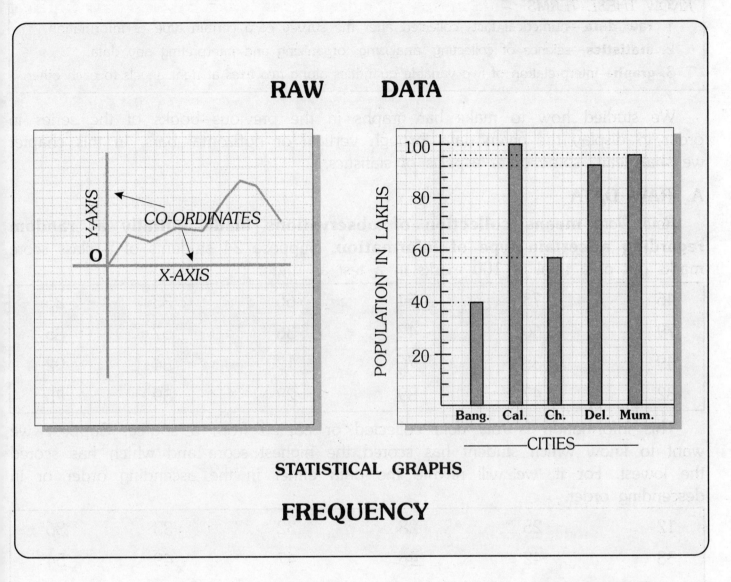

RAW   DATA

CO-ORDINATES

Y-AXIS

O

X-AXIS

POPULATION IN LAKHS

100

80

60

40

20

Bang. Cal. Ch. Del. Mum.

CITIES

STATISTICAL GRAPHS

FREQUENCY

26 STATISTICS

We studied how to make bar graphs in the previous books of the series in order to display the given data through vertical or horizontal bars. In this chapter we shall learn some other aspects of statistics.

A. RAW DATA

Raw Data **means collection of observations made initially at random regarding a certain type of information.** Suppose 24 students of a class score marks out of a total of 100 marks in a test as under :

46	73	54	66	33	25
79	60	42	36	57	85
49	38	76	12	84	92
32	47	89	28	59	75

This information is *raw data* collected or copied from a source. Suppose we want to know which student has scored the highest score and which has scored the lowest. For it, we will rewrite the data either in the ascending order or in descending order.

12	25	28	32	33	36
38	42	46	47	49	54
57	59	60	66	73	75
76	79	84	85	89	92

Now we can easily report that the **lowest score** is 12 while the **highest score** is **92**.

The difference between the *lowest score* and the *highest score* is called the **Range**. So, we can say :

The **range** of the *above observations* is 92 – 12 = **80**

From this information, we can also calculate the *average marks* obtained by a student. This average is called the **Arithmetical Mean**.

The jobs mentioned above are collectively called **statistics.**

Remember the following definitions :

1. *Statistics* **is the science of collecting, analysing, organising and interpreting numerical data.**

2. **The collection of numerical facts of a particular type of information is called** *data.*

3. **The collection of observations gathered initially at random is called** *raw data.*

4. *Range* **means the difference between the highest and the lowest values in an observed data.**

5. *Mean* **or** *Arithmetical Mean* **is the quotient obtained by dividing the** *total of the observations* **by the** *number* **of the observations,** *i.e.*

$$\text{Mean} = \frac{\text{sum of all observations}}{\text{number of observations}}$$

In the example on page 238 :

$$\text{Mean} = \frac{12+25+28+32+33+36+\ldots\ldots\ldots 92}{24} = \frac{1347}{24} = \mathbf{56{\cdot}042}$$

Let us now solve some examples :

Example 1. **The weights of 10 students of a class are 50, 48, 51, 49, 46, 43, 52, 47, 45, 44 kilograms respectively. Find the range and the mean weight of a student.**

Solution : Arranging the weights in descending order

52, 51, 50, 49, 48, 47, 46, 45, 44, 43

Clearly the highest weight = 52 kg.

The lowest weight = 43 kg.

∴ Range = (52 – 43) kg. = **9 kg.** *Ans.*

And Mean = $\dfrac{52+51+50+49+48+47+46+45+44+43}{10 \text{ (No. of students)}}$

$$= \frac{475}{10} = \mathbf{47{\cdot}5} \ Ans.$$

FREQUENCY DISTRIBUTION

Frequency **means the number of times a particular observation (item of data) occurs in the interpretation of data.**

For example—

We collect and interpret the data of heights of 18 children of a class in cm.

122	125	130	122	124	130
127	126	127	130	121	124
130	127	120	130	122	127

Arranging the heights in descending order :

130, 130, 130, 130, 130, 127, 127, 127, 127, 126, 125, 124, 124, 122, 1222, 122, 121, 120

We see that—

(a) height of 122 cm. occurs 3 times   (b) height of 124 cm. occurs 2 times

(c) height of 127 cm. occurs 4 times   (d) height of 130 cm. occurs 5 times

So, we say that :

(a) **frequency of 122 cm. is 3**   (b) **frequency of 124 cm. is 2**

(c) **frequency of 127 cm. is 4**   (d) **frequency of 130 cm. is 5**

This data can be expressed in a tabular form. This tabular expression is called **frequency distribution**.

We use *tally marks* to express the frequency as under :

I mark for   1   II marks for   2   III marks for 3

IIII marks for   4   IIII marks for   5

TABULAR EXPRESSION

Frequent Item	Tally Marks	Frequency
122 cm.	III	3
124 cm.	II	2
127 cm.	IIII	4
130 cm.	IIII	5
	Total	14

Mean = $\dfrac{\text{Sum of the products of observations and their frequencies}}{\text{Sum of the frequencies}}$

In the above case—

Data in the ascending order :

121, 122, 122, 122, 124, 124, 124, 125, 126, 127, 127, 127, 127, 130, 130, 130, 130, 130

Heights	Frequency	Products
121	1	$121 \times 1 = 121$
122	3	$122 \times 3 = 366$
124	2	$124 \times 2 = 248$
125	1	$125 \times 1 = 125$
126	1	$126 \times 1 = 126$
127	4	$127 \times 4 = 508$
130	5	$130 \times 5 = 650$
Total	17	2144

Sum of the *products of observations* and their *frequencies* = 2144

Sum of the frequencies = 17 ∴ Mean = $\dfrac{2144}{17}$ = **126·117** *Ans.*

GROUPING OF DATA

When the number of observations is fairly large, the data may be classified into several groups and the frequency of each group may be recorded.

*The data classified in several groups along with the frequency of each group is called **grouped data**. Each group of a classified data is called a **class interval**.*

HOW TO CLASSIFY DATA

Suppose the marks obtained by 50 students of a class are as under :

47	57	55	51	53	59	52	62	65	67
64	72	77	78	92	5	8	12	18	15
2	23	24	25	27	81	89	26	29	22
34	35	30	37	36	42	48	28	21	27
17	13	35	31	32	36	41	40	43	45

First of all, we shall arrange the data in the ascending order :

2	5	8	12	13	15	17	18	21	22
23	24	25	26	27	27	28	29	30	31
32	33	34	35	36	36	37	40	41	42
43	45	47	48	51	52	53	55	57	59
62	64	65	67	72	77	78	81	89	92

Now we shall classify the data into groups as under :

Group I : 0 — 20   Group II : 20 — 40

Group III : 40 — 60   Group IV : 60 and above

GROUP or CLASS INTERVAL I (0 — 20)
2 5 8 12 13 15 17 18   **(8 observations)**
More than or equal to 0 but less than 20

GROUP or CLASS INTERVAL II (20 — 40)
21 22 23 24 25 26 27 27 28 29
30 31 22 33 34 35 36 36 37   **18 observations**
More than or equal to 20 but less than 40

GROUP or CLASS INTERVAL III (40 — 60)
40 41 42 43 45 47 48 51 52 53
55 57 59   **13 observations**
More than or equal to 40 but less than 60

GROUP or CLASS INTERVAL IV 60 and above)
62 64 65 67 72 77 78 81 89 92   **(10 observations)**
More than or equal to 60

Now we shall make the FREQUENCY TABLE

Class Interval	Tally Marks	Frequency
0 — 20	ЖЖ III	8
20 — 40	ЖЖ ЖЖ ЖЖ III	18
40 — 60	ЖЖ ЖЖ III	13
60 and above	ЖЖ ЖЖ	10
	Total	49

PRACTICE EXERCISES 54

A. Define :

1. Raw Data : ....

....

2. Range : ....

....

3. Mean : ....
....

4. Frequency : ....
....

5. Class Interval : ....
....

B. 6. Given below are the heights of 12 boys of a team in centimetres. Find the *upper limit, lower limit, range, mid-value* and *mean* of the given heights.

Heights : 146   136   143   148   132   128
             139   140   152   154   142   150

7. A player scores runs in ten matches as given below. Find the *highest score, lowest score, range, mid-value* and *mean* of the runs.

Runs :   27   28   30   31   55   60   65   70   85   100

C. 8. The number of children in the 20 families of a village are as given below. Prepare the frequency table.

2   2   1   1   2   3   2   2   1   3
2   2   3   1   2   1   1   3   2   2

9. Given below are the numbers of accidents during a certain month in 30 cities. Prepare their frequency table and find the mean of the data.

23   12   45   34   23   12   12   11   1   2
23   12   12   10   9   8   10   1   23   34
10   9   10   9   8   1   2   1   11   12

D. 10. The marks obtained by 45 students of a class in a test were as given below. Divide the data into suitable groups starting from 0—5, 5—10........ and prepare a frequency table.

5   16   12   17   18   18   8   3   12   7   6   23   8   18   16
13   5   10   3   21   5   7   0   1   7   13   9   21   21   13
20   15   10   9   2   24   23   16   2   23   5   17   7   12   18

11. Given below are weights of 36 persons in kilograms. Classify the data in suitable groups starting from 40—45 and prepare a frequency table.

43   51   47   62   48   40   50   62   53   56   40   48
56   53   50   42   55   52   48   46   45   54   52   50
47   44   54   55   60   63   58   55   60   58   53   52

27 | GRAPHS

We have learnt how to draw bar graphs and how to interpret them. These graphs were related to ungrouped data. So, only heights of bars (rectangles) were the main consideration to show the data. In this lesson, we shall go a step further. We shall learn how to draw graphs of grouped frequency distribution. These graphs consist of rectangles (bars) that show **class intervals** as the *bases* and the corresponding **frequencies** as the *heights*. Such graphs are called **histograms**.

A. HISTOGRAMS

A *histogram* **is a graphical diagram that consists of columns showing frequencies of various classes of the collected observations regarding a certain type of information.**

HOW TO DRAW A HISTOGRAM

While drawing a histogram, we take the following steps :
1. We prepare a frequency table for the given data.
2. Along the *horizontal axis*, we show class-intervals with a proper scale.
3. We show frequencies in the ascending order with a proper scale along the *vertical axis*.
4. We draw a column for each frequency matching its height to the frequency.
5. The mid-point of the base of each bar corresponds to the score.

Example 1. The marks obtained by the 24 students of a class in English are as under. Draw a histogram for this data.

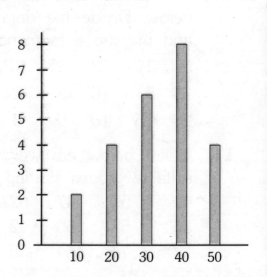

Marks obtained	No. of Students
0 — 10	2
10 — 20	4
20 — 30	6
30 — 40	8
40 — 50	4

Solution :   1. Along the horizontal axis mark the class intervals.

2. Along the vertical axis mark the frequencies.

Example 2. Draw a histogram in order to represent the data given below :

Class Intervals	Rs.300-400	Rs.400-500	Rs.500-600	Rs.600-700	Rs.700—800
Frequencies	15	10	8	20	10

STEPS :   1. Take the class intervals along the horizontal axis.

2. Take the frequencies along the vertical axis.

3. As there are no frequencies for 0—100, 100—200, 200—300, so three kinks are indicated near the origin to show that the graph begins with 300, not with 0.

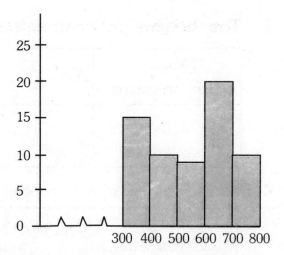

Example 3.   Look at the histogram given in front and interpret the following facts from it :

1. **No. of teachers between 45 years and 50 years.**

2. **No. of teachers between 30 and 35 years.**

3. **No. of teachers who are above 40 years of age.**

4. **Why has a kink been given in the beginning ?**

Solution :   1. Teachers between 45 yrs and 50 yrs = 12

2. Teachers between 30 yrs and 35 yrs = 4

3. Teachers who are above 40 years of age = 10 + 12 + 5 + 6 = 33

4. As the histogram starts from 30, we have to give a kink to indicate 0—30.

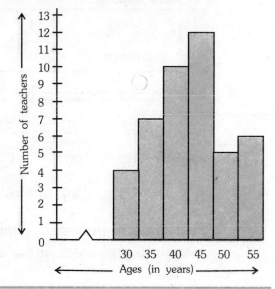

A. 1. Define a histogram :

....

....

....

2. Which five steps will you take while drawing a histogram ?

B. Draw histograms for the following data :

3. The heights in centimetres of 15 teenagers are as under :

Height (Class intervals)	120—125	125—130	130—135	135—140	140—145
No. of teengers (Frequencies)	1	2	4	2	6

4. The monthly salaries in rupees of 78 workers of a factory were as under :

Salary (Class Intervals)	300—310	310—320	320—330	330—340	340—350
No. of workers (Frequencies)	12	18	28	15	5

5. Weights of 31 men were as under in kilograms :

Weight (Class Intervals)	45—50	50—55	55—60	60—65	65—70
No. of Men (Frequencies)	2	8	11	7	3

6. The marks obtained by 24 students in a certain test are as under :

12	12	15	20	35	45	55	60
68	70	90	88	75	66	55	58
57	54	36	80	89	89	45	90

Prepare a frequency table for the above data choosing suitable class-intervals and then draw a histogram.

D. Interpret the following histograms :

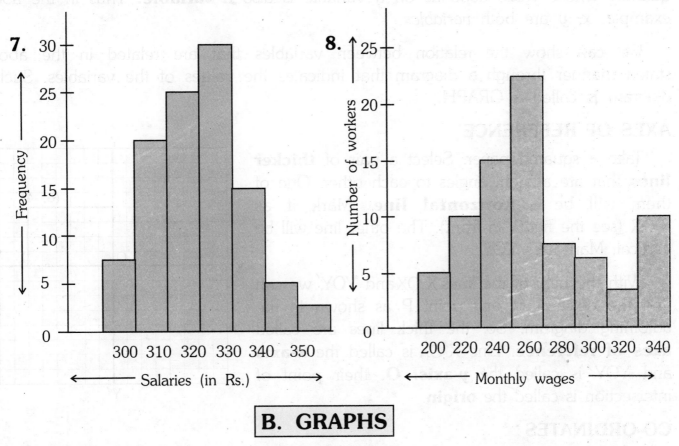

7.

8.

B. GRAPHS

We generally see that two quantities are often related such that if a change is made in one, a corresponding change occurs in the other as well. Suppose tea costs Rs. 80 a kg. If we double the weight, the cost also gets doubled and if we treble the weight, the cost is trebled. So, we say that the **cost** is *directly proportional to the* **weight.**

Similarly any expression involving *x* will have different values for different values of *x*. For example, if *x* has a series of values 3, 2, 1, 0, –1, –2, –3, the expression 2*x* + 5 will have its values as under :

x	3	2	1	0	–1	–2	–3
$2x$	6	4	2	0	–2	–4	–6
$2x + 5$ or y	11	9	7	5	3	1	–1

If we suppose that 2*x* + 5 = *y*, then *y* will have these values. Clearly, these values of *y* depend on the values of *x*.

A quantity that may have a series of values is called a **variable** and the quantity whose value depends on a variable is also a **variable.** Thus in the above example, *x, y* are both *variables*.

We can show the relation between variables that are related in the above-stated manner through a diagram that indicates the values of the variables. Such a diagram is called a GRAPH.

AXES OF REFERENCE

Take a squared paper. Select a pair of **thicker lines** that are at right angles to each other. One of them will be a **horizontal line**. Mark it as X′OX (see the figure in front). The other line will be vertical. Mark it as YOY′.

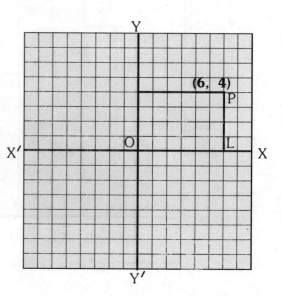

With the help of the lines X′OX and YOY′, we can find the position of any point P as shown in the adjoining diagram. So, the thick lines are called **axes of reference**. Line X′OX is called the **x-axis** and YOY′ is called the **y-axis. O**, their point of intersection is called the **origin**.

CO-ORDINATES

Now observe the point P shown in the above diagram. It is clear that we can get right under P by moving/marking 6 divisions along OX, *i.e.* to the point L. Then moving 4 divisions vertically upwards from L, we can reach P. Alternatively, we can say that we can get just abreast of P by moving 4 divisions along OY. From there we can move 6 divisions to the right to reach P.

These distances of 6 and 4 divisions along OX and OY are called **Co-ordinates** of the point P.

The *co-ordinate* along or parallel to OX is called **abscissa.**

The co-ordinate along or parallel to OY is called **ordinate.**

In practice, the *abscissa* is denoted by *x* while the *ordinate* is denoted by *y*.

When we speak of a point on the diagram, we say it a **point (x, y)**, *i.e.* the abscissa is always named first. This *process of marking the position of a point on a squared paper is called* **plotting a point.**

QUADRANTS AND THEIR SIGNS

Both the axes of reference divide the plane of the squared paper into four divisions—YOX, YOX′, Y′OX′, Y′OX . Each of these divisions is called a **quadrant**. They are called the *first, second, third* and *fourth* quadrants respectively.

Clearly, in each of the four quadrants, there is a point corresponding to point P. All these points will have their co-ordinates just as P has, *i.e. 6 units* and *4 units*.

In order to distinguish between the four various position of point P, we use **+ve** and **–ve** signs as under :

(a) 1. Units measured along *x-axis* to the right of O are **+ve.**

2. Units measured along *x-axis* to the left of O are **–ve.**

(b) 1. Units measured along *y-axis* upwards from O are **+ve.**

2. Units measured along *y-axis* downwards of O are **–ve.**

Observe the point P in each quadrant and note down the use of signs with its co-ordinates.

Let us now learn how to plot points on a squared paper.

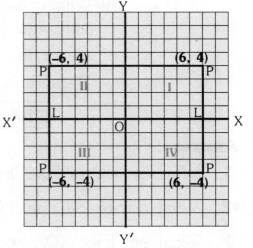

Example 1. Plot the points :

(a) **(6, 8)**   (b) **(–2, 2)**

(c) **(7, –4)**   (d) **(–6, –8)**

Solution :   (a) ∵ both co-ordinates are **+ve**

∴ The point is in Quad. I. So, we take 6 units along OX and then 8 units right upwards to plot the required point P.

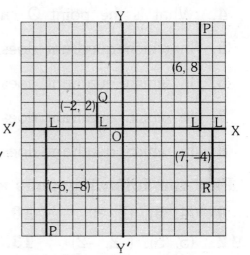

b) ∵ *x*–co-ordinate is **–ve**

∴ The point is in Quad. II. So, we take 2 units along OX' and then 2 units upwards to plot the point Q.

(c) ∵ *y*–co-ordinate is **–ve**

∴ The point is in Quad. IV. So, we take 7 units along OX and then 4 units right downwards to plot the point R.

(d) ∵ both the co-ordinates are **–ve**

∴ The point is in Quad. III. So, we take 6 units along OX' and then 8 units right downwards.

Example 2. Plot the points P (6, 8) and Q (–2, 2) and find the distance between them.

Solution :   Point P has both co-ordinates **+ve**

∴   We plotted it in Quad. I.

Point Q has **x-co-ordinate –ve**

∴   We plotted it in Quad. II.

To find the distance between P and Q

(a) Join PQ

(b) With Q as centre and QP as radius draw an arc that cuts the horizontal line passing through Q at R. Clearly QP = QR.

Count the units from Q to R ; they are 10

∴   Distance between P, Q = **10 units** *Ans.*

PRACTICE EXERCISES 56

A. Answer :

1. What do we call the line X′OX ?   ....

2. What do we call the line YOY′ ?   ....

3. What are lines XOX′ and YOY′ called ?   ....

4. What is the point O called where X′OX and YOY cut ?   ....

5. In which quadrant does the point (4, 5) lie ?   ....

6. In which quadrant does the point (–2, –5) lie ?   ....

7. In which quadrant does the point (–4, 6) lie ?   ....

8. In which quadrant does the point (4, –6) lie ?   ....

B. Plot the following pairs of points :

9. (4, 5), (2, 8)   **10.** (–4, 5), (–2, 8)   **11.** (3, 11), (0, 6)

12. (5, 5), (–2, –2)   **13.** (0, 0), (–3, 5)   **14.** (–3, 8), (–2, 6)

C. Plot the pairs of the points and find the distance between the points of each pair :

15. (4, 0), (0, 3)   **16.** (9, 8), (5, 5)   **17.** (15, 0), (0, 8)

18. (20, 12), (–15, 0)   **19.** (20, 9), (–15, –3)   **20.** (10, 4), (–5, 12)

D. 21. Plot the points (3, 3), (–3, 3), (–3, –3), (3, –3). Find the number of squares contained in the rectangle given by these points.

A. Define :

1. statistics	2. data	3. raw data	4. range
5. frequency	6. graph	7. mean	8. frequency distribution
9. class interval	10. histogram	11. kink	12. ordinate
13. x-axis	14. y-axis	15. abscissa	16. quadrant

B. 17. Given below are the raw data collected at random regarding the scores of 24 students out of a total of 100. Arrange it in the ascending order and report the lowest as will as the highest scores. Also, find the rancge of the data and its mean.

46	73	54	66	33	25
79	60	42	36	57	85
49	38	76	12	84	92
32	47	89	28	59	75

18. Given below are the raw data of the heights of the 18 children of a class in centimeters. Arrange the data in ascending order and indicate their frequency in a tabular form giving the *heights*, the *frequencies* with their *tally marks* and the *products* of observation. Also calculate the *mean*.

122	125	130	122	124	130
127	126	127	130	121	124
130	127	120	130	122	127

Heights	Frequencies	Tally Marks	Products	Sum of Products

Sum of the Products   = ...

No. of Frequencies   = ...

$\text{Mean} = \dfrac{\text{Sum of Products}}{\text{No. of Frequencies}} =$ ....

19. Given below are the raw data of marks obtained by 50 students of a class n a test out of 100 marks. Among the data in their ascending order and group them into four groups as under.

      (a) 0 - 20   (b) 20 - 40   (c) 40 - 60   (d) above 60.

Also prepare a *frequency table*.

47	57	55	51	53	59	52	62	65	67
64	72	77	78	92	5	8	12	18	15
2	23	24	25	27	81	89	26	29	22
34	35	30	37	36	42	48	28	21	27
17	13	35	31	32	36	41	40	43	45

20. Draw a histogram to represent the data given below :

Groups of Data	0 - 10	10 - 20	20 - 30	30 - 40	40 - 50
No. of Frequencies	2	4	6	8	4

21. Plot the points of each pair and find the distance between them.

      (a) 6, 8   (b) – 3, 3   (c) 6, – 5   (d) – 5, –7

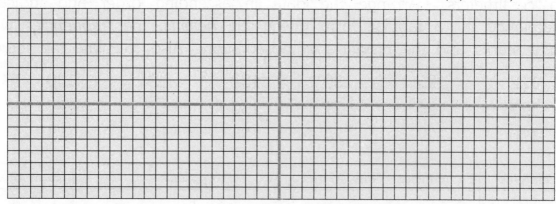

MEMORABLE FACTS

1. **Statistics** means *collecting, scanning, arranging* and *interpreting* any data.
2. The data collected *at random* is called **raw data**.
3. The *heights* and the *lowest* limits of a data mark of their **range**.
4. The *number of times* any item of any data occurs in it is called its **frequency**.
5. The frequency of any data is expressed through **tally marks**.
6. A **histogram** is a graphic diagram that uses *columns* to indicate frequencies.
7. A *graph* is a diagram that shows the relation between two variable quantities either of which is measured along one of a *pair of axes* at right angles to each other.

ANSWERS

A. **1.** both   **2.** rational number   **3.** both   **4.** $\frac{a}{1}$.   **5.** based on reasoning

6. $\frac{0}{2}$ **7.** no   **8.** 0 itself   **9.** no number   **10.** $\frac{15}{22}$

11. $\frac{-2}{3}$, 0, $\frac{2}{3}$ **12.** $0.\overline{1}$ **13.** $(\frac{a}{b})^m$ **14.** $\frac{1}{10}$, $\frac{1}{100}$ **15.** 1.5×10^6 **16.** 2.9×10

B. **17.** A *rational number* is a number that can be expressed in the form $\frac{a}{b}$ where b is not equal to 0. But an *irrational number* is a number that cannot be expressed in the form $\frac{a}{b}$.

18. The +ve and –ve forms of a rational number are the *additive inverse* of each other. But the *multiplicative inverse* of a rational number is formed by changing the places of its numerator and denominator.

19. The *density* of two consecutive rational numbers is their capacity to hold rational numbers between them. But the *absolute value* of an integer is its numerical value whatever sign may occur before it.

20. A decimal with finite decimal part is a *terminating decimal* but a decimal with a never-ending decimal part is a *non-terminating (concurring decimal)*.

21. A recurring decimal with unmixed recurring decimal digits is a *pure recurring decimal*. But a recurring decimal with mixed recurring and non-recurring decimal digits is an impure or mixed recurring decimal.

22. In any term a small numeral on its top right to show its power is called its *index*. While the term itself is called the *base*.

23. Two quantities are in *direct variation* if their ratio remains the same when both of them are decreased and increased together. But they are in *inverse variation* if their product remains the same when they increase or decrease opposite to each other.

24. A *factor* is a quantity that divides another quantity exactly while a *common factor* is a quantity that can divide two or more quantities exactly.

25. A literal number that can be replaced by more than one numerical values is a *variable* while a literal number with only one numerical value is a *constant*.

26. The *centroid* of a triangle is the point where its *medians* intersect but the *orthocentre* of a triangle is the point where its *altitudes* intersect.

27. The *circumcentre* of a triangle is the point where the *right bi-sectors* of its sides intersect but the *incentre* of a triangle is the point where the *bisectors of its angles* intersect.

28. *Concurrent* means two or more lines passing through the same point but *concentric* means two or more *circles* having the same centre.

29. A *chord* is a line-segment that joins two different points on the circumference of a circle while an *arc* is any part of the circumference between two points taken on it.

30. *Area* means total *expanse* of a surface that has two dimensions but *volume* means the total *space* occupied by an object due to its three dimensions

31. Perimeter means the *sum of the lengths* of the sides of a plane figure while *diameter* is the biggest chord in a circle passing through its centre.

C. 32. $\dfrac{-6}{7}, \dfrac{3}{-4}, \dfrac{1}{-2}, \dfrac{-5}{11}$ and $\dfrac{-5}{11}, \dfrac{1}{-2}, \dfrac{3}{-4}, \dfrac{-6}{7}$

33. no answer required   **34.** $\dfrac{-95}{72}$ **35.** no answer required   **36.** $\dfrac{-1}{3}, 0, \dfrac{1}{3}$

37. no answer needed   **38.** (a) 12·2929   (b) 0·1428

39. (a) $\dfrac{19}{90}$ (b) $\dfrac{139}{1100}$ **40.** $\dfrac{49}{99}$ **41.** $\dfrac{-1}{7}$ **42.** no answer needed   **43.** 30 minutes

D. 44. 26 days   **45.** 160 men   **46.** 28 days   **47.** 4 days   **48.** 7·2 seconds
49. 1 min. 48 sec **50.** 30   **51.** 1400   **52.** 50% above the cost   **53.** 10%
54. 1% loss   **55.** Rs. 3600, Rs. 2400

E. 56. $2x^3 - 3x^2 + 5x + 21$ **57.** 1·468   **58.** $(a - b + 3)(a - b - 3)$
59. $x = 15\dfrac{5}{9}$ **60.** 65, 66, 67, 68

F. 61. (a) six   (b) none   (c) 90°, 45°, 45°   (d) 5 cm.

G. 62. (a) median   (b) concurrent   (c) incentre   (d) SSS, SAS, ASA

H. 63. (a) four, four   (b) 180°   (c) common   (d) 4 rt. $\angle$s

I. 64. (a) false   (b) false   (c) true   (d) true
(e) true   (f) true   (g) true   (h) false

K. 68. 20 cm.   **69.** Rs. 188·10   **70.** 48 sq. m   **71.** 23 cm.   **72.** Rs. 120

PRACTICE EXERCISES 1. (Page 17)

A. 1. yes   **2.** no   **3.** no   **4.** no   **5.** yes
B. 6. yes   **7.** no   **8.** yes   **9.** no   **10.** yes
C. 11. 25   **12.** 49   **13.** 9   **14.** 81
D. 15. 27 + 26 = 53   **16.** 103 + 102 = 205   **17.** 569 + 568 = 1137
E. 18. yes   **19.** no   **20.** no   **21.** no
F. 22. $(13)^2$ **23.** $(30)^2$ **24.** $(42)^2, (43)^2$ **25.** $(110)^2, (111)^2$

G. 26. $\dfrac{(4444)^2}{1+2+3+4+3+2+1}$ **27.** $\dfrac{(55555)^2}{1+2+3+4+5+4+3+2+1}$

H. 28. $2^2 = 4$ **29.** $3^2 = 9$ **30.** $4^2 = 16$ **31.** $5^2 = 25$

32. $49 = 1 + 3 + 5 + 7 + 9 + 11 + 13$;

$64 = 1 + 3 + 5 + 7 + 9 + 11 + 13 + 15$;

$36 = 1 + 3 + 5 + 7 + 9 + 11$

33. (a) 3, 5   (b) 8, 10   (c) 5, 13

I. 34. A triplet of three natural numbers is called a Pythagorean Triplet if the sum of the squares of two of them equals the square of the third ; as—

(3, 4, 5) ; (6, 8, 10) ; (5, 12, 13) ; (10, 24, 26)

35., 36. Factorize and prove

PRACTICE EXERCISES 2 (Page 19)

A. **1.** see page 17

B. **2.** 36   **3.** 42   **4.** 29   **5.** 84   **6.** 231

7. 546   **8.** 51   **9.** 1000

C. **10.** 5, 30   **11.** 5, 25   **12.** 39   **13.** 11   **14.** 6, 140

D. **15.** $\dfrac{1}{3}$ **16.** $\dfrac{11}{13}$ **17.** $\dfrac{16}{19}$ **18.** $1\dfrac{4}{5}$ **19.** 132

20. 182   **21.** 288   **22.** 48   **23.** 72   **24.** 60

E. **25.** 10, 100   **26.** 11   **27.** 3   **28.** 1000, 9999 ; 10, 1111   **29.** 3

PRACTICE EXERCISES 3. (Page 22)

A. **1.** 23   **2.** 81   **3.** 729   **4.** 329   **5.** 603

6. 2098   **7.** 554   **8.** 1213   **9.** 539   **10.** 239

11. 9070   **12.** 8027   **13.** 1317   **14.** 999   **15.** 317

16. 4519   **17.** 3607   **18.** 13204   **19.** 4297   **20.** 34021

B. **21.** 24·7   **22.** 9·21   **23.** 12·13   **24.** ·751   **25.** 39·15

26. ·0243   **27.** ·752   **28.** 13·276   **29.** ·0197   **30.** ·0606

31. 34·91   **32.** ·0374   **33.** ·612   **34.** 9·99   **35.** 2·403

C. **36.** $\dfrac{23}{29}$ **37.** $\dfrac{21}{31}$ **38.** $3\dfrac{4}{7}$ **39.** $4\dfrac{39}{58}$ **40.** $4\dfrac{8}{13}$

41. $2\dfrac{2}{5}$ **42.** $4\dfrac{23}{27}$ **43.** $2\dfrac{5}{7}$ **44.** $6\dfrac{3}{29}$ **45.** $\dfrac{73}{309}$

46. $5\dfrac{10}{11}$ **47.** $1\dfrac{83}{203}$ **48.** $33\dfrac{5}{9}$ **49.** $5\dfrac{35}{38}$ **50.** $\dfrac{16}{23}$ **51.** $\dfrac{9}{17}$

D. **52.** 11·25 **53.** 10 **54.** 16·02 m **55.** 501·95

PRACTICE EXERCISES 4 *(Page 27)*

A. **1.** 1·732 **2.** 2·646 **3.** 2·449 **4.** 1·414 **5.** 2·828

6. ·948 **7.** 1·673 **8.** ·632 **9.** ·894 **10.** 2·366

11. 1·264 **12.** ·447 **13.** 4·381 **14.** ·126 **15.** 1·897

16. ·7905 **17.** ·471 **18.** ·816 **19.** $\dfrac{1}{3}$ **20.** ·763

B. **21.** 3·266 **22.** $5\dfrac{2}{5}$ **23.** $6\dfrac{1}{4}$ **24.** $3\dfrac{1}{6}$ **25.** $\dfrac{16}{23}$

26. ·654 **27.** 1·615 **28.** ·707 **29.** 198 **30.** $\dfrac{9}{17}$

31. $\dfrac{4}{5}$ **32.** $1\dfrac{4}{13}$

C. **33.** 2·53 **34.** ·0193 **35.** 5·26 m **36.** 20·4 m **37.** 18·97 m

38. 2·55 m **39.** 3·6055 **40.** 15·4146

41. 9·798 nearly **42.** *(a)* 3·742 *(b)* 3·74

43. *(a)* yes *(b)* yes *(c)* no *(d)* yes

44. *(a)* $\cdot\overline{84}\ \overline{82}\ \overline{41}$ *(b)* $4\ \overline{40}\ \overline{16}\ \overline{04}$ *(c)* $\overline{82}\ \overline{26}\ \overline{49}\ \overline{00}$

(d) $8\ \overline{43}\ \overline{21}\cdot\overline{16}\ 7$ *(e)* $\cdot\overline{00}\ \overline{00}\ \overline{82}\ \overline{81}$ *(f)* $\overline{07}\ \overline{17}\ 6$

PRACTICE EXERCISES 5 *(Page 34)*

A. **1.** irrational **2.** rational **3.** irrational **4.** irrational **5.** rational

6. rational **7.** irrational **8.** irrational **9.** irrational **10.** irrational

B. **11.** 2·449 ; 3·316

C. **12.** $2 + \sqrt{3},\ 2 - \sqrt{3}$ **13.** $\sqrt{3} + 2,\ \sqrt{3} - 2$ **14.** $\sqrt{8},\ \sqrt{2}$

15. $\sqrt{18},\ \sqrt{2}$ or $\sqrt{8}\ ,\ \sqrt{2}$ **16.** $\sqrt{3}$

D. **17** to **20** No answers required.

E. **21.** no **22.** yes **23.** yes **24.** yes **25.** yes

26. yes **27.** yes **28.** yes **29.** no **30.** yes

F. **31.** 2·943 **32.** 1·991 **33.** ·584 **34.** ·252

35. 1 **36.** 0·102 **37.** Needs no answer.

PRACTICE EXERCISES 6 (Page 38)

A. **1.** 729   **2.** 4913   **3.** 6859   **4.** 2744   **5.** 4096
6. 1000   **7.** 8000   **8.** 27000   **9.** 64000   **10.** 125000
11. ·125   **12.** 1·728   **13.** ·512   **14.** ·000216   **15.** 15·625
16. $\dfrac{8}{27}$ **17.** $\dfrac{64}{125}$ **18.** $\dfrac{4913}{2744}$ **19.** $\dfrac{1}{4913}$ **20.** $\dfrac{1331}{2744}$
21. -343 **22.** $-p^3$ **23.** $-4\dfrac{17}{27}$ **24.** $-\dfrac{x^3}{y^3}$ **25.** $-\dfrac{c^3}{d^3}$

B. **26.** no   **27.** no   **28.** no   **29.** yes   **30.** no
31. yes   **32.** yes   **33.** yes   **34.** no   **35.** no
36. 5   **37.** 5   **38.** 1331 cu. m   **39.** No answer needed.

PRACTICE EXERCISES 7 (Page 42)

A. **1.** 6   **2.** 12   **3.** 7   **4.** 8   **5.** 9
6. 105   **7.** 54   **8.** 60   **9.** 28   **10.** $1\dfrac{4}{5}$

B. **11.** 7   **12.** -7 **13.** ·7   **14.** ·3   **15.** ·06
16. -12 **17.** 12   **18.** 12   **19.** -66 **20.** 28

C. **21.** $\dfrac{3}{5}$ **22.** $\dfrac{-4}{10}$ **23.** ·011   **24.** -18 **25.** 30   **26.** 60

E. **33.** 5   **34.** 5   **35.** 9   **36.** 7
37. 6   **38.** 3·2 m   **39.** 70 cm.   **40.** 16·51

PRACTICE EXERCISES 8 (Page 45)

A. **1.** 1·817   **2.** 3·915   **3.** 8·434   **4.** 8·862   **5.** 30·94   **6.** ·529
7. ·406   **8.** 9·094   **9.** 19·44   **10.** 9·252   **11.** ·5235   **12.** ·329

B. **13.** 4·626   **14.** 18·566   **15.** 8·582

PRACTICE EXERCISES 9 (Page 49)

A. **1.** 4096   **2.** $\dfrac{1}{729}$ **3.** 1   **4.** $\dfrac{8a^9}{b^4}$
5. $\dfrac{75b^{2n}}{a^{3m}}$ **6.** $\dfrac{1}{2}$ **7.** 16   **8.** $\dfrac{1}{784}$
9. 24   **10.** a^2m^2 **11.** $\dfrac{16a^3}{b^7}$

B. **12.** 9   **13.** $\dfrac{1}{4}$ **14.** 6   **15.** 24   **16.** 20
17. $3\dfrac{3}{8}$ **18.** 12   **19.** 11   **20.** 8

C. **21.** 64   **22.** 10   **23.** $\dfrac{1}{x^2}$ **24.** $\dfrac{1}{225}$ **25.** ·00243   **26.** $\dfrac{1}{144}$

D. **27.** $\dfrac{y^8}{x^4}$ **28.** $\dfrac{1}{7\sqrt{a^5}}$ **29.** 62·5   **30.** 8

A. **1.** $\sqrt{12}$ **2.** $\sqrt{50}$ **3.** $\sqrt{80}$ **4.** $\sqrt[3]{32}$

5. $\sqrt{45}$ **6.** $\sqrt{75}$ **7.** $\sqrt{20}$ **8.** $\sqrt{108}$

B. **9.** $5\sqrt{2}$ **10.** $2\sqrt{21}$ **11.** $2\sqrt[3]{9}$ **12.** $3\sqrt[3]{4}$

13. $5\sqrt{3}$ **14.** $3\sqrt{5}$ **15.** $2\sqrt{5}$ **16.** $2\sqrt{3}$

C. **17.** $5\sqrt{3}$ **18.** $3\sqrt{5}$ **19.** $4\sqrt{5}$ **20.** $4\sqrt{2}$

21. $11\sqrt{3} + 3\sqrt{2}$ **22.** $\sqrt{5}$ **23.** $4\sqrt{3}$ **24.** $\sqrt{10} + \sqrt{2}$ **25.** $7\sqrt{3} - 2$

D. **26.** $\sqrt{6}$ **27.** 2 **28.** 72 **29.** $2\sqrt{3}$ **30.** $24\sqrt{3}$

31. 6 **32.** $24\sqrt{3}$ **33.** 420 **34.** $96\sqrt{15}$

E. **35.** $\sqrt{2}$ **36.** $\frac{9}{4}\sqrt{7}$ **37.** $\sqrt{6}$ **38.** $6\sqrt{15}$ **39.** $\sqrt{10 \cdot 5}$

40. 6 **41.** $\sqrt{10}$ **42.** $\frac{3}{4}$ **43.** 650 **44.** 24

F. **45.** $\frac{7}{3}\sqrt{3}$ **46.** $\frac{5}{8}\sqrt{8}$ **47.** $\frac{a}{b}\sqrt{b}$ **48.** $\frac{3 - \sqrt{5}}{4}$

49. $\frac{5}{3}(\sqrt{6} + \sqrt{3})$ **50.** $\frac{27 + 10\sqrt{2}}{23}$ **51.** $2 - \sqrt{3}$ **52.** $7 - 4\sqrt{3}$

53. $5 + 2\sqrt{6}$ **54.** $\frac{7 + 2\sqrt{10}}{3}$ **55.** $3 - 2\sqrt{2}$ **56.** $\frac{3 + \sqrt{5}}{2}$

G. **57.** 16 **58.** 8 **59.** $-16\sqrt{10}$ **60.** $a - b$

A. **1.** to **11** need no answer. **B.** **12.** to **16** need no answer

D. **17.** 900 **18.** $1 + 3 + 5 + 7 + 9 + 11 + 13$; $1 + 3 + 5 + 7 + 9 + 11$ **19.** 3

20. (a) 1111 (b) 2098 (c) 21·15 (d) ·0091 (e) $18\frac{3}{13}$ (f) $33\frac{5}{9}$

21. (a) 10 (b) 10·25

E. **22.** ·138 **23.** 2·236 **24.** 1·443 **25.** 3·818 **26.** 1·673 **27.** 2·366

F. **28.** 1·991 **29.** 2·427 **30.** $2 + \sqrt{3}$

G. **34.** 6 **35.** 36

H. **36.** $\frac{-4}{11}$ **37.** 3·2 **38.** ·11 **I.** **39.** 15 cm. **40.** 70 cm.

A. **1.** Rs. 3.24 **2.** 12½% **3.** Rs. 30 **4.** 7½% **5.** Rs. 4000

6. Rs. 32.50 **7.** Rs. 48 per dozen

B. **8.** Rs. 100 **9.** Rs. 693 **10.** 10% **11.** 5% **12.** Rs. 50, 25%

13. Rs. 57.75 **14.** $11\frac{1}{9}$% **15.** (a) Rs. 111.75 (b) Rs. 99

C. **16.** Rs. 250 **17.** Rs. 42 **18.** 5%

A. **1.** Rs. 2100   **2.** Rs. 6050   **3.** Rs. 1349·84   **4.** Rs. 1157.63   **5.** Rs. 2420

    6. Rs. 5832   **7.** Rs. 13310   **8.** Rs. 2645   **9.** Rs. 35595·70   **10.** Rs. 8836

B. **11.** Rs. 4630·50 ; Rs. 630·50   **12.** Rs. 2890 ; Rs. 330   **13.** Rs. 21632 ; Rs. 1632

    14. Rs. 1681 ; Rs. 81   **15.** Rs. 14641 ; Rs. 4641   **16.** Rs. 4741·63 ; Rs. 645·63

C. **17.** Rs. 17576, Rs. 1951   **18.** Rs. 4356, Rs, 260   **19.** Rs 8998·91, Rs. 998·91

    20. Rs. 21632 ; Rs. 1632

D. **21.** Rs. 45562·50 ; Rs. 13562·50   **22.** Rs. 23328   **23.** Rs. 1157·63

    24. Rs. 662   **25.** Rs. 22218 ; Rs. 6218   **26.** Rs. 16675

A. **1.** Rs. 2000   **2.** Rs. 25000   **3.** Rs. 6400   **4.** Rs. 16000

    5. Rs. 256   **6.** Rs. 62500

B. **7.** Rs. 500000   **8.** Rs. 10000   **9.** Rs. 4095   **10.** Rs. 20000   **11.** Rs. 2560   **12.** Rs. 2560

C. **13.** Rs. 15625   **14.** Rs. 8000   **15.** Rs. 7500   **16.** Rs. 15000

D. **17.** 20%   **18.** 2 years   **19.** 2 years   **20.** 10% per annum

    21. 15%   **22.** 1 year   **23.** 6 months   **24.** 21%

    25. Rs. 450   **26.** Rs. 4000   **27.** 10%; Rs. 768   **28.** 3 years ; Rs. 1300

    29. Rs. 1600, Rs. 160   **30.** 2 years ; Rs. 880   **31.** Rs. 1,000   **32.** Rs. 4591·20

    33. Rs. 21344   **34.** Rs. 482   **35.** Rs. 1000   **36.** Rs. 5000

    37. 2 years   **38.** Rs. 20,000

A. **1.** + (plus)   **2.** − (minus)

B. **3.** 30870   **4.** 27783   **5.** 92450   **6.** 168920

    7. 35152   **8.** 29484   **9.** 8400   **10.** 2·853%

    11. 1·246%   **12.** 20·5%

A. **1.** to **4** (see terms to know)

B. **5.** 14·4% yearly   **6.** 12.024% yearly   **7.** Rs. 47385   **8.** Rs. 7938

    9. 14·87%, 7·177%   **10.** 16704 years   **11.** $(900)^{10}$ crore

    12. $8·67747 \times 10^7$ **13.** 2364·4664 lakh tons   **14.** Rs. 2·5020504 crore   **15.** 110400

A. **1.** Amount at C.I. $= P\left(1 + \dfrac{r}{100}\right)^T$　　**2.** C.I. $= P\left(1 + \dfrac{r}{100}\right)^T - P$

3. Increase Formula $=$ Original Value $\left(1 + \dfrac{\text{Growth Rate}}{100}\right)^{\text{Time units}}$

4. Decrease Formula $=$ Original Value $\left(1 - \dfrac{\text{Growth Rate}}{100}\right)^{\text{Time units}}$

B. **5.** 2 years　　　　　**6.** Rs. 1000　　　　**7.** Rs. 45562·50

8. 14%　　　　　**9.** Rs. 8998·912　　**10.** Rs. 8170　　**11.** Rs. 4096

12. 2 years　　　　**13.** Rs. 47385　　　**14.** $8\frac{1}{3}$%　　**15.** Rs. 8781·25

C. **16.** True　　　　　**17.** True

D. **18.** 33600, 30,000　**19.** Rs. 35,00　　　**20.** Rs. 1500　　**21.** 20200

22. Rs. 84　　　　**23.** Rs. 100　　　　**24.** Rs. 600　　**25.** Second ; Re 0

26. Rs. 1001.25　　**27.** Rs. 15625

B. **11.** $-3 + 7x + 5x^2$　　　　　　**12.** $-8x + 4xy - 3x^2y + 5x^4$

13. $-5x + 2xy + y^3 - x^4 - 3x^3y^2$　　**14.** $3x^4y + 2x^3y^3 + 5xy^6 + 15x^8$

15. $-15x^2 + 5xy^2 - 2x^3y + 3x^4y$　　**16.** $3 - 7x + 5x^2 - 3x^4 + x^5$

17. $1 - 8x + 3x^2 + 5x^3 + 7x^4$　　　**18.** $-\frac{1}{2}xy^2 + 3x^2y + 4x^3 + 5y^3$

C. **19.** $5x^4 - 4x^3 + 2x^2 + x - 3$　　　**20.** $16x^8 - 5xy^6 - 4x^3y^3 + 5x^4y$

21. $-3x^3y^2 - 6xy^3 + 5x^2y + 4xy$　　**22.** $y^6 + 4x^2y^3 - 6x^2y^2 - 4x^2y - x^2 + 8x$

23. $9x^4 + 8x^3 + 5x^2 + 7x + 3$　　　**24.** $4x^4 + 6x^2y + 5xy - 7x - 11$

D. **25.** $6x^2 - 2xy + 6y^2 - 6x + 11$　　**26.** $19x^2 + 3xy - 9y^2 + 5x + 2$

27. $3y^3 + \frac{3}{4}y^2 - \frac{1}{3}y + 18$　　　**28.** $9x^3 + 4\frac{1}{3}x^2y + 5y^2 - \frac{1}{2}xy^2 + 4\frac{1}{3}y^3$

29. $2x + \sqrt{3}x^3$

E. **30.** $-x^3 + \frac{1}{5}x^2y - xy^2 + 3y^3$　　**31.** $2x^3 + 8x^2y - 3xy^2 - 2y^3$

32. $3x^3 + 11x^2 - 16x + 39$　　　**33.** $\frac{1}{3}x^3 + 3x^2 - \frac{11}{7}xy + \frac{2}{3} - y^3$

34. $\sqrt{2} - x - \sqrt{3}x^2 + (3 + \sqrt{3})x^3$

F. **35.** $4 + 4x^2 - 2x^3$　　　　　　**36.** $x^5 - 4x^4 + 10x^3 - 13x^2 + 11$

G. **37.** $9x^3 + 4\frac{1}{3}x^2y + 4\frac{1}{2}xy^2 + 4\frac{1}{3}y^3$　**38.** $\frac{1}{2}x^2 + \frac{1}{6}x + \frac{17}{42}$

39. $\sqrt{2}x^2 + \frac{1}{4}x$　　　　　　**40.** $2\sqrt{3}x^2 + x - 4\sqrt{3}$

B.   **4.** $-42x^5$ **5.** $-6x^3y^3$ **6.** 1 **7.** $12a^3b^4$ **8.** $-10c^3d^3$

     9. a^2 **10.** $-84x^5y^4z^3$ **11.** $\frac{1}{2}x^2y^3z^2$ **12.** $\frac{2}{5}x^3y^2z$

C.   **13.** $6x^5 - 12x^4 + 21x^3 - 15x^2$ **14.** $10x^7 - 6x^5 - 2x^3$ **15.** $-8x^6y + 2x^4y^3 + 18x^2y^5$

     16. $\frac{-3}{16}x^4y^4z^4$ **17.** $6x^4 - 19x^3 + 18x^2 - 22x + 5$ **18.** $6x^4 - 16x^3 + 29x^2 - 29x + 10$

     19. $5x^3 + 8x^2y - 17xy^2 - 9xy + 12y^3 - 3x^2$ **20.** $15x^2y - 6xy^2 + 9x^2 + 17xy - 8y^2 + 12x - 4y$

D.   **21.** $x^5 - x^4 + 3x^3 + 4x^2 + 2x + 5$ **22.** $25x^4 - 49x^2y^2 + 84xy^3 - 36y^4$

     23. $3x^8 - 6x^7 + 2x^6 + 13x^5 - 26x^4 + 19x^3 - 13x^2 + 13x - 4$

     24. $\frac{3}{8}x^4 - \frac{1}{12}x^3 - \frac{11}{12}x^2 + \frac{19}{27}x - \frac{1}{9}$ **25.** $10x^4 + 17x^3 - 62x^2 + 30x - 3$

     26. $x^7 + x^6 - 19x^5 + 105x^3 + 117x^2 - 122x + 22$

     27. $x^5 + 3x^4 - 5x^3 + 14x^2 + 30x - 16$

     28. $16x^6 - 40x^5 + 18x^4 + 33x^3 - 70x^2 + 67x - 24$

     29. $6x^5 + 37x^4 - 37x^3 + 34x^2 + 3x - 1$ **30.** $-2x^6 - 2x^5 + x^4 - 4x^3 - 4x^2 + 6x + 5$

A.   **1, 2, 3** see page 114,115   **4.** quantity left over in an inexact division

B.   **5.** $-4xy^2$ **6.** $3x^2z^2$ **7.** $3a$ **8.** $-3ab^4c^5$

     9. $12xy^3z^5$ **10.** $-2x^2 - 3x + 4$ **11.** $-\frac{1}{2}x^2 + \frac{2}{3}xy - \frac{5}{6}y^2$

     12. $\frac{8}{3}x^3 - \frac{5}{3}y^2 + 8xz^3$ **13.** $\frac{1}{3}x - \frac{13}{18} + \frac{6}{x} - \frac{13}{14x^2} + \frac{10}{x^3}$

     14. $\frac{1}{2b} - \frac{3}{2a} + \frac{b}{12a^2}$ **15.** $10x^2 - 45x + 51y - 18y^2$

C.   **16.** $x + 2$ **17.** $2x - 7$ **18.** $x^2 - 8x + 3$

     19. $x^2 + x + 1$ **20.** $x^3 - x^2 + 3x - 5$ **21.** $3x - 8$; Remainder $= 7$

D.   **22.** $2x - 1$ **23.** $x^2 + 1$ **24.** $5x^2 + 7xy - 6y^2$

     25. $5x^2 - 9x + 3$ **26.** $x^2 + 4x - 2$

E.   **27.** $Q = 5x^4 + 2x^3 + 6x^2 + 3x + 9$; $R = 7$ **28.** $Q = x^3 - x^2 - 2x + 5$; $R = 6x + 1$

     29. $Q = 2x^2 + 2x$; $R = -2x^2 + 11x - 8$ **30.** $Q = x^3 + 3x^2 - 6x + 3$

F. 31. On dividing, no remainder is left out

32. On dividing, no remainder is left out

G. 33. 1   **34.** $x^2 + 5x + 9$

H. 35. Divisor × Quotient + Remainder = Dividend   **36.** Factor   **37.** Smaller

38. Division   **39.** Addition   **40.** Subtraction

PRACTICE EXERCISES 19 *(Page 97)*

A. 1. *see page 95*

B. 2. rational expression **3.** polynomial **4.** rational expression **5.** polynomial

6. rational expression **7.** polynomial **8.** rational expression **9.** polynomial **10.** polynomial

C. 11. $\dfrac{7\,(x^2 - x + 1)}{(2x - 5)\,(3x + 2)}$

12. $\dfrac{4x^2 - 2x + 7}{(2x - 5)\,(x + 2)}$

13. $\dfrac{2\,(x^3 + x - 5)}{x^2 - 1}$

14. $\dfrac{y^3 + 2y^2 + 2y - 3}{y^2 - 1}$

15. $\dfrac{8y^2 - 11y + 1}{(y - 3)\,(2 + y)}$

16. $\dfrac{8y^2 + 15y - 7}{(y + 3)\,(2 - y)}$

17. $\dfrac{24x^2 + 23x - 23}{(3x - 2)\,(2x - 1)}$

18. $\dfrac{13x^2 - 9x - 19}{(2x + 3)\,(3x + 2)}$

19. $\dfrac{2x^3 + 17x^2 + 48x + 43}{(x + 2)\,(x + 3)}$

D. 20. $\dfrac{x^2 - 17x + 3}{(3x + 2)\,(2x - 5)}$

21. $\dfrac{3\,(4x - 1)}{(2x - 5)\,(x + 2)}$

22. $\dfrac{-\,2y\,(2y - 5)}{y^2 - 1}$

23. $\dfrac{2\,(x^3 - 3x^2 + x - 1)}{x^2 - 1}$

24. $\dfrac{7x + 4}{(x + 1)\,(2x - 1)}$

25. $\dfrac{-\,2x^2 + 7x + 8}{(3x + 1)\,2x + 3)}$

26. $\dfrac{2x^3 - 6x^2 + 11x + 7}{(2 + x)\,(x - 3)}$

27. $\dfrac{-\,2x^3 - 6x^2 + 8x - 1}{(x + 3)\,(2 - x)}$

28. $\dfrac{-\,y^3 + 5xy^2 - 5x^2y + x^2 + y^2 - 3xy}{(x - y)\,(x + 1)}$

29. $\dfrac{-\,x^2 - 2x - 4}{(2x + 3)\,(x + 1)}$

E. 30. $\dfrac{2x^3 + 8x^2 - 11x - 50}{(x + 5)\,(x + 4)}$

31. $\dfrac{2x^3 - 4x^2 - 34x + 135}{(x - 3)\,(x + 5)}$

32. $\dfrac{-\,6a^2 + 11a + 42}{(a + 2)\,(a - 4)}$

33. $\dfrac{2y^3 + 14y^2 - 63y + 24}{(y - 2)\,(y + 3)}$

34. $\dfrac{a^4 + 4a^3 + a^2 + a + 2}{(a + 2)\,(a - 1)}$

35. $\dfrac{48x^3 + 21x^2 + 8x + 1}{(3x + 1)\,(3x - 1)\,(2x + 1)}$

A. 1. $\dfrac{-4x^5}{5y^3}$ 2. $\dfrac{2}{3x^3}$ 3. $\dfrac{-3}{2q^6r^3}$ 4. $\dfrac{x-5}{x-1}$

B. 5. $\dfrac{2x}{x-y}$ 6. 1 7. $\dfrac{2x+1}{x+2}$ 8. $\dfrac{x+6}{x-6}$

9. $x^2 + x - 6$ 10. $\dfrac{5x\,(x+3)}{32x^2 + 4x - 1}$

C. 11. $\dfrac{c}{a^3b}$ 12. $\dfrac{1}{3y}$ 13. $\dfrac{-4\,(x^2 + 5x + 8)}{x^2 - 4}$

14. $\dfrac{x^3 - 1}{x + 3}$

D. 15. $(x+3)^2$ 16. $\dfrac{2x^3 + 2x^2 + x + 1}{2x}$

17. $\dfrac{a-b}{a+b}$ 18. $m^2 - 16$ 19. $\dfrac{x\,(x-3)}{(x+2)^2}$

20. *(a)* $\dfrac{2a^2}{a^2 - 1}$ *(b)* $\dfrac{-2a}{a^2 - 1}$ *(c)* $\dfrac{a-1}{a+1}$ *(d)* $\dfrac{a^2}{a^2 - 1}$

E. 21. *(a)* see page 121   *(b)* see page 121

A. 1. $x^2 + 12x + 35$ 2. $x^2 - 6x - 16$ 3. $x^2 - 11x + 30$

4. $x^2 + 2x - 63$ 5. $9x^2 - 9x - 28$ 6. $4x^2 - 2x - 12$

7. $x^2 - \dfrac{1}{6}x - \dfrac{1}{6}$ 8. $x^2 - \dfrac{19}{12}x + \dfrac{5}{8}$ 9. $a^2 - \dfrac{1}{3}a - \dfrac{2}{9}$

B. 10. 14552   11. 10506   12. 2444

13. 11340   14. 9506   15. 3190

C. 16. $(x+2)(x+3) = x^2 + x\,(2+3) + 2 \times 3$

17. $\left(x + \dfrac{3}{4}\right)\left(x - \dfrac{1}{4}\right) = x^2 + x\left(\dfrac{3}{4} - \dfrac{1}{4}\right) + \dfrac{3}{4} \times \dfrac{-1}{4}$

18. $(p+2)(p-1) = p^2 + p\,(2-7) + 2 \times (-7)$

D. 19. $4x^2 + 9y^2 + 16z^2 + 12xy + 24yz + 16zx$

20. $9x^2 + y^2 + 4z^2 - 6xy + 4yz - 12zx$

21. $81x^2 + 4y^2 + z^2 + 36xy + 4yz + 18zx$

22. $9p^2 + \dfrac{1}{4}q^2 + 4r^2 + 3pq - 2qr - 12rp$

23. $4x^2 + 9y^2 + 25z^2 - 12xy - 30yz + 20zx$

24. $x^2 + y^2 + 4 - 2xy + 4y - 4x$

25. $\dfrac{x^2}{4} + \dfrac{1}{x^2} + 1$ **26.** $27x^2 + \dfrac{x^2}{25} + \dfrac{1}{25x^2} - \dfrac{52}{25}$

27. $9 + 2\sqrt{6} + 4\sqrt{2} + 4\sqrt{3}$

E. **28.** 15129   **29.** 12321   **30.** 132496   **31.** 64516

F. **32.** 27 ; 727   **33.** 5   **34.** 8   **35.** 8   **36.** 1 ; − 1

G. **37.** 20449   **38.** 39601   **39.** 56·25   **40.** 160801

PRACTICE EXERCISES 22 *(Page 109)*

A. **1.** $8x^3 + 27y^3 + 36x^2y + 54xy^2$ **2.** $\dfrac{x^3}{27} + \dfrac{y^3}{64} + \dfrac{x^2y}{12} + \dfrac{xy^2}{16}$

3. $125x^3 + 729y^3 + 675x^2y + 1215xy^2$ **4.** $27p^3 + 8q^3 + 54p^2q + 36pq^2$

5. $x^3 + \dfrac{1}{x^3} + 3x + \dfrac{3}{x}$ **6.** $a^3 + \dfrac{1}{a^3} + 3a + \dfrac{3}{a}$

7. $27x^3 + 27y^3 + 81x^2y + 81xy^2$ **8.** $27x^3 + 64y^3 + 108x^2y + 144xy^2$

9. $27x^3 + \dfrac{1}{8}y^3 + \dfrac{27x^2y}{2} + \dfrac{9xy^2}{4}$

B. **10.** $64x^3 - 125y^3 - 240x^2y + 300xy^2$ **11.** $27x^3 - 64y^3 - 108x^2y + 144xy^2$

12. $x^3 - y^3 - 3x^2y + 3xy^2$ **13.** $64 - 27x^3 + 108x^2 - 144x$

14. $27x^3 + 135x^2y + 225xy^2 + 125y^3$ **15.** $8x^3 + 27 + 36x^2 + 54x$

16. $8x^3 - \dfrac{1}{8x^3} - 6x + \dfrac{3}{2x}$ **17.** $\dfrac{a^3}{27} + \dfrac{8b^3}{27} + \dfrac{2a^2b}{9} + \dfrac{4ab^2}{9}$

18. $x^3 - \dfrac{1}{x^3} - 3x + \dfrac{3}{x}$

C. **19.** 25672375   **20.** 997002999   **21.** 970·299

D. **22.** 65   **23.** 26   **24.** 100   **25.** 539   **26.** 5886

E. **27.** 140   **28.** 36   **29.** 970   **30.** 52   **31.** 52

32. 364   **33.** 18   **34.** 110

F. **35.** $-8(27x^2 + 16)$ **36.** $18y(3y^2 + 4x^2)$ **37.** $\dfrac{q^3}{4} + \dfrac{p^2q}{3}$

38. $14(3a^2 + 49)$ **39.** $\dfrac{y^3}{32} + \dfrac{x^2y}{6}$ **40.** $10(12x^2 + 25)$

A. **1.** $x^3 + y^3$ **2.** $64x^3 + 27y^3$ **3.** $x^3 + 8$

    4. $x^3 + 27y^3$ **5.** $8x^3 + 27y^3$ **6.** $27x^3 + y^3$

B. **7.** $x^3 - y^3$ **8.** $125x^3 - 8y^3$ **9.** $125a^3 - 27b^3$

    10. $p^3 + 8q^3$ **11.** $x^3 - 27$ **12.** $125 - 8x^3$

C. **13.** $27x^3 - \dfrac{y^3}{8}$ **14.** $\dfrac{8x^3}{125} - \dfrac{27y^3}{343}$ **15.** $27x^3 + \dfrac{y^3}{8}$

    16. $\dfrac{27p^3}{8} - \dfrac{q^3}{27}$ **17.** $\dfrac{1}{8}p^3 - \dfrac{1}{27}q^3$ **18.** $\dfrac{8x^3}{125} - \dfrac{27y^3}{64}$

D. **19.** $4a^2,\ b^2$ **20.** $\dfrac{y^2}{49}, \dfrac{3xy}{7}\ ;\ \dfrac{y^3}{343}$ **21.** $2x, \dfrac{y}{6}, 8x^3$ **22.** $5, 3, 3\sqrt{3}$

E. **23.** $28b^3 - 117a^3$ **24.** $2x^3 - 19$ **25.** $\dfrac{-y^3}{4}$

F. **26.** **27** need no answers

G. **28.** $81x^2 + 4y^2 + z^2 + 36xy + 4yz + 18zx$

    29. $9x^2 + 4y^2 + z^2 - 12xy + 4yz - 6zx$

    30. $25x^2 + y^2 + 4z^2 + 10xy - 4yz - 20zx$

    31. $9q^2 + 4 + 4p^2 + 12q - 8p - 12pq$

H. **32.** $a^3 + b^3 + c^3 - 3abc$ **33.** $8x^3 - 27y^3 + 125z^3 + 90xyz$

    34. $l^3 - m^3 - 8 - 6lm$

I. **35.** 27   **36.** 70   **37.** 180   **38.** 108

J. **39.** needs no answer.   **40.** $- 327600$ **41.** 41040   **42.** $- 605·28$

    43. $3 (a - b) (b - c) (c - a)$ **44.** $8x^3 - 17x^2 + 16x - 14$ **45.** 49

    46. $xy = 4$ **47.** $xy + yz + zx = 50$

A. **1.** $2a (4a - 3b + 1)$ **2.** $3xy (x + 3y - 5)$ **3.** $4x (x^2 + 2y - 5z)$

    4. $2xy (xy - 2z^2 + 3yz)$ **5.** $x^2 (x^2 - y^2 - xy)$ **6.** $(1 + 7x^2) (1 + 7x^2)$

B. **7.** $7 (y - x)$ **8.** $(a + 5) (a + 7)$ **9.** $4 (2x - 3y) (2x - 3y + 2)$

    10. $(x + y) (2a - 3b)$ **11.** $2 (3x - 4y) (3 - 12x + 16y)$

    12. $2 (3x + 5y) (6x + 10y - 3)$

C. **13.** $(x + 1) (x^2 + 1)$ **14.** $(a - 3) (a^2 + 1)$ **15.** $(a - 1) (a + b)$

    16. $(x - 1) (x - y)$ **17.** $(x - a) (y + b)$ **18.** $(b + 2c) (6a - b)$

    19. $(3a + 4b) (x - 2y)$ **20.** $(a + b + 1) (a + b - 1)$

A. **1.** $(x + 1)(x + 5)$ **2.** $(x - 4)(x - 3)$ **3.** $(x + 5(x - 3)$

4. $(x + 3)(x - 4)$ **5.** $(x + 9)(x + 16)$ **6.** $(x - 6)(x - 3)$

7. $(x - y)(x - 2y)$ **8.** $(x + 12)(x - 6)$ **9.** $(x + 28)(x - 3)$

10. $(x - 11)(x + 3)$ **11.** $(x + 11)(x - 3)$ **12.** $(p - 30)(p + 4)$

13. $(x + 3)(x - 2)$ **14.** $(x - 4)(x + 3)$ **15.** $(x - 4)(x - 2)$

16. $(x + 5)(x - 3)$ **17.** $(x + 10)(x + 12)$ **18.** $(a - 2)(a - 1)$

19. $(x + 8)(x + 1)$ **20.** $(x + a)(x + 2a)$ **21.** $(y - 17)(y - 3)$

22. $(a + b)(a - 5b)$ **23.** $(p - 7)(p - 5)$ **24.** $(x + 6)(x + 8)$

B. **25.** $(x - 1)(7x - 8)$ **26.** $2(p + 4)(2p - 9)$ **27.** $4(a + 1)(2a - 1)$

28. $(x + 4)(3x - 2)$ **29.** $(x - 5y)(5x + 2y)$

30. $(2x - 1)(2x - 7)$ **31.** $(p + 6q)(10p - q)$ **32.** $(x - 1)(3x + 20)$

33. $(x - 4y)(5x + 6y)$ **34.** $(5m + 3)(m - 1)$

35. $(2z - 1)(3z + 2)$ **36.** $(2x - 2)(x - 2)$ **37.** $(4p - 3q)(3p - q)$

38. $(a + b)(9a + 2b)$ **39.** $(x + p)(3x - p)$ **40.** $(2x + 3)(3x - 1)$

41. $(a - 2)(3a + 2)$ **42.** $(x - 4)(5x - 6)$ **43.** $(a + 2)(2a + 5)$

44. $(a - 1)(4a - 3)$ **45.** $(y + 1)(5y - 13)$ **46.** $(3x + 4)(7x - 1)$

47. $(x + 3)(9x - 4)$ **48.** $(a - 1)(6a - 15)$

A. **1.** $(2x + 5)(2x + 5)(2x + 5)$ **2.** $(5x + 2y)(5x + 2y)(5x + 2y)$

3. $(x + 5y)(x + 5y)(x + 5y)$ **4.** $(6a + 7b)(6a + 7b)(6a + 7b)$

5. $\left(\dfrac{2}{3}a + \dfrac{1}{b}\right)\left(\dfrac{2}{3}a + \dfrac{1}{b}\right)\left(\dfrac{2}{3}a + \dfrac{1}{b}\right)$ **6.** $\left(\dfrac{5}{x} + \dfrac{2}{y}\right).\left(\dfrac{5}{x} + \dfrac{2}{y}\right)\left(\dfrac{5}{x} + \dfrac{2}{y}\right)$

B. **7.** $(a - 6)(a - 6)(a - 6)$ **8.** $(x - 3y)(x - 3y)(x - 3y)$

9. $\left(\dfrac{x}{3} + \dfrac{y}{2}\right)\left(\dfrac{x^2}{9} - \dfrac{xy}{6} + \dfrac{y^2}{4} + \dfrac{y}{x}\right)$ **10.** $(2x - y)(2x - y)(2x - y)$

11. $\left(\dfrac{a}{4} - \dfrac{b}{5}\right)\left(\dfrac{a}{4} - \dfrac{b}{5}\right)\left(\dfrac{a}{4} - \dfrac{b}{5}\right)$ **12.** $(4x - y)(4x - y)(4x - y)$

A. **1.** $(2x + 5)(4x^2 - 10x + 25)$ **2.** $(2x + 7)(4x^2 - 14x + 49)$

3. $(1 + 2p)(1 - 2p + 4p^2)$ **4.** $2(4x + 3y)(16x^2 - 12xy + 9y^2)$

5. $(2a + b)(4a^2 - 2ab + b^2)$ **6.** $\left(\dfrac{x}{3} + \dfrac{y}{4}\right)\left(\dfrac{x^2}{9} - \dfrac{xy}{12} + \dfrac{y^2}{16}\right)$

7. $(3x + 4y)(9x^2 - 12xy + 16y^2)$ **8.** $(6x + 1)(36x^2 - 6x + 1)$

9. $\left(\dfrac{x}{6} + \dfrac{y}{5}\right)\left(\dfrac{x^2}{36} - \dfrac{xy}{30} + \dfrac{y^2}{25}\right)$

B. 10. $(x - 2)(x^2 + 2x + 4)$ **11.** $(5x - 4y)(25x^2 + 20xy + 16y^2)$

12. $\left(\dfrac{x}{3} - \dfrac{y}{4}\right)\left(\dfrac{x^2}{9} + \dfrac{xy}{12} + \dfrac{y^2}{16}\right)$ **13.** $\left(\dfrac{a}{4} - \dfrac{b}{5}\right)\left(\dfrac{a^2}{16} + \dfrac{ab}{20} + \dfrac{b^2}{25}\right)$

14. $4(2p - 3q)(4p^2 + 6pq + 9q^2)$ **15.** $(0{\cdot}1\,a - 0{\cdot}2b)(0{\cdot}01a^2 + 0{\cdot}02ab + 0{\cdot}04b^2)$

16. $(4 - 7a)(16 + 28a + 49a^2)$ **17.** $(5x - y)(25x^2 + 5xy + y^2)$

18. $(3ab - c)(9a^2b^2 + 3abc + c^2)$ **19.** $(a + b)(a - b)(a^2 - ab + b^2)(a^2 + ab + b^2)$

20. $xy(x - y)(x^2 + xy + y^2)$ **21.** $(x + 3)(19x^2 + 39x + 21)$

C. 22. $3(x - y)(y - z)(z - x)$ **23.** $(2x + 3y - z)(4x^2 + 9y^2 + z^2 - 6xy + 3yz + 2zx)$

24. $3pqr(p - q)(q - r)(r - p)$ **25.** $3 \times 2{\cdot}7 \times (-1{\cdot}6) \times (-1{\cdot}1)$

26. $(y - 3x - z)(y^2 + 9x^2 + 3xyz^2 - 3zx + yz)$

D. 27. 1 **28.** $.08$ **29.** $7x + 9$ **30.** -175500

31. $\dfrac{71}{512}$ **32.** 129024 **33.** -383040 **34.** 12 **34.** 123750

PRACTICE EXERCISES 28 (Page 124)

A. 1. $x = 4$ **2.** $x = 4$ **3.** $x = \dfrac{3}{7}$ **4.** $a = 2$

5. $x = 2$ **6.** $x = -5$

B. 7. $x = 3\dfrac{1}{2}$ **8.** $x = 12$ **9.** $x = 1$ **10.** $x = 5\dfrac{3}{8}$

11. $x = \dfrac{5}{17}$ **12.** $x = -2\dfrac{2}{5}$ **13.** $x = 1$

14. $x = \dfrac{9m - 2}{3}$ **15.** $x = -\dfrac{8}{11}$ **16.** $x = 1$ **17.** $x = -45$ **18.** $x = -7$

C. 19. $x = -2\dfrac{5}{11}$ **20.** $x = \dfrac{1}{41}$ **21.** $a = 8$ **22.** $x = \dfrac{-11}{9}$

23. $x = -3$ **24.** $x = \dfrac{-1}{7}$ **25.** $x = \dfrac{-5}{34}$ **26.** $x = 11$

27. $x = 3\dfrac{7}{9}$ **28.** $x = \dfrac{13}{15}$ **29.** $x = 2$ **30.** $x = \dfrac{11}{16}$

31. $x = 2\dfrac{3}{25}$ **32.** $x = -2\dfrac{1}{2}$ **33.** $p = 15\dfrac{3}{4}$

PRACTICE EXERCISES 29 (Page 127)

A. 1. 8 yrs, 40 yrs.   **2.** 30, 80   **3.** 28   **4.** $\dfrac{2}{9}$ **5.** 42

6. 10 yrs, 40 yrs.   **7.** 50°, 100°, 30°   **8.** 3 km./hr.   **9.** 100 gram

10. Rs. 80, Rs. 60, Rs. 45   **11.** 28 cm, 21 cm.   **12.** 13 km./hour

13. Rs. 40 ; Rs. 120   **14.** 96, 24   **15.** Gold $21\dfrac{1}{9}$ gm., copper $= 8\dfrac{8}{9}$ gm.

16. $\dfrac{17}{13}$ **17.** 40 km, 30 km.   **18.** 96   **19.** 8 m, 17 m.   **20.** 18 km/hr.

21. 14 yrs, 38 yrs.   **22.** 51, 53, 55   **23.** 82, 84, 86

A.   **1.** $15x^2 + xy + 4y^2$ **2.** $2y^3 - 2x^3 + 3xy^2 - 8x^2y$

    3. *(a)* $6x^4 - 16x^3 + 29x^2 - 29x + 10$ *(b)* $\dfrac{3x^5}{8} + \dfrac{x^4}{4} - \dfrac{13x^3}{12} - \dfrac{x^2}{6} + \dfrac{19x}{27} - \dfrac{1}{9}$

    4. *(a)* Quotient $= x^4 - 2x^3 + 5x^2 - x - 3$

        (b) Quotient $= x^2 + 4x - 2$; Remainder $= 9x + 5$

B.   **5.** $9x^2 + \dfrac{1}{4x^2} - 3$ **6.** $\dfrac{x^2}{25} + \dfrac{y^2}{36} - \dfrac{xy}{15}$

    7. $x^2 + 4y^2 + 25z^2 - 4xy + 20yz - 10zx$ **8.** $4p^2 + 9q^2 + z^2 - 12pq - 6qz + 4pz$

C.   **9.** 40   **10.** 23, 527   **11.** 14, 194   **12.** 9080   **13.** 65

D.   **14.** $\dfrac{-\,y(2y^2+7y+11)}{(4+y)\,(2-y)}$ **15.** $\dfrac{16x^3-60x^2-48x-11}{12(2x+1)\,(2x-1)}$ **16.** $\dfrac{2x^3 +2x^2 + x +1}{2x}$

    17. $18b\,(3b^2 + a^2)$

E.   **18.** $27x^3 + \dfrac{1}{8}y^3$ **19.** $\dfrac{8}{27}p^3 - \dfrac{1}{27}q^3$

    20. *(a)* $(2x + y + 3z)\,(2x + y + 3z)$ *(b)* $(x - 9)\,(x + 6)$

        (c) $(x - 2y)\,(x - y)$ *(d)* $(3x + 4y)\,(9x^2 - 12xy + 16y^2)$

        (e) $(7x - 4)\,(49x^2 + 28x + 16)$

    21. *(a)* 14552   *(b)* 77760   **22.** *(a)* 27   *(b)* $3xyz$

    23. *(a)* $(2x - 7)\,(4x^2 + 14x + 49)$ *(b)* $(x - 2y)\,(9x - 4y)$

    24. *(a)* $x = 2\dfrac{3}{4}$ *(b)* $y = -\,6\dfrac{2}{9}$ *(c)* $x = 3$

    25. 2 km/hr.   **26.** 65 km. and 70 km. per hour

PRACTICE EXERCISES 30 *(Page 135)*

2. $\angle ACB = 50°$ **3.** *(a)* because SR and AB are both parallel to PQ   *(b)* Trapeziums

4. *(a)* yes, opposite sides of a rectangle   *(b)* yes, both $\parallel$ CD   *(c)* yes, both $=$ CD

    (d) yes, AB and EF are equal and parallel   *(e)* yes   **7.** $\angle x = 115°$, $\angle y = 120°$

PRACTICE EXERCISES 31 *(Page 139)*

4. 3 cm.

PRACTICE EXERCISES 32 *(Page 141)*

1. 4 cm.   **2.** *(a)* 6 cm. *(b)* 4 cm.   **3.** 6 cm.

5. 2·25 cm.   **6, 7, 8** need no answers.   **9.** OD $= 4$ cm.

PRACTICE EXERCISES 33 *(Page 146)*

A. aeroplane, jumper, clown, butterfly, leaf and flag

B. B, O, W, A, V, M

D. *(a)* see page 143   *(b)* see page 145   *(c)* see page 143

Practice Exercises - 34 need no answers.

PRACTICE EXERCISES 35 (Page 159)

A. **1.** True **2.** False **3.** False **4.** True **5.** True **6.** False **7.** False **8.** True

PRACTICE EXERCISES 36 (Page 164)

A. **1.** yes **2.** yes **3.** yes **4.** yes **5.** yes **6.** yes **7.** yes

B. **8.** They have their—(a) corresponding angles equal (b) corresponding sides proportional

9. (a) They are enlarged (b) They are dimensioned

C. **10.** see page 187 **11.** see page 186 **12. & 13.** see page 188 **14.** see page 189

D. **15.** $\triangle ABC \sim \triangle APC$; $x = 2\cdot4$ cm. $y = 3\cdot2$ cm. **16.** $6\cdot25$ cm.

17. AB = $3\cdot2$ PR = $6\cdot9$ **18.** 96 m. **19.** AE = 6 cm. CE = 8 cm.

PRACTICE EXERCISES 37 (Page 170)

2. OA = 6 cm. **3.** 12 cm. **5.** (a) 90° (b) 90° (c) yes **6.** 120° each

7. 90° each **8.** 60° each **9.** Nonagon **10.** Pentagon

13. yes, yes, yes, yes **15.** yes, yes, yes, yes

PRACTICE EXERCISES 38 (Page 175)

1. $\overset{\frown}{AC}$ = 80°, $\overset{\frown}{BC}$ = 100°, $\overset{\frown}{ABC}$ = 280° **2.** 288° **3.** 60°, 300°

4. minor $\overset{\frown}{MC}$ = 60°, $\overset{\frown}{NC}$ = 120°, $\overset{\frown}{MNC}$ = 300° **5.** 72°, 288°

7. minor $\overset{\frown}{AC}$ = 70°, minor $\overset{\frown}{BD}$ = 70° ; minor $\overset{\frown}{BC}$ = 110°

8. major $\overset{\frown}{PQ}$ = 300° ; major $\overset{\frown}{QR}$ = 220° ; minor $\overset{\frown}{QR}$ = 140° ; minor $\overset{\frown}{PR}$ = 160°

9. 45° **10.** needs no answer **11.** $154\frac{2}{7}^{\circ}$ and $205\frac{5}{7}^{\circ}$

PRACTICE EXERCISES 39 (Page 178)

A. **1.** 58° **2.** 158° **3.** 60°

B. **4.** 50° **5.** 50°

C. **6.** 30° **7.** 42° **8.** 45° **9.** (a) ∠BOD = 55° ; (b) ∠ABC = 25° ; (c) ∠CBD = $37\frac{1}{2}^{\circ}$

PRACTICE EXERCISES 40 (Page 180)

A. **1.** 40° **2.** 40°, 80° **3.** 30°, 30° **4.** 90°, 90° and 5°, 5° **5.** 45°, 50°, 35°

6. 105° **7.** 50° **8.** 50° **9.** 45°

PRACTICE EXERCISES 41 (Page 183)

A. **1.** see page 182 **2.** see page 182

B. **3.** 120° **7.** ∠x = 85°. ∠z = 95°, ∠y = 95° **8.** 30° **9.** 35° **10.** 60°

PRACTICE EXERCISES 42 (Page 187)

A. **1.** see page 166 **2.** see page 166 **3.** see page 166

B. **4.** (a) APB (b) GFEA, TSMB (c) QOP (d) QOP, EM (e) P

C. **5.** yes **6.** no **7.** no **8.** produce it both ways

D. **9.** 90° **10.** It needs no answer. **11.** 8 cm. **14.** 12 cm.

PRACTICE EXERCISES 44 (Page 195)

A. **1.** Length × Breadth **2.** ½ (Diagonal)^2 or (side)^2 **3.** $\sqrt{s\,(s-a)\,(s-b)\,(s-c)}$

B. **4.** Rs. 4620 **5.** 1344 sq. m ; 44·8 m. **6.** Rs. 840 **7.** 420 sq. m **8.** 4·205 sq. m

9. Rs. 795 **10.** 3 metres **11.** 125 m, 75 m **12.** Base 900 m ; alt = 300 m.

13. 100 m **14.** 16.8 sq. m. **15.** 432 sq. cm

16. 925 m^2 ; Rs. 1665 **17.** Rs. 1750

PRACTICE EXERCISES 45. (Page 198)

A. **1.** 231 sq. cm **2.** Base = 32 cm. ; Height = 16 cm. **3.** Base = 30 cm, Height = 10 cm.

4. 7·5 cm. **5.** 246 sq. m **6.** 360 sq. m **7.** 405 sq. cm **8.** 216 sq. cm

9. 11·9 cm. **10.** Area = 150 sq. cm ; Perimeter = 50 cm. **11.** 24 sq. cm

12. Area = 24 sq. cm **13.** Rs. 585 **14.** 138 sq. m **15.** 1344 sq. m **16.** 1369·84 sq. m

17. 5 m **18.** 32 m **19.** 35 m, 20 m **20.** 152 sq. m

PRACTICE EXERCISES 46 (Page 202)

A. **1.** 10.5 sq. m **2.** 150 sq. m **3.** 56.25 sq. m **4.** 120 sq. m **5.** 66 sq. m

B. **6.** 1161·9 sq. m **7.** 251·52 sq. m **8.** 105.32 sq. m **9.** 66 sq. m

PRACTICE EXERCISES 47 (page 207)

A. **1.** see page 204 **2.** 22 : 7

B. **3.** 132 cm. **4.** 88 cm. **5.** 396 cm. **6.** 66 cm. **7.** 11 m **8.** 61·6 cm.

C. **9.** 105 m, 52·5 m **10.** 42 cm. ; 21 cm. **11.** 4·9 cm, 2·95 cm.

12. 28 cm, 14 cm. **13.** O^{ce} = 4·4 m **14.** 1980 m **15.** 3·5 cm.

16. 2000 revolutions **17.** 19·8 cm. **18.** 164 m **19.** Rs. 64·68

PRACTICE EXERCISES 48 (Page 210)

A. **1.** Diameter × $\dfrac{22}{7}$ **2.** O^{ce} ÷ $\dfrac{22}{7}$ **3.** πr^2 **4.** Diameter ÷ 2

B. **5.** 75·46 sq. cm **6.** 13·86 sq. cm **7.** 38·5 sq. cm **8.** 1386 sq. cm

9. 616 sq. cm **10.** 186·34 sq. cm

C. **11.** 13·86 sq. cm **12.** 3850 sq. cm **13.** 13·86 sq. m **14.** 124·74 sq. cm

15. 98·56 sq. m **16.** 5544 sq. m

D. **17.** 154 sq. m **18.** 616 sq. m **19.** 3850 sq. m **20.** 1886·5 sq. m

21. 5544 sq. cm **22.** 49896 sq. m

E. **23.** 22 m **24.** 44 m **25.** 550 sq. m **26.** 1424·5 sq. m

27. 2310 sq. m **28.** Rs. 885.5 **29.** Rs. 265534500

30. 4 : 9 **31.** 15.9 m nearly **32.** 352 m **33.** Rs. 11230

A.   **1.** see page 212   **2.** see page 214   **3.** see page 213   **4.** see page 213

B.   **5.** 34·65 sq. cm   **6.** 148 sq. cm   **7.** 15·4 sq. m   **8.** 12·58 sq. cm

9. $8\frac{8}{21}$ sq. cm   **10.** 183·3 sq. cm

C.   **11.** 15·09 cm   **12.** 6 times   **13.** 105 cm   **14.** Rs. 10780·80

15. Area = 2856 sq. m, Perimeter = 248 m

D.   **16.** 3·8 cm, 6·3 cm.   **17.** 17·7 sq. cm   **18.** 231 sq. m

19. 42 sq. cm ; 154 sq. cm ; 94·5 cm ; 50·3 sq. cm

A.   **1.** (edge)^3 **2.** $6 \times$ (side)^2 **3.** Length $\times$ Breadth $\times$ Height

4. 2 (LB + BH + LH)   **5.** $\sqrt{\text{Length}^2 + \text{Breadth}^2 + \text{Height}^2}$

B.   **6.** 512 cu. m ; 384 sq. m   **7.** 274·625 cu. m ; 253·5 sq. cm   **8.** 729 cu. m ; 486 sq. m

9. 42·875 cu. cm ; 73·5 sq. cm

C.   **10.** 37·5 cu. m ; 70 sq. m   **11.** 168 cu. m ; 194 sq. m   **12.** 360 cu. m ; 396 sq. m

D.   **13.** 512 cu. cm   **14.** 486 sq. cm   **15.** 25000 bricks   **16.** 22·5 cm.

17. 1223·14 litres ; 7·29 sq. m   **18.** 15·7 cm.   **19.** 1 m.

A.   **1.** $\pi \times r^2 \times h$ **2.** $2 \times \pi \times r \times h$ **3.** $2 \times \pi \times r \, (r + h)$

B.   **4.** 6237 cu. cm ; 1188 sq. cm ; 1881 sq. cm   **5.** 616 cu. m ; 352 sq. m ; 429 sq. m

6. 808·5 cu. cm ; 462 sq. cm ; 539 sq. cm   **7.** 7700 cu. cm ; 2200 sq. cm ; 2508 sq. cm

C.   **8.** 616 cu. m ; 1·54 m   **9.** 28 m   **10.** 550 cu. cm (·55 litre) ; 242 cu. cm

11. Rs. 2200   **12.** 754·29 sq. cm ; 352 sq. cm

13. 385 cu. cm, 297 sq. cm   **14.** Rs. 801·50 ; 0·5544 litre

15. Second by 112 cu. cm   **16.** 18·6 cm.   **17.** 4 cm.   **18.** 4 m.

A.   **1.** $\frac{1}{3} \times \pi \times r^2 \times h$ **2.** $\pi \times r \times l$ **3.** $\pi \times r \times (r + l)$

B.   **4.** 9856 cu. cm   **5.** 2079 cu. cm   **6.** 8250 cu. cm

C.   **7.** **10 cm.**   **8.** 50 cm.   **9.** 13 cm.   **10.** 5 cm.

D.   **11.** 10010 sq. cm ; 13860 sq. cm   **12.** 900.9 sq. m ; 1247·4 sq. m

E.   **13.** 9856 cu. cm ; 2200 sq. cm ; 2816 sq. cm   **14.** 2079 cu. cm ; 54 cm

15. 66 metres ; Rs. 1204·50   **16.** Vol = 3769·92 cu. cm ; C. Surface = 1319·47 sq. cm

17. 6 cm.   **18.** 24 cm.

19. V. = 37·68 cu. m ; C. Surface 47·1 sq. m   **20.** 37 cm.

A. 1. $\frac{4}{3} \times \pi \times r^3$　　2. $4 \times \pi \times r^2$　　3. $\frac{2}{3} \pi \times r^3$

4. $2 \times \pi \times r^2$　　5. $3 \times \pi \times r^2$

B. 6. 4851 cu. cm ; 1386 sq. cm　　7. 1437·3 cu. cm ; 616 sq. cm

8. 735·9 cu. cm ; 394·24 sq. cm

C. 9. 1437·3 cu. m　　10. 5544 sq. cm　　11. 4851 cu. cm

12. 1386 sq. cm　　13. 28 cm.　　14. 423·5 cu. cm

15. ·3679 litre ; 84.62 cu. cm　　16. 84000 lead shots　　17. 1 cm.

18. 178·09 sq. cm　　19. 4·2 cm.

20. Surface = 417·8 sq. cm,　Weight = 1·694 kg.

MISCELLANEOUS EXERCISES V (Page 234)

B. 5. Length × Breadth　　6. $\frac{1}{2}$ × Base × Height　　7. $\sqrt{s\,(s-a)\,(s-b)\,(s-c)}$

8. (side)^2　　9. Base × Height　　10. $\frac{1}{2}$ × Diagonal × Diagonal

11. $\frac{1}{2}$ × Sum of parallel sides × Height　　12. πr^2

13. $\pi r^2 \times \dfrac{\text{sector angle}}{360}$　　14. $\dfrac{O^{ce} \times \text{Angle of the arc at the centre}}{360}$

15. (edge)^3　　16. Length × Breadth × Height　　17. $\pi r^2 h$

18. $2\pi rh$　　19. $\frac{1}{3} \times \pi r^2 \times h$

20. πr × Slant Height　　21. $\frac{4}{3} \times \pi \times r^3$　　22. $4 \times \pi r^2$

C. 23. 11·2 cm.　　24. Rs. 42500　　25. 352 sq. m.

26. 901·9 cu. m　　27. 15·09 m. nearly　　28. 12 cm.

29. 4·8 m nearly　　30. 2 cm.　　31. 2·4 cm.

32. 36·06 kg.　　33. 418 sq. cm. ; 982 grams nearly

34. 63·36 kg.

PRACTICE EXERCISES 56 (Page 250)

1. x-co-ordinate　　2. y-co-ordinate　　3. co-ordinates　　4. origin

5. First　　6. Third　　7. Second　　8. Fourth